Palgrave Studies on Leadership and Learning in Teacher Education

The series focuses on original and research informed writing related to teachers and leaders' work as it addresses teacher education in the 21st century. The editors of this series adopt a more comprehensive definition of Teacher Education to include pre-service, induction and continuing professional development of the teacher. The contributions will deal with the challenges and opportunities of learning and leading in teacher education in a globalized era. It includes the dimensions of practice, policy, research and university school partnership. The distinctiveness of this book series lies in the comprehensive and interconnected ways in which learning and leading in teacher education are understood. In the face of global challenges and local contexts it is important to address leadership and learning in teacher education as it relates to different levels of education as well as opportunities for teacher candidates, teacher educators education leaders and other stakeholders to learn and develop. The book series draws upon a wide range of methodological approaches and epistemological stances and covers topics including teacher education, professionalism, leadership and teacher identity.

Sulaiman M. Al-Balushi
Lisa Martin-Hansen • Youngjin Song
Editors

Reforming Science Teacher Education Programs in the STEM Era

International and Comparative Perspectives

palgrave
macmillan

Editors
Sulaiman M. Al-Balushi
College of Education
Sultan Qaboos University
Muscat, Oman

Lisa Martin-Hansen
Department of Science Education
California State University Long Beach
Long Beach, CA, USA

Youngjin Song
Department of Science Education
California State University Long Beach
Long Beach, CA, USA

ISSN 2524-7069 ISSN 2524-7077 (electronic)
Palgrave Studies on Leadership and Learning in Teacher Education
ISBN 978-3-031-27333-9 ISBN 978-3-031-27334-6 (eBook)
https://doi.org/10.1007/978-3-031-27334-6

This Palgrave Macmillan imprint is published by the registered company Springer Nature Switzerland AG.
The registered company address is: Gewerbestrasse 11, 6330 Cham, Switzerland

Contents

Notes on Contributors

Tuğba Abanoz Assistant professor at Ankara University, Turkey. She's been involved in educational work, including participating in various educational events organized by public schools in Boston, USA. Her research interests are STEM in early childhood, science education, self-regulation, resilience, teacher professional development, and art education in early childhood.

Sevil Akaygun Associate Professor of Chemistry Education in the Department of Mathematics and Science Education at Boğaziçi University. Her research focuses on visualization in chemistry education, STEM education and nanotechnology education. She has coordinated national and international projects, given workshops to STEM teachers, published articles in these areas.

Valarie L. Akerson Professor of Science Education at Indiana University. She researches elementary teachers' ideas about and teaching of Nature of Science. She is past president of the Association for Science Teacher Education and past president for NARST. She is a 2021 recipient of the Distinguished Contributions Through Research Award.

Sulaiman M. Al-Balushi Professor of Science Education, former dean of the College of Education at Sultan Qaboos University, Oman (2014–2020), a visiting scholar at the University of Exeter, UK (2020–2021), and a board member of different journal editorial boards. He holds a PhD from The University of Iowa, USA.

Mohammed Al Amri Professor of Art & Education, and Ex. Head of Curriculum & Instruction Department at College of Education, Sultan Qaboos University, Oman. He was a visiting scholar at Harvard University. Al-Amri has an MA in Art Education from University of Warwick and a PhD from University of Manchester.

Yoshiaki Aoki Leading senior mentor at the Shizuoka STEM Academy at Shizuoka University, supported by Japan Science and Technology Agency. He was the past director for Shizuoka Science Museum, Ru · Ku · Ru. He was the principal at several elementary schools at the Shizuoka City.

Marta Romero Ariza Ph.D. and associate professor in the Department of Didactics of Sciences at the University of Jaén. She has participated in international projects to test innovative approaches and resources to enhance STEM learning and critical thinking, supporting teacher professional development in this field.

Fatma Aslan-Tutak Associate Professor of Mathematics Education in the Department of Mathematics and Science Education at Boğaziçi University. Her research interests are mathematical knowledge, mentoring in teacher education, comparative teacher education studies, professional development to improve teacher practices, critical mathematics education, classroom-based assessment, and STEM education.

Kathryn M. Bateman She obtained her PhD from The Pennsylvania State University in Curriculum & Instruction. She is a former Philadelphia middle school science teacher and Marine Biologist. Her research is embedded in the everyday practices of teachers through a lens of post-modern philosophy with a goal of advocacy for equitable education.

Amy S. Bauer Doctoral candidate in mathematics education, Department of Teaching, Learning and Teacher Education at the University of Nebraska-Lincoln. She has formerly worked as a middle school mathematics and science teacher. Her research focuses on integrated STEM in elementary education.

Shashidhar Belbase Assistant professor in the College of Education, UAE University. His research interest ranges from teacher and student beliefs about teaching-learning mathematics with technology, interdisciplinary STEM/STEAM education, and other cross-cutting issues of education and environment. Belbase has published several peer-reviewed articles and book chapters.

G. Michael Bowen Associate professor, Mount Saint Vincent University, Halifax, Nova Scotia. Bowen has taught science in public and private schools in Canada and the USA. His research examines graphical/data literacy, inquiry science, online/STEM technologies, representations of science/scientists in news and entertainment media, science teacher preparation, and science fairs.

Gayle A. Buck Associate Dean of Research and Professor of Science Education at Indiana University. Her scholarship focuses on relationships between learners, teachers, and science. Her research explores (1) student populations traditionally underserved in science education, (2) neglected epistemological assumptions in science education, and (3) pragmatic and participatory approaches to educational research.

Muhammad Abd Hadi Bunyamin Senior Lecturer of Physics Education at Universiti Teknologi Malaysia (UTM), Johor Bahru, Malaysia. He is also a research executive at UTM Vice-Chancellor Office. He was the recipient of a teaching award at the college level in May 2020.

Sedef Canbazoğlu-Bilici Professor in the Department of Science Education at Gazi University, Turkey. She worked as a visiting scholar at the University of Minnesota, STEM Education Center in 2011–2012. Her research interests include developing technology-enriched activities for developing science teachers' TPACK and STEM education.

Ximena Carrasco Environmental Engineer from the Universidad Federico Santa María (Chile), Professor of Chemistry at the Pontificia Universidad Católica de Valparaíso, and Master in Education in Science and Technology from the Technion University, Israel. Currently, she is pursuing doctoral studies in Science Education.

Ashley Carter graduate student, Mount Saint Vincent University, Halifax, Nova Scotia. Carter is a graduate student in Mount Saint Vincent University's Curriculum Studies program and is employed as an elementary school teacher where she incorporates STEM technologies in her classroom.

Yu Chen Research assistant professor in the Faculty of Education at the University of Macau, Macau, China. Her research interests are science/STEM education.

M. Sencer Corlu Professor of Mathematics Education at the Oslo Metropolitan University in Norway. Furthermore, he has acted as the director of the BAUSTEM Center at Bahçeşehir University in Turkey since 2016. Corlu's areas of expertise include mathematics teacher education, STEM Education, and international schools.

Isha DeCoito Associate professor (cross-appointed to the Faculty of Science), Western University, Canada. My scholarship targets three major aspects of STEM education: curriculum, pedagogical perspectives and practices that reflect equity, diversity, inclusion, and decolonization (EDID); mentoring and professional development of educators; and digital technologies to improve scientific and technological literacy.

Jordi Domènech-Casal Secondary education teacher and Associate Lecturer of Science Education at Universitat Autònoma de Barcelona.PhD in genetics and a degree in social sciences. His research interests are devoted to PBL, CLIL and STEM.Authored "Aprendizaje Basado en Proyectos para STEM. Breve manual práctico" book (2023) and articles on STEM education.

Heba EL-Deghaidy Department chair and Professor of Science Education, The American University in Cairo. She leads the STEAM education initiative as an international approach to an interdisciplinary learning model. Her doctoral degree in science education comes from the University of Birmingham, UK. She was the PI of different international and national projects.

Mohamed El Nagdi Adjunct faculty, The American University in Cairo. He has a diverse educational background and expertise especially in STEM Education. His publication focuses on STEM teacher identity, equity, assessment, curriculum development, and professional development.

Allison Gonsalves Assistant Professor, McGill University, Montreal, Quebec. Gonsalves' research interests are in the area of science identities with a focus on gender and equity in higher education and out of school science learning contexts. She has taught elementary/secondary science teaching methods courses at McGill University for over ten years.

Yoshiyuki Gunji Associate Professor of Science Education, Faculty of Education, Shizuoka University. He is also the director of the STEAM Education Institute. He is the vice chair for Environmental Education

Committee at Shizuoka City Government. His major works are in the area of STEAM education especially on Chemistry and Engineering Education.

Elizabeth F. Hasseler Postdoctoral associate at the University of Nebraska-Lincoln. She was formerly a rural science teacher and mechanical engineer. Her doctorate focused on secondary science and engineering programs, and her research experience includes various topics, such as ornithoptic wings and effective science teaching.

Qianwen He Doctoral student in the Department of Science and Environmental Studies at the Education University of Hong Kong. Her research interests are science education, STEM education and teacher professional development.

Sophia Jeong Assistant Professor of Science Education in the Department of Teaching and Learning at The Ohio State University. Her scholarly work draws on theories of new materialisms to examine ontological complexities of subjectivities and socio-material relations in the science classrooms.

Katie L. Johnson Doctoral candidate in mathematics education, Department of Teaching, Learning and Teacher Education at the University of Nebraska-Lincoln. She has formerly worked as a middle school mathematics teacher.

Samia Khan Associate Professor and Director of the Master of Educational Technology Program, University of British Columbia, Vancouver, British Columbia. Formerly a public school science teacher in Canada, Khan completed her doctorate from the University of Massachusetts-Amherst. She researches model-based teaching and learning, STEM teacher education, and educational technologies.

Eva Knoll Associate professor, Université du Québec à Montréal, Montreal, Quebec. Knoll is a professor in the Mathematics Department where she teaches mathematics and mathematics education courses to pre-service and in-service teachers and graduate researchers. Her research focuses on the mathematical reasoning involved in making art using a phenomenological approach.

Yoshisuke Kumano Professor emeritus, appointed professor, vice director of STEAM Education Institute, Shizuoka University. He is also currently the director of NPO Shizuoka STEAM Education Development

Center and the director of Shizuoka STEM Academy Supported by Japan Science and Technology Agency. He was the past president of EASE.

B. Sumeyye Kurutas Doctoral student and graduate assistant in mathematics education at the University of Delaware in USA. Her research interests are teacher learning, teacher professional development, instructional coaching, and reflective journaling.

Digna Couso Lagarón Tenured Lecturer of Science Education at the Universitat Autònoma de Barcelona, where she teaches pre-service primary and secondary school teachers.Her research interests include communities of practice, research-based design of teaching and learning sequences and equity and gender balance in STEM education.

Tian Luo Assistant professor working at Capital Normal University, China. Her research interests include science education, STEM education, teacher education, and so on. She has published some first-author research papers in SSCI journals and participated in the editorial work of several academic books.

Teresa Lupión-Cobos Associate Professor of Science Education at the University of Málaga with a degree in Chemistry and PhD in Organic Chemistry.Secondary education teacher and science teacher trainee.Her research focused on scientific literacy and teachers' professional development to incorporate the inquiry approach, through STEAM experiences in pre-service and in-service teaching.

Ricardo Martinez Assistant Professor of Mathematics Education in the Department of Curriculum and Instruction, College of Education, Pennsylvania State University. Martinez's research focuses on teaching and learning mathematics for Emergent Bilinguals, ethnomathematics, teacher education, critical mathematics education, and community engagement through Youth Participatory Action Research (YPAR).

Lisa Martin-Hansen Professor of Science Education and former Department Chair of Science Education (2013–2022) at California State University, Long Beach in California, USA. Lisa served as president of the Association for Science Teacher Education (ASTE), 2015–2016. She holds a PhD from The University of Iowa in Iowa City, USA.

Ainoa Marzabal Professor of Science Education in the Faculty of Education at the Pontificia Universidad Católica de Chile (Chile). During that period (2004–2010), she also worked as a Physics, Chemistry and Mathematics teacher in the Spanish school system.

Dominic Mashoko Senior Lecturer of Science Education and Chemistry at Great Zimbabwe University, Masvingo Province of Zimbabwe. He teaches science methods, chemistry, and science technology courses. He has authored several articles in refereed journals. His research focuses on indigenous knowledge (IK), culture, and STEM education.

Toshihiko Masuda Leading senior mentor in the Shizuoka STEM Academy at Shizuoka University, supported by Japan Science and Technology Agency. He was the past director for Shizuoka Science Museum, Ru · Ku · Ru. He was the principal at several middle schools at the Shizuoka City.

Deepika Menon Assistant Professor of Science Education, in the Department of, Teaching, Learning and Teacher Education, at the University of Nebraska-Lincoln. Her research focuses on preservice and in-service integrated STEM education, self-efficacy, and identity development. She serves as the coordinator of the elementary preservice science education program.

Cristian Merino Professor of Science Education in the Chemistry Institute at the Pontificia Universidad Católica de Valparaíso (Chile). Cristian is director of the Center for Excellence in Teaching and Learning (PUCV).

Brant G. Miller Professor of Science Education in the Department of Curriculum and Instruction at the University of Idaho (USA). Prior to his current position and graduate work, he was an eighth-grade science teacher in Western South Dakota.

Nor Farahwahidah Abdul Rahman Social science researcher majoring in STEM education. Currently, she is working as a senior lecturer at the School of Education, Faculty of Social Sciences and Humanities, Universiti Teknologi Malaysia. Her works mainly focus on scientific epistemology, education for sustainability, and engineering education.

Reyhan Ada Safak Doctoral candidate of Mathematics Education in the Department of Teaching and Learning at The Ohio State University.

Mutlu Şen-Akbulut Assistant professor in the Department of Computer Education and Educational Technology at Boğaziçi University. She completed her PhD from the University of Georgia in the area of Learning, Design, and Technology. Her research interests include instructional design, technology integration in education, and pre-service teacher education.

Pratim Sengupta Professor of Learning Sciences and Research Chair of STEM Education, University of Calgary, Calgary, Alberta.Following his PhD in Learning Sciences at Northwestern, Sengupta founded the Mind, Matter & Media Lab at University of Calgary conducting research in a broad range of areas including modelling complex systems.

Mohamed A. Shahat Assistant Professor of Science Education at Sultan Qaboos University (SQU), Oman, and an associate professor at Aswan University, Egypt. He holds a PhD from the University of Duisburg-Essen, Germany. Currently, he is leading various national strategic research projects, including STEM and entrepreneurial education, at SQU.

Marie-Claire Shanahan Professor of Learning Sciences, and Research Chair of Science Education and Public Engagement with Science, University of Calgary, Calgary, Alberta.

Wendy Simms Professor, Vancouver Island University, Nanaimo, British Columbia. Simms teaches science and research methods, sustainability, and teacher identity. Her research focuses on citizen science in classroom settings and the design of learning environments that foster identity exploration and development. She is actively involved in science and sustainability outreach.

Winnie Wing-Mui So Professor in the Department of Science and Environmental Studies and director of the Centre for Environment and Sustainable Development at the Education University of Hong Kong. Her research interests include STEM education, Science Education and Environmental Education.

Youngjin Song Lecturer in the Department of Science Education at California State University, Long Beach. She previously worked at University of Northern Colorado as an associate professor. As a former chemistry teacher, she is interested in STEM teachers' professional growth. She holds a PhD from the University of Georgia, USA.

Hassan H. Tairab Professor of Science Education, UAE University, with a responsibility of teaching and supervising science education students. Tairab has published and presented science education research in various international journals and meetings. His research interest focuses on issues related to teaching and learning of science.

Amanda Thomas Associate professor in the Department of Teaching, Learning and Teacher Education at the University of Nebraska-Lincoln. She also serves as Elementary Teacher Education Coordinator. Thomas' research primarily focuses on preservice elementary mathematics and technology education.

Guy Trainin Professor in the Department of Teaching, Learning and Teacher Education at the University of Nebraska-Lincoln. He has served as Elementary Teacher Education Coordinator, Graduate Chair, and Department Chair. Trainin's research is on teacher education, literacy integration with technology and the arts, and innovative schooling.

William R. Veal Professor of Science Education and Chemistry at the College of Charleston, South Carolina. He teaches science methods, chemistry, and environmental science courses. His research focuses on science teacher preparation as it relates to pedagogical content knowledge, creativity, and standards.

Dawn Wiseman Associate professor, Bishop's University, Sherbrooke, Quebec. Wiseman's teaching, research and service are very much interconnected and interrelated focusing on the manner in which Indigenous and Western ways of knowing, being, and doing might circulate together in STEM/STEAM teaching and learning (kindergarten through post-secondary education).

Defne Yabaş Assistant professor at Bahçeşehir University, Turkey. She works also as associate director at the university's STEM education research center: BAUSTEM. Her major is in mathematics education. After graduation, she completed her MA, and PhD studies in curriculum and instruction with a focus on mathematics education.

Takahiro Yamamoto Assistant Professor, Concentration in Science Education, Major in Subject Education Faculty of Education, Shizuoka University. He is also Assistant Professor, Training Course for School Teachers, Graduate School of Education, Shizuoka University. His specialized research and study is Biological Education in Science Education.

Chi Ho Yeung Associate professor in the Department of Science and Environmental Studies at the Education University of Hong Kong. His research interests include statistical physics, spin and disordered systems, transportation networks, optimization and routing, recommendation systems, complex and social networks, artificial intelligence, educational technology and STEM education.

List of Figures

List of Tables

CHAPTER 1

STEM Teacher Education: An Overview

Youngjin Song, Lisa Martin-Hansen, Valarie L. Akerson, Gayle A. Buck, and Sulaiman M. Al-Balushi

Introduction

In the media and in educational circles, we've heard the acronym STEM (science, technology, engineering, and mathematics) referenced in many ways in the last two decades. STEM is important and central to preparing scientifically literate citizens who are ready to make decisions in a world full of information and complex choices. Furthermore, STEM education

Y. Song • L. Martin-Hansen (✉)
Department of Science Education, California State University Long Beach, Long Beach, CA, USA
e-mail: Youngjin.Song@csulb.edu; Lisa.Martin@csulb.edu

V. L. Akerson • G. A. Buck
Indiana University, Bloomington, IN, USA
e-mail: vakerson@indiana.edu; gabuck@iu.edu

S. M. Al-Balushi
College of Education, Sultan Qaboos University, Muscat, Oman
e-mail: shalushi@squ.edu.om

S. M. Al-Balushi et al. (eds.), *Reforming Science Teacher Education Programs in the STEM Era*, Palgrave Studies on Leadership and Learning in Teacher Education,
https://doi.org/10.1007/978-3-031-27334-6_1

is considered as a means to foster a scientific and technical workforce for national competitiveness, innovation, and economic growth. Several influential education, policy, and business groups created reports describing the need for expanding and improving STEM education (e.g., AAAS, 1990, 1993; Carnegie Corporation Of New York, 2009; NCMSTC, 2000; NGA, 2007; NRC, 1996, 2007, 2012a; NSB, 2007; PCAST, 2012; cited in NRC, 2014).

The emphasis on STEM education has called for reshaping science education globally. STEM education has influenced science education standards, designs, and practices in various K-12 schools and higher education institutions, often in different ways. New school curricula, extra-curricular programs, instructional methods, and university programs have been created across different STEM education communities. At the center of these changes have been educators (elementary and secondary teachers), who have been considered to be the main implementers of STEM-related initiatives. Accordingly, teacher preparation institutions have made efforts to prepare current and prospective K-12 teachers for STEM education. This edited book presents different international and cultural practices in redesigning teacher education programs that prepare science teachers in response to the progressive development in STEM education.

This chapter first seeks to answer the question, "What is STEM?" by providing an overview of the nature of each STEM discipline as the acronym STEM has often been used as an "ambiguous slogan" (Bybee, 2013). The next section briefly explores how the concept of STEM has played out in teacher education programs, followed by contributions of the current book. Lastly, the summaries of each chapter are provided.

Defining STEM

There are several different definitions of STEM that exist in the field. Bybee (2013) described nine different perspectives of STEM education, ranging from one simply considering STEM to be one of the single-fields (science, or math, or engineering or technology) to the view of STEM as a transdisciplinary with each component (S-T-E-M) fully integrated. In the last perspective a major issue, such as global pandemic, for example, could be taught in a way that includes all four disciplines in a meaningful way, when it makes sense to learn the subjects in a meaningful and integrated/interdisciplinary manner. Similarly, other scholars characterized STEM education into different levels depending on how each field is integrated (e.g., Akaygun & Aslan-Tutak, 2016; Mpofu, 2019; Vasquez et al., 2013).

Bybee notes the presence of different perspectives does not necessarily mean one is preferable over the other. It may simply mean that individuals may prefer one definition to the others given their own perspectives and instructional/learning settings. In this volume, we find these various perspectives and preferences. Thus, it is necessary to define the natures of the individual disciplines to be able to recognize them and their interdependence. In the subsections below, we provide a brief overview of the natures of the STEM disciplines.

Nature of Science. Nature of Science (NOS) has been recommended to be part of the inclusion of science education for decades, though it has still not often been included in K-12 classrooms. Lederman and Lederman (2020) define NOS as the non-controversial characteristics that define the type of scientific knowledge developed through scientific inquiry. First, students should conceptualize the distinction between observations and inferences, with observations being descriptive statements of natural phenomena as obtained by the senses. Inferences would be interpretations of those observations. Second, similar to observations and inferences, students should understand the distinction between scientific theories and laws. Theories and laws are different types of scientific knowledge and one does not develop into the other. Laws are statements or descriptions of the relationships among observable phenomena. Theories are inferred explanations for observable phenomena. Third, even though scientific knowledge is derived from observations of the natural world, it also includes human imagination and creativity. Science involves the invention of explanations from data. Fourth, related to that is that scientific knowledge is subjective, or theory laden. Scientists' background knowledge, experience, training, and expectations influence their work. These factors develop a mindset that influences the kinds of scientific questions explored and interpretations made. Also related, is that science is practiced within a larger culture, and scientists are part of that culture. This culture is influenced by science, but it also influences science. Sixth, scientific knowledge is never certain, as scientific claims can change as new evidence is collected, or existing evidence is interpreted differently. Thus, scientific knowledge is reliable, but tentative.

Nature of Technology. According to Cullen and Guo (2020) technology is both the tools that are used and also the systematic processes by which problems are solved. Views about nature of technology are shaped by individuals' cultures, experiences, and backgrounds. Nature of technology is not included in any standards documents, and so the impetus to teach it may be less than disciplines where it is included. Arthur (2009) claims that the "ology" part is missing from research on technology. Wahab et al. (2012) state there are some common characteristics that could be considered as comprising the nature of technology, including (1) physical production, (2) knowledge, skills, and approach of application, and (3) organization into system. Kruse (2013) reminds us that technology is not just electronics, but should include identifying technology, the technological process, the idea that technology is not neutral, the limitations of technology, tradeoffs, and interactions of technology and culture.

Nature of Engineering. Deniz et al. (2020) noted that with the advent of the NGSS, there came special emphasis on engineering, and engineering was to be a discipline included in U. S. science classrooms. Engineering can be seen as including three domains, with engineering as a body of knowledge, engineering as a set of practices, and engineering as a way of knowing, which would be called the nature of engineering (NOE) knowledge (Hartman, 2016). There is no full consensus about ideas that should be incorporated in NOE. However, Deniz et al. (2020) conducted a search that led them to recommend the following aspects being considered as important ideas about NOE. It begins with a definition of Engineering as engineers systematically engaging to achieve solutions for specific problems. They apply scientific knowledge to design these solutions. The aspects that are part of the NOE then, are that (1) NOE requires data and evidence, and is therefore empirical, (2) NOE is tentative as engineering design solutions can change, (3) engineers are creative and imaginative in coming up with designs for problem solutions, (4) there is no unique solution to a design problem; some solutions may be more suited to meet the criteria and constraints of the problem, (5) engineering design solutions are constructed through social negotiation, (6) engineering is a human activity, and is part of a social and cultural context, (7) engineering has criteria and constraints—criteria for what needs to be done, and constraints of materials, time, funding, and (8) engineering is failure-laden—failure in engineering design is inevitable, and therefore much testing and retesting is part of engineering design.

Nature of Mathematics. Hudson et al. (2020) stated that mathematicians classify mathematics into two separate, but complementary fields—pure mathematics and applied mathematics. Pure mathematics is mathematics for its own sake, and applied mathematics is mathematics used with other disciplines. They describe that these two different fields within mathematics complicate trying to define a nature of mathematics. Pair (2017) stated that there were core characteristics that can be agreed upon as nature of mathematics, at least for pure mathematics. These characteristics are that mathematical ideas and practices are part of cultural identity; mathematical knowledge is dynamic and subject to modification; mathematical inquiry is an exploration of mathematical ideas; and that these ideas are tested via social argumentation. Hudson et al. (2020) argue for the nature of mathematics to include (1) mathematics as a way of knowing, (2) mathematics is tentative because mathematical claims are based on assumptions, and (3) that mathematics is creative.

With our understanding of the natures of the STEM disciplines, it's clear that each discipline comprising STEM has its unique nature of knowledge developed differently. As a compilation of four disciplines, STEM should be a meaningful integration among all disciplines that make up STEM.

STEM Education and Teacher Preparation

With the current emphasis on STEM education globally, science educators in the K-12 system have been expected to adapt and teach new STEM-related initiatives in- and out-of- their classrooms. STEM education generally seeks to move from a discipline-based teaching and learning approach in science to an interdisciplinary approach in the context of real-world situations or problems (Breiner et al., 2012). In reviewing the relevant literature, the Committee on Integrated STEM Education pointed out that integrated STEM education has shown positive impacts on students' conceptual learning within the disciplines, interest development, and transformation of identities with respect to the STEM subjects (NRC, 2014).

Successful implementation of STEM education in ways that produce positive outcomes for students depends on the expertise of STEM educators (Bybee, 2013; NRC, 2014). Consequently, teacher preparation institutions have reformed their education programs for pre-service teachers or have provided professional development for in-service teachers to address a more integrated approach to STEM (Akaygun & Aslan-Tutak, 2020; Enderson et al., 2020). Several research studies about STEM professional development demonstrated teachers increased content knowledge, confidence for integrating STEM content areas, and improved classroom practices in STEM fields (e.g., Baxter et al., 2014; Guzey et al., 2014; Nadelson et al., 2012). At the pre-service level, researchers have investigated the learning outcomes of pre-service teachers in an innovative STEM class or program and reported pre-service teachers increased confidence around STEM, problem-solving skills, STEM teaching efficacy, facilitation of STEM literacies, and interdisciplinary collaboration (e.g., Akaygun & Aslan-Tutak, 2020; Alan et al., 2019; Murphy & Mancini-Samuelson, 2012; Rinke et al., 2016).

All the above research shows promise of supporting both new and experienced teachers in the STEM fields. However, it was pointed out "comparatively little attention has been given to growing need for STEM teacher preparation" (Rinke et al., 2016, p. 300) in spite of the international movement for STEM education. The Committee on integrated STEM Education also mentioned "little is known from research about how best to support the development of educator expertise" in integrated STEM education (NRC, 2014, p. 115) with very few teacher education programs that have made efforts to prepare STEM teachers in the United States. Moreover, we have noticed that research articles about STEM teacher preparations in scholarly journals written in English do not reflect the many voices of diverse countries. For instance, in a review article about teachers' perception of STEM integration by Margot and Kettler (2019), 80% of the analyzed studies were conducted in the United States. Thus, the current book presents a variety of different international practices in reforming science teacher education programs to respond to STEM education.

Contributions of the Current Book

The current book sheds light upon different international practices in reforming science teacher education programs to respond to STEM education. The chapter contributors represent 12 countries from Africa, Asia, Europe, the Middle East, North America, and South America, with great varieties in STEM teacher preparation structure and emphasis. The contexts include science-centric versions of STEM programs and more integrated models of STEM. This contextual diversity will help the readers learn about the design, opportunities, and challenges of STEM teacher preparation in different circumstances. We believe our contribution will inspire teacher preparation institutions to develop their STEM teacher education programs or benefit from the international practices presented in the book to integrate different STEM-based experiences into their existing in-service programs. Researchers interested in collaborating with other countries can have a glimpse into some of the variety that exists. In this way, it is possible to look to these examples to create innovations and improvements in our respective efforts in STEM education.

Although some published books (Goodell & Koç, 2020; Green, 2014; Leonard et al., 2019) focus on preparing STEM teachers as the main topic, these books are mainly centered on the US experience. Conversely, the current book is more diversified and presents a wide range of international experiences. It illustrates different global perspectives and shares practices of different educational contexts. This perspective helps the reader understand how different international settings have dealt with various challenges in preparing STEM teachers. These examples can help institutions consider possible improvements in their current STEM teacher preparation programs.

Others (e.g., Penprase, 2020) highlight different teaching practices of STEM-related disciplines at the college level. In contrast, the current book focuses on teacher education programs that prepare STEM school teachers. Another book by Uzzo et al. (2018) characterizes the pedagogical content knowledge (PCK) in STEM that STEM teachers and trainers need. Our book differs from this book by illustrating how STEM teacher education programs have been re-defined and re-designed in several countries around the globe. Furthermore, a book by Banks and Barlex (2020) presents different pedagogical approaches for teachers to teach STEM topics. Our book has a different focus as it concerns teacher education programs. The models will illustrate various STEM programs that can inspire new ideas and changes in current programs.

Chapter Overviews

Dominic Mashoko and William Veal in Chap. 2 examined implementation of the STEM policy in science teacher preparation programs in different African countries in the south. Through the lens of a neoliberal framework, the interview data from ten lecturers presented how they conceptualized STEM, how STEM policy has influenced science teacher preparation, and what kinds of challenges they encountered.

In Chap. 3, Isha DeCoito gives an in-depth look at Canada's first STEM teacher preparation program as well as the STEM Specialty Focus and accompanying courses which highlight the nature and integration of the disciplines of STEM. Detail is provided about opportunities for teacher candidates to deepen their understanding of STEM concepts and enhance STEM skills as well as successes and challenges in the program.

A number of scholars from Canada, in Chap. 4, have provided multiple perspectives of STEM teacher preparation in several provinces. Authors within four large geopolitical regions in Canada include G. Michael Bowen, Dawn Wiseman, Marie-Claire Shanahan, Samia Khan, Allison Gonsalves, Pratim Sengupta, Wendy Simms, Eva Knoll, and Ashley Carter. In this chapter, the authors provide a description of the programs at their institution as well as other institutions within their jurisdiction. They also summarize current practices, identify systemic issues that may limit how and where STEM teacher education is occurring. Lastly, they describe potential solutions to those issues.

In Chap. 5, Cristian Merino Rubilar, Ainoa Marzabal, Brant G. Miller and Ximena Carrasco Romero present how recent national policies for teacher education and a new science curriculum have reshaped science teacher education in the STEM era in Chile. The detailed descriptions of STEM-oriented teacher preparation programs at two higher education institutions in Chile are expected to provide exemplary experiences for science educators who are in the process of transforming science teacher education more toward STEM approaches.

Heba EL-Deghaidy and Mohamed El Nagdi, in Chap. 6 evaluate the impact of a STEM diploma program offered to the fresh graduates of science teacher education programs and to the existing science teachers to respond to the increasing demands in Egypt for STEM specialists. The program's graduates expressed its positive impact on their classroom practices and perceived it as a valuable route to their professional growth.

STEM teacher preparation policies are addressed in conjunction with the STEM education initiatives in Hong Kong in Chap. 7 by Yu Chen, Chi Ho Yeung, Tian Luo, Qianwen He, and Winnie Wing-Mui So. In particular, it provides in-depth descriptions of pre-service teacher preparation programs at both primary and secondary levels. The chapter informs future direction of STEM teacher preparation based on the research on STEM teacher preparation in Hong Kong.

The authors of Chap. 8 provide an in-depth description of one exemplary pre-service STEM/STEAM-based teacher education program to illustrate the STEM reform initiative in Japan. This includes detailed information of the major changes in education policy. The chapter also illustrates the partnership between the university and the local schools, in which pre-service teachers play a critical role in implementing the STEM curriculum.

Muhammad Hadi Bunyamin and Nor Farahwahidah Abdul Rahman present in Chap. 9 an initial exploration of the integration of the STEM fields in pre-service and in-service programs in Malaysia. In their teacher education program, STEM is offered as an elective course that not all teacher candidates are required to enroll in. Their chapter also explores the perceptions of school practitioners on the importance of integrating STEM education in schools and teacher education programs.

Mohamad Shahat and Mohammed Al Amri evaluate whether the programs prepare their candidates to teach for STEM in Chap. 10. Thus, the chapter lists examples of STEM topics, assignments, and experiences in different courses and components of both pre-service programs in Oman. The authors also discuss various shortcomings and provide recommendations to improve the current pre-service programs to prepare prospective teachers to teach for STEM.

In Chap. 11 Teresa Lupión-Cobos, Digna Couso Lagarón, Marta Romero Ariza, and Jordi Domènech Casal describe the different STEM modules offered to pre-service science teachers in Spain and how different STEM approaches have informed student teachers' school practices. The authors discuss levels of STEM integration, the role of disciplinary content knowledge, and the development of critical competencies. The authors stress that STEM provides new opportunities to share high-quality pedagogical content knowledge through the initiatives described in the chapter.

Defne Yabaş, Sedef Canbazoğlu-Bilici, Tuğba Abanoz, B. Sümeyye Kurutaş, and M. Sencer Corlu in Chap. 12 illustrate an in-service professional development STEM program in Turkey designed and delivered collaboratively by university teacher educators and experienced science teachers. The authors propose that the unique design of this STEM PD could be provided to prospective teachers to develop their experience with STEM education.

In Chap. 13, Authors Sophia Jeong, Kathryn M. Bateman, Sevil Akaygun, Fatma Aslan-Tutak, Mutlu Şen-Akbulut, and Reyhan Ada Safak describe different educational contexts for science and mathematics teacher preparation in the United States and Turkey. For the United States of America (US), they use the context of two research-intensive, public universities as well as a small liberal arts college in the Mid-Atlantic region of the United States. Mathematics and science educators from Turkey describe specific contexts which frame and conceptualize their science and mathematics teacher preparation programs for STEM education in Turkey with their interdisciplinary, collaborative, and integrated nature of STEM education.

Deepika Menon, Amy S. Bauer, Katie Johnson, Elizabeth F. Hasseler, Amanda Thomas, Ricardo Martinez, and Guy Trainin, in Chap. 14, share an in-depth perspective of one institution of higher education in the United States of America. This team of multi-disciplinary STEM educators and researchers re-designed learning pathways threaded throughout concurrent elementary science, mathematics, and technology methods courses within a STEM semester. Successes and challenges associated with curricular changes are described along with recommendations for ways other teacher educators could restructure their elementary education programs for STEM integration.

In Chap. 15, Valarie L. Akerson and Gayle A. Buck begin with their definition of STEM and then introduce readers to the Next Generation Science Standards (NGSS) as the framework from which STEM teacher preparation programs can be enacted within the United States of America. Akerson and Buck highlight the potential of NGSS to encourage and support STEM instruction in a meaningful way. They then give an example of STEM instruction in a teacher preparation program in a US institution of higher education including examples for how NGSS can be used to encourage STEM education in meaningful ways from various grade levels, including primary and intermediate elementary grades, as well as middle and high school levels.

Hassan Tairab and Shashidhar Belbase discuss in Chap. 16 a central challenge in the United Arab Emirates that science teachers face when teaching STEM curriculum: the ability to integrate STEM fields within the undertaken topic. The authors argue that the integration issue has drawn considerable attention to reforming school science and mathematics curricula and teacher preparation programs. The chapter provides an overview of curriculum reforms in response to STEM education and the impacts on science teacher education policies and challenges. Different examples of STEM curriculum reforms around the globe are illustrated.

Looking across the various types of STEM instruction in these worldwide examples, we find that there are generally four types of STEM models of teacher preparation.

- ***Fully integrated STEM teacher preparation programs***: The international practices presented in this book do not reflect fully integrated

STEM teacher preparation programs. However, there is one case in Egypt presented in Chap. 6 of a professional diploma that admits in-service teachers from different STEM disciplines. One of the program's main aims is to prepare them to work at STEM-based schools by exposing them to various practices related to STEM education, such as utilizing engineering design in teaching.

- ***Integrated curriculum and experiences in teacher preparation programs:*** Most of the international contributions in this book present teacher education programs that offer new modules or experiences within their study plans to focus on STEM education. These modules expose pre-service teachers to learning theories, teaching methods, and practices related to STEM/STEAM approaches.
- ***Partnerships with schools:*** Some teacher preparation programs presented in this book collaborate with schools to deliver STEM-based professional development programs to in-service teachers (while the teacher preparation program may be single-subject specific). Although the teacher educators (i.e., faculty) of these teacher education programs are the primary instructors of the STEM-based professional development programs, their students (i.e., pre-service teachers) assist in the delivery. This experience enhances their knowledge, skills, and dispositions of STEM education.
- ***No STEM integration (not represented in these chapters, self-selection issue):*** As this book project invited authors to write about STEM education, programs that did not see themselves enacting STEM, but rather focusing on a single (or dual) subject, self-selected out and therefore were not included in the book chapters as examples. Because of this situation, the editors reached out to colleagues who could share examples of single or dual subject-specific teacher preparation (versus a "STEM" emphasis). Doris Jorde, Professor of Science Education at the University of Oslo in Norway, explained that STEM is a very American idea. Norwegian teacher preparation programs integrated "aspects of technology into our programs in higher education and school science and math courses. We never talk about engineering, and technology is only a minor course idea at junior high school which has never really found a place in our curriculum." (D. Jorde, personal communication,

Sept. 20, 2020). Additionally, in Germany, the situation is somewhat complex. Teacher preparation in STEM is a program for each science discipline because in Germany those in teacher preparation programs study two subjects. For example, one can study mathematics and physics to become a teacher. It is a dedicated program, where one takes classes in physics with the physics students and in education with students studying pedagogy (Neumann et al., 2017). In the UK, STEM is generally viewed as a collection of subjects rather than integrated subject[s] and aim for requirements in STEM disciplines for a STEM career agenda (Wong et al., 2016). Therefore, UK teacher preparation is similar to those programs in Norway and Germany with in-depth study in sciences, but with mathematics and technology connections when necessary to learn the specific science subjects. There is seldom an emphasis on engineering.

Final Thoughts

In conclusion, science teacher programs around the globe have different interpretations of STEM education, and the changes in these programs illustrate diverse professional practices. Furthermore, the contributing authors discuss the impact of these STEM-based practices and approaches on the pre-service teachers' awareness, teaching practices, and perceptions. In some chapters, partnership and collaboration with in-service teachers, practitioners, and their schools are central themes. We hope the book provides teacher educators and researchers with various innovative approaches to align science teacher preparation programs and creative educational projects with the continuous development of STEM education.

References

Akaygun, S., & Aslan-Tutak, F. (2016). STEM images revealing stem conceptions of pre-service chemistry and mathematics teachers. *International Journal of Education in Mathematics, Science and Technology, 4*(1), 56–71.

Akaygun, S., & Aslan-Tutak, F. (2020). Collaboratively learning to teach STEM: A model for learning to integrate STEM education in preservice teacher education. In V. L. Akerson & G. A. Buck (Eds.), *Critical questions in STEM education* (pp. 147–163). Springer.

Alan, B., Zengin, F. K., & Kececi, G. (2019). Using STEM applications for supporting integrated teaching knowledge of pre-service science teachers. *Journal of Baltic Science Education, 18*(2), 158–170.

American Association for the Advancement of Science. (1990). Science for all Americans. Oxford University Press.

(American Association for the Advancement of Science), & American Association for the Advancement of Science. (1993). Benchmarks for science literacy. Project 2061 Oxford University Press.

Arthur, W. B. (2009). *The nature of technology: What it is and how it evolves.* Simon & Schuster.

Banks, F., & Barlex, D. (2020). Teaching STEM in the secondary school: Helping teachers meet the challenge. *Routledge.* https://doi.org/10.4324/9780429317736

Baxter, J. A., Ruzicka, A., Beghetto, R. A., & Livelybrooks, D. (2014). Professional development strategically connecting mathematics and science: The impact on teachers' confidence and practice. *School Science and Mathematics, 114*(3), 102–113.

Breiner, J. M., Harkness, S. S., Johnson, C. C., & Koehler, C. M. (2012). What is STEM? A discussion about conceptions of STEM in education and partnerships. *School Science and Mathematics, 112*(1), 3–11.

Bybee, R. W. (2013). *The case for STEM education: Challenges and opportunities.* NSTA Press.

Carnegie Corporation of New York. (2009). The Opportunity Equation: Transforming Mathematics and Science Education for Citizenship and the Global Economy. Available at https://www.carnegie.org/publications/theopportunity-equation-transforming-mathematics-and-science-education-for-citizenship-and-the-globaleconomy/ 2013 (Retrieved online: March 23, 2023).

Cullen, T. A., & Guo, M. (2020). The nature of technology. In V. L. Akerson & G. A. Buck (Eds.), *Critical questions in STEM education* (pp. 21–32). Springer.

Deniz, H., Yesilyurt, E., Newman, S. J., & Kaya, E. (2020). Toward defining nature of engineering in the next generation science standards era. In V. L. Akerson & G. A. Buck (Eds.), *Critical questions in STEM education* (pp. 33–44). Springer.

Enderson, M. C., Reed, P. A., & Grant, M. R. (2020). Secondary STEM teacher education. In C. C. Johnson, M. J. Mohr-Schroeder, T. J. Moore, & L. D. English (Eds.), *Handbook of research on STEM education* (pp. 349–360). Routledge.

Goodell, J. E., & Koç, S. (Eds.). (2020). *Preparing STEM teachers: The UTeach replication model.* Information Age Publishing, Inc.

Green, S. L. (2014). STEM education: How to train 21st-century teachers. *Nova Science Publishers.* Incorporated.

Guzey, S. S., Tank, K., Wang, H.-H., Roehrig, G., & Moore, T. (2014). A high-quality professional development for teachers of grades 3–6 for implementing engineering into classrooms. *School Science and Mathematics, 114*(3), 139–153.

Hartman, B. D. (2016). *Aspects of the nature of engineering for K-12 science education: A Delphi study.* Doctoral dissertation, Oregon State University. https://ir.library.oregonstate.edu/concern/graduate_thesis_or_dissertations/t148fk693

Hudson, R. A., Creager, M. A., Burgess, A., & Gerber, A. (2020). The nature of mathematics and its impact on K-12 education. In V. L. Akerson & G. A. Buck (Eds.), *Critical questions in STEM education* (pp. 45–57). Springer.

Kruse, J. W. (2013). Implications of the nature of technology for teaching and teacher education. In M. Clough & J. Olson (Eds.), *The nature of technology* (pp. 345–369). Sense.

Lederman, N. G., & Lederman, J. (2020). Nature of scientific knowledge and scientific inquiry. In V. L. Akerson & G. A. Buck (Eds.), *Critical questions in STEM education* (pp. 3–20). Springer.

Leonard, J., Burrows, A. C., & Kitchen, R. S. (Eds.). (2019). Recruiting, preparing, and retaining stem teachers for a global generation. *Brill Sense.* https://doi.org/10.1163/9789004399990

Margot, K. C., & Kettler, T. (2019). Teachers' perception of STEM integration and education: A systematic literature review. *International Journal of STEM Education, 6*(1), 1–16.

Mpofu, V. (2019). A theoretical framework for implementing STEM education. In K. G. Fomunyam (Ed.), *Theorizing STEM education in the 21st century.* IntechOpen. https://www.intechopen.com/chapters/68740

Murphy, T. P., & Mancini-Samuelson, G. J. (2012). Graduating STEM competent and confident teachers: The creation of a STEM certificate for elementary education majors. *Journal of College Science Teaching, 42*(2), 18.

Nadelson, L. S., Seifert, A., Moll, A. J., & Coats, B. (2012). I-STEM summer institute: An integrated approach to teacher professional development in STEM. *Journal of STEM Education, 13*(2), 69–83.

NCMSTC (National Commission on Mathematics and Science Teaching for the 21st Century). (2000). Before It's Too Late: A Report to the Nation from the National Commission on Mathematics and Science Teaching for the 21st Century. Available at https://journals.ekb.eg/article_31944.html (Retrieved March 23, 2023).

National Governors Association (NGA). (2007). Innovation America: A Final Report. Available at https://files.eric.ed.gov/fulltext/ED504101.pdf (Retrieved: March 23, 2023).

National Research Council (NRC). (1996). National Science Education Standards. Washington: National Academy Press. Available at https://www.nap.edu/catalog.php?record_id=4962 (Retrieved March 23, 2023).

National Research Council (NRC). (2007). Taking Science to School: Learning and Teaching Science in Grades K-8. Washington: National Academies Press. Available at https://www.nap.edu/catalog.php?record_id=11625 (Retrieved March 23, 2023).

National Research Council (NRC). (2012a). A Framework for K–12 Science Education: Practices, Crosscutting Concepts, and Core Ideas. Washington: National Academies Press. Available at https://www.nap.edu/catalog.php?record_id=13165 (Retrieved March 23, 2023).

National Research Council (NRC). (2013). Next generation science standards: For states, by states.

National Research Council (NRC). (2014). *STEM integration in K-12 education: Status, prospects, and an agenda for research.* National Academies Press.

National Science Board (NSB). (2007). National Action Plan for Addressing the Critical Needs of the U.S. Science, Technology, Engineering and Mathematics Education System. Available at https://www.nsf.gov/nsb/documents/2007/stem_action.pdf (Retrieved March 23, 2023).

Neumann, K., Härtig, H., Harms, U., & Parchmann, I. (2017). Science teacher preparation in Germany. In J. Pedersen, T. Isozaki, & T. Hirano (Eds.), *Model science teacher preparation programs: An international comparison of what works best* (pp. 29–52). Information Age Publishing.

Pair, J. D. (2017). *The nature of mathematics: A heuristic inquiry.* Unpublished doctoral dissertation. Middle Tennessee State University.

President's Council of Advisors on Science and Technology (PCAST). (2012). Report to the President. Engage to Excel: Producing One Million Additional College Graduates with Degrees in Science, Technology, Engineering and Mathematics. Available at https://files.eric.ed.gov/fulltext/ED541511.pdf (Retrieved: March 23, 2023).

Penprase, B. E. (2020). STEM education for the 21st century. *Springer Nature.* https://doi.org/10.1007/978-3-030-41633-1

Rinke, C. R., Gladstone-Brown, W., Kinlaw, C. R., & Cappiello, J. (2016). Characterizing STEM teacher education: Affordances and constraints of explicit STEM preparation for elementary teachers. *School Science and Mathematics, 116*(6), 300–309.

Uzzo, S. M., Graves, S. B., Shay, E., Harford, M., Thompson, R., & (Eds.). (2018). *Pedagogical content knowledge in STEM: Research to practice.* Springer International Publishing. https://doi.org/10.1007/978-3-319-97475-0

Vasquez, J. A., Sneider, C., & Comer, M. (2013). *STEM lesson essentials, grades 3–8: Integrating science, technology, engineering, and mathematics.* Heinemann.

Wahab, S. A., Rose, R. C., & Osman, S. I. W. (2012). Defining the concepts of technology and technology transfer: A literature analysis. *International Business Research, 5*(1), 61–71.

Wong, V., Dillon, J., & King, H. (2016). STEM in England: Meanings and motivations in the policy arena. *International Journal of Science Education, 38*(15), 2346–2366. https://doi.org/10.1080/09500693.2016.1242818

CHAPTER 2

Implementing STEM Policy in African Nations' Teacher Education Programs: Insights from Some Southern African Countries

Dominic Mashoko and William R. Veal

Introduction

STEM has recently become a new tool, idea, policy driver, and theme for updating and transforming teacher education in science education. For example, STEM education in Zimbabwe in 2016 started as a strategy to boost economic development (Dekeza & Kufakunesu, 2017). While there

D. Mashoko
School of Education, Great Zimbabwe University, Masvingo, Zimbabwe
e-mail: dmashoko@gzu.ac.zw

W. R. Veal (✉)
Departments of Teacher Education and Chemistry, College of Charleston, Charleston, SC, USA
e-mail: vealw@cofc.edu

S. M. Al-Balushi et al. (eds.), *Reforming Science Teacher Education Programs in the STEM Era*, Palgrave Studies on Leadership and Learning in Teacher Education,
https://doi.org/10.1007/978-3-031-27334-6_2

are multiple definitions of STEM found in different organizations in the United States (e.g., National Science Foundation, National Research Council), countries in the southern part of Africa have produced policy statements for the establishment of STEM in primary and secondary education (e.g., South Africa and Lesotho). These policy documents focus on a general mandate to infuse STEM education into curriculum of different universities and not necessarily any direct reference for teacher preparation. For an example, Zimbabwe uses a more practical definition that focuses on the development of an individual to succeed in society and contribute to the economic growth of the country (Government of Zimbabwe, 2008).

At the university level, to enter STEM fields of study the focus of the student has to coincide with a progressive agenda that matches a "changing global landscape…in an increasingly technological and complex world" (Tytler & Self, 2020). To accomplish this goal, pre-service teacher education programs must prepare their pre-service teachers to develop university students for entrepreneurship.

The implementation of STEM education policy presents multiple challenges to most science teacher educators. Gadzirayi et al. (2016) noted barriers related to STEM implementation in Zimbabwe inclusive of lack of clarity on the basics and rationale for STEM and the lack of context in which STEM education is delivered in Zimbabwe. Mpofu (2019) proposed that for STEM education to be well implemented, "teachers will require a lot of support in terms of guiding frameworks, professional development, material development and many other resources" (p. 12). There are barriers related to advancing STEM education as an interdisciplinary study in education. These include the lack of investment in teacher professional development, poor preparation, and poor conditions and facilities. As a result of these challenges, there is poor implementation of STEM policy at the university levels. These barriers are exacerbated at the university level for teacher preparation due to a lack of specific policy statements for teacher preparation. It is against this backdrop that this chapter sought to explore the implementation of STEM policy in pre-service teacher education programs in universities in different African countries in the south.

Research Purpose

This research examined the policies and influences on the implementation of STEM into universities on science teacher preparation in different African countries in the south. To achieve the above research aim, the objectives of the study were to:

- Identify the implementation of STEM policy in universities and science teacher preparation in different African countries in the south
- Explore some of the challenges and opportunities of implementing STEM policy in universities on science teacher preparation in the south

Theoretical Framework

Given the current level of polarization within the political systems of many countries, and the economic drivers behind workforce development, the understanding of STEM implementation in the current educational landscape is best conducted through the lens of a neoliberal framework, defined as "an ensemble of economic and social policies, forms of governance, and discourses and ideologies" (Lipman, 2011, p. 8). Similarly, Harvey (2005) defines neoliberalism as "a theory of political economic practices that proposes that human wellbeing can best be advanced by liberating individual entrepreneurial freedoms and skills within an institutional framework " (p. 2). Thus, neoliberalism is a nexus point for government policies, culture, and education. The "interconnectivity of politics, history, and culture" provide the basis for viewing education and the policies impacting STEM across different countries (Carney, 2009, p. 70).

The literature is varied on what actually characterizes a neoliberal education system. For example, Apple (2000) argued that "the world, he says, is seen as intensely competitive economically, and students, as the future workforce, must be given the necessary skills and dispositions to compete efficiently and effectively" (p. 59). Manteaw (2008) concurred with this contention and further argued that "schools, according to this plan, must serve two overriding functions: ideological and labor training" (p. 121). Thus, STEM policy in teacher education in the context of a neoliberal framework involves the "production of knowledge and dispositions which are appropriate for servicing the economy'" (Gray et al., 2018, p. 475). In the context of a neoliberal marketing approach, Kandiko (2010) believed that there are shifts in higher education funding towards the hard and applied sciences (fields close to the market) and away from the social sciences and humanities (p. 157), so as to attain highest quality or greater economic payoff. This leaves schools of education and teacher preparation with less money to implement STEM policy.

Literature Review

This section reviews literature on the implementation of the STEM policy in education. It does so by defining policy, conceptualizing STEM education, and rationalizing the STEM policy integration. The section then rounds off by examining challenges to curriculum implementation of the STEM policy initiatives.

Defining Policy

Policy in general provides a general plan of action and lays rules and procedures. Gadzirayi et al. (2016) argued that "policy can be expressed in official statements and codified in formal documents subject to the vision, mission, goals and objectives of the decision makers with regards to their stakeholders" (p. 15). In this regard, policy entails a prescription of what should or should not be done with regards to a particular issue. It is envisaged that policy can be written or unwritten. In the context of a university, policy formulations are expressed in documents including program regulations, ministerial directives, and committee and senate reports. Hence, this study sought to examine universities' implementation of the STEM policy for teacher preparation in various African countries in the south.

Conceptualizing the Implementation of STEM Education

Breiner et al. (2012) report that the idea behind STEM originated in the United States as a strategy to strengthen its science and mathematics education in the early 1980s (e.g., National Commission on Excellence in Education [NCEE], 1983; National Science Foundation [NSF] and U.S. Department of Education, 1980). Gadzirayi et al. (2016) argued that STEM education is an integrated, interdisciplinary approach to learning that provided hands-on and relevant learning experiences for students. Czerniak and Johnson (2014) believed STEM integration as "interdisciplinary, multidisciplinary, transdisciplinary, thematic, integrated, connected, nested, sequenced, shared, blended, networked, and fused approach" (p. 398). Tsupros et al. (2009) defined STEM education as an interdisciplinary approach to learning where rigorous academic concepts were coupled with real-world lessons as students applied STEM in contexts that made connections between school and the outside world. From an African perspective, Mpofu (2019) presented a continuum of STEM integration that included four different approaches: disconnected, connected, complementary, and integrated.

Hurley (2001) identified five types of STEM integration that have historically been used as sequential, parallel, partial, enhanced, and total. This is in sync with Mpofu's (2019) characterization of STEM in terms of four levels. The first level is the separatist approach, S-T-E-M, which involves adding STEM with little or no integration to the school curriculum or each subject area. This is similar to a 'silo' (Dugger, 2010) or 'disconnected' (Akaygun & Aslan-Titak, 2016) approach. Level 2 involves the integration of two of the four disciplines (SteM) (e.g., integrating technology and engineering ideas into science and mathematics subjects). Akaygun and Aslan-Titak (2016) referred to Level 2 as a 'connected' approach. Level 3, S-T/E-M, focuses on E and T based pedagogy into science and mathematics subjects. Akaygun and Aslan-Titak (2016) referenced Level 3 as a 'complimentary' approach to curriculum. Level 4, STEM, approach combines all four subjects into one hybrid system of knowledge. This level is what Dugger (2010) called 'infusion' or Akaygun and Aslan-Titak (2016) called an 'integrated approach' of all STEM subjects. Then lastly, level 5, comprising of science, mathematics, arts, technology, and engineering (SMATE) subjects. This involves merging all STEM fields and capturing arts subjects. This level is in sync with what the Zimbabwe Ministry of Primary and Secondary Education regards as Science, Technology, Engineering, Arts, and Mathematics (STEAM) curriculum that encompasses arts subjects (Chitate, 2016).

Asunda (2014) articulately argued that STEM education represents, "connection points and overlap among science, technology, engineering, and mathematics" (p. 3). Kalolo (2016) affirmed that, "STEM education is more than just the grafting of 'technology' and 'engineering' layers onto standard science and mathematics curricula." In keeping with Kalolo's (2016) viewpoint, Voogt and Roblin (2012) argue that STEM is necessary to meet demands for twenty-first century skills for learners, namely: transversal (not directly linked to a specific field); multidimensional (includes knowledge, skills and attitudes); and association with higher order skills and behaviors.

Dugger (2010) presented the following ways of conceptualizing STEM implementation:

- S-T-E-M: This treats each discipline as in a 'silo' as an independent subject with little or no integration.
- SteM: This is when one teaches each of the four STEM disciplines with more emphasis going to one or two of the four (which is what is happening in most U.S. schools today).
- The third way is to integrate one of the STEM disciplines into the other three being taught. For example, engineering content can be integrated into science, technology, and mathematics courses.
- The fourth way is a more comprehensive way. It infuses all four disciplines into each other and teaches them as integrated subject matter. For example, there is technological, engineering, and mathematical content in science, so the science teacher would integrate the T, E, and M into the S.

The above views are in sync with Mutseekwa's (2021) assertion that "integrated STEM education therefore entails combining the subjects, using one subject to support the teaching of the other, utilizing the thematic approach in teaching and finding connections amongst the disciplines" (p. 77).

In Sub-Saharan Africa, Barrette et al. (2019) observed various STEM integration approaches, namely, integrated science curriculum (Zambia); the science technology, robotics, engineering, arts, and mathematics (STREAM) program (South Africa); 'vocationalisation' (Namibia); the innovation, science, practice, application, conceptualisation, entrepreneurship and systems (iSPACES) curriculum (Tanzania); and the science technology innovation (STI) policy (Lesotho). The policy statements in each of these countries promoted STEM as the basic component to further education initiatives that included teacher education.

Rationale for STEM Education

STEM education was adopted by many stakeholders in education across the globe, inclusive of developed and developing countries. In this study, a few examples of these countries shall suffice for our purpose here due to limitations of space. The launch of STEM in Zimbabwe came at a time when the country was economically hemorrhaging. STEM curriculum was introduced targeting sponsorship for students who enrolled for Advanced Level science subjects (Moyo, 2016). According to the Zimbabwean Ministry of Higher and Tertiary Education, Science and Technology Development (Editor, 2016), STEM provides competencies such as problem-solving, critical thinking, creativity, teamwork, communication skills, and conflict resolution (Chitate, 2016). The desire to improve economic stability was also reflected by the promulgation of the Zimbabwe Agenda for Sustainable Economic Transformation in 2018, and a Social Development Pillar for STEM in their Vision 2030 policy document that read, "Education: Education Curricula: To increase skills development in the country, emphasis will be placed on Science, Technology, Engineering and Mathematics (STEM) subjects" (Zimbabwe, 2018, p. 38). Murwira (2018) reported that the focus of STEM shifted to "manpower and infrastructure development." As a result, pre-service instructors and programs had to modify their courses to include information and experiences for future teachers so that their instruction could impact the students in schools.

The idea and implementation of STEM in education has become an increasingly important policy initiative in countries around the world to increase research, productivity, and industry (Anderson & Li, 2020). The idea that science and technology relate to all aspects of life allows STEM to easily be the foundation for advancement of industry and the economy in countries. In Africa, competition and economic survival have influenced the rapid growth of STEM in the workplace that has necessitated a focus on STEM in the school education system, which has direct impacts for teacher preparation. Pimthong and Williams (2020) argued that it would be in the best interest of a government to push for better education in the STEM subjects since they can "relate…to everyday life" (p. 290). Anderson and Li (2020) stated that STEM brings "new perspectives about possible foci and the value of school education" (p. 16). Badmus and Omosewo (2020) observed that "At the moment, Africa is a major consumer of technology, the implication is that a significant amount of her economy is drained to America, Europe, and Asia, owing to the purchases of useful but foreign technologies" (p. 103). Therefore, teaching with an emphasis on STEM would open African economies to more regional and global prospects.

With a national emphasis on improving STEM education to support the economy, effective STEM educators and curriculum are needed. Badmus and Omosewo (2020) stated, "Its [STEM] emergence in the classroom is…to shift the limit of human thinking and problem-solving ability, which may result in meaningful development and improved living" (p. 100). Tytler et al. (2019) stated that STEM encompasses development of critical and creative thinking skills. In South Africa, STREAM students are expected to invent, create, design, and solve community problems (Barrette et al., 2019).

Challenges and Barriers to STEM Integration

Ejiwale (2013) listed barriers of advancing STEM education in K-12 schools as: poor preparation and shortage in supply of qualified teachers; lack of investment in teacher professional development; lack of connection with individual learners; lack of research collaboration across STEM fields; poor content delivery and methods of assessment; poor conditions and facilities; and lack of hands-on training for students. These barriers can also be attributed to science teacher preparation due to the professional requirement of implementing core standards as a classroom teacher. Kalolo (2016) reported STEM integration threats in terms of negative perceptions towards STEM education by stakeholders, lack of policy connectivity, lack of inspiration, and lack of support. In Zimbabwe, National Assembly (2016) identified the lack of clarity on the basics and rationale of STEM as the main challenges to STEM education. Not only do pre-service teachers face the same challenges, but there is also a lack of preparation on experiencing and conducting hands-on STEM activities.

Methods

This chapter presents how teacher preparation institutes in Zimbabwe, Zambia, South Africa, Tanzania, Lesotho, Botswana, Malawi, and Namibia have altered their teacher preparation program to infuse characteristics of STEM due to neoliberal influences. Purposeful sampling was used to select ten science lecturers/professors from nine institutions of higher learning in eight different countries for interviews aimed at providing a deeper understanding of real-life experience on STEM implementation (Patton, 2002). The Covid-19 pandemic prompted innovative interviewing strategies such as telephoning and zoom meetings with participants.

This cross-cultural examination supported different neoliberal reasons for STEM implementation in these countries using different cases as units of analyses. Findings from this chapter add a voice to how and why STEM is being implemented in African countries in the south through a neoliberal framework.

Each conversational interview followed a semi-structured format focusing on understanding the policies that govern STEM implementation into teacher preparation in each country and how these policies influence the structure of the various institutions' science teacher preparation programs. Some of the questions, for example, asked what the definition of STEM in the country is; what the university emphasis on STEM education is, and what policy factors influence STEM integration. It was also asked; how STEM education was being implemented into the primary and secondary pre-service teacher education programs and what the challenges and barriers for STEM implementation were. Finally, it was asked how STEM implementation was assessed in their countries and what were the influences that impact implementation of STEM ideas into science teacher preparation courses and programs. Each interview lasted approximately 45 minutes. Some participants emailed answers to the questions back to the authors. All the interviews were conducted using Zoom and recorded for sharing with the entire research team and for ease in analysis. Additionally, interview participants were asked to provide any links/copies of any documents, policies, and the like that would assist in attaining a deeper understanding of the STEM implementation in their countries. Additional documents were added by the research team, for example the Zimbabwe National Qualifications Framework (2018) and the *International Handbook of Teacher Education* (Karras & Wolhuter, 2019).

Participants

Purposeful sampling was used to select ten science lecturers/professors from 9 institutions of higher learning in eight different countries The participants resided in Zimbabwe, Zambia, South Africa, Tanzania, Lesotho, Botswana, Malawi, and Namibia. Their appointments ranged from instructor and lecturer to professor in science education, and the list included two people working in the Ministry of Education in their countries and taught at a university. These participants were interviewed using a multiple case study, unit analysis aimed at providing a deeper understanding of real-life experience on STEM implementation (Patton, 2002). Additional informal interviews and discussions were conducted with colleagues within Zimbabwe who taught science methods courses or in teacher preparation programs focused on STEM integration.

Data Analysis

Documents analyzed included course outlines, national STEM policy statements, notes, syllabi, and reports. Document analysis and thematic reduction of interviews were used to evaluate the phenomena (Bryman, 2012). Interview transcripts were systematically evaluated for *a priori* themes and coded for relationships to neoliberal ideas. This cross-national examination supported different neoliberal reasons for STEM implementation in these eight countries.

Findings and Discussions

Three salient themes were identified: conceptualization of STEM by science educators and policy documents at the national and university levels, emphasis of STEM in the universities impacting pre-service teacher education, and barriers to STEM implementation at the pre-service level.

Conceptualization of STEM

The term STEM was conceptualized differently by participants in the study. One science lecturer in Zimbabwe defined it as "an integration of Science, Technology, Engineering and Mathematics skills in teaching and learning." Another science lecturer in South Africa concurred with this definition and further viewed it as, "one that deals with the teaching and learning of science, mathematics, engineering and technology so as to develop practical skills that can help drive or push economic development." One Professor in Zambia brought a slightly different dimension to the issue and argued that, "STEM can be an integrated approach that develops human skills and knowledge useful for national economic development." A government official in Lesotho stated, "Our policy is to implement STEM, so our universities use this to guide their curriculum. Yes, the idea does directly impact the pre-service programs so that the pre-service teachers must learn STEM."

The above excerpts show that STEM involves integration of science, technology, engineering, and technology in education and focuses on economic development of the country. These definitions concur with the definitions given by Chitate (2016) who suggest that STEM education should produce students with twenty-first century skills for use in everyday life. It can also be deduced that other participants believe that STEM is not limited to science subjects only but includes arts subjects as well. This matches with 'STEAM' curriculum that encompasses arts subjects as well (Chitate, 2016) and is interdisciplinary (Czerniak & Johnson, 2014).

University STEM Emphasis

Respondents agreed that their universities' emphasis on STEM education involves the integration of the four subjects of STEM, which should lead to the production of goods and services. This drive entails teaching students innovation and industrialization at the secondary and tertiary levels and a focus on competence-based curriculum at the primary level and heritage-based curriculum at the tertiary level. This has direct implications for training pre-service teachers to be prepared for implementing these ideas in the school curriculum. For example, one science lecturer in Zimbabwe commented further:

> Learning content at primary and secondary school level is guided by competence-based philosophy while at tertiary level teaching and learning is framed within heritage-based curriculum, which is Education 5.0 (teaching, research, community engagement, innovation, and industrialization) policy pushes STEM education at my university.

Another science lecturer in Zambia indicated that, "universities focus on production factors, where emphasis is placed on producing end products (students) who are self-reliant that are equipped with sustainable development skills." This was seen at the pre-service program level through the analyses of syllabi of science methods courses. Most of the syllabi reviewed contained statements that mentioned student learning outcomes related to problem-solving skills and integration of content and pedagogy. Also, another lecturer in Botswana added, "At tertiary level, STEM education promotes acquisition of knowledge and skills through information communication technologies (ICTs) driving teaching and learning for pre-service teachers." The above views are in line with the Zimbabwe's Ministry of Primary and Secondary Education (MoPSE,

2015). The policy document states that STEM implementation is guided by a particular philosophy for education.

In tandem with the national drive to uphold STEM vision, all institutions of higher learning for the eight countries involved in this study carried out curriculum review in the context of the initiative. For example, in Zimbabwe, universities "drafted course outlines for the teaching of natural sciences incorporating sciences such as chemistry, physics, biology, and computer science as well as agriculture." The approach compelled them to re-engineer their courses. As reported by one science lecturer in Zambia, "This re-engineering of Technical Teacher Education Program has seen a significant growth effect in engineering subjects in secondary schools." Three lecturers from Lesotho, Botswana, and South Africa reported that universities attempted to re-engineer their courses/modules to resonate with the objectives of STEM. The re-engineering was done at the pre-service level due to the influence of the government policy and STEM professors.

Universities are promoting user-friendly technology pedagogy that is scientifically oriented and represents STEM implementation. For example, many lecturers use information communication technologies (ICTs) methodologies in delivering lectures. One science methods instructor in Namibia indicated that they have, "constructed a state-of-the-art computer laboratory which is equipped with the latest technological devices used to promote effective learning." Another senior lecturer in Malawi echoed similar sentiments indicating that they have a functional ICT program to facilitate STEM teaching: "We have the now popular and well-known 'jewel brand' [that] is technologically compliant and plays a key role in STEM promotion in Teacher Education." In another example, in Zambia, mobile phones have been used to enhance teaching and learning of science and mathematics at universities in which pre-service teachers have learned how to integrate mobile phones for science data collection. In these examples, STEM was framed within ICT-driven approaches.

Institutions drafted robust strategic plans through adjustment of their policies and practices to support the shift towards STEM education. For example, one university training for primary school teachers in Zimbabwe intends to develop a teacher who is innovative and scientifically oriented. Similarly, one university training secondary school teachers in Zimbabwe views STEM as a transformation of "the teacher through nurturing of entrepreneurship, innovation, and creativity." In universities for all countries involved in the study, curriculum was made applicable to vocations to embrace the STEM philosophy in subjects such as agriculture, building design and woodwork, which did little to help the pre-service teacher programs.

Lecturers at some universities indicated that their focus in tandem with STEM was to produce students who can produce functional products. For example, one science lecturer at a primary teachers' college in Zambia commented, "STEM should enable students to produce functional materials." A lecturer at university in Zimbabwe indicated that there were currently involved in research on "indigenous herbs for sustainable human and domestic animal livelihoods in Zimbabwe."

Barriers to STEM Implementation

A few barriers to STEM implementation were cited by participants. For example, science lecturers in Zimbabwe and South Africa listed a plethora of barriers: In Zimbabwe, one lecturer indicated that "Lack of institutional, physical support, for example, lack of mathematics and science laboratories, lack of collaboration across STEM fields, lack of contexts where students can apply science and lack of investment on professional development on STEM education." In South Africa, one lecturer cited the "Lack of well-defined policy, largely theoretical to education curriculum, lack of coordination between colleges/universities and the school system in curriculum development."

Conclusions

The implementation of STEM policy in teacher education in Southern Africa has received different interpretations and hence approached differently in institutions of higher learning. A major finding is the lack of agreement on a conceptual definition and how STEM should be implemented in all levels of schooling. Along the lines of the Mpofu's (2019) four levels of STEM implementation (alluded to earlier in this chapter), all levels were found and mentioned by the participants indicating a lack of a coherent vision for STEM integration and implementation. Evidence was provided on analyzed national STEM guidelines. In Zambia, results show that research focuses on agricultural science STEM, general STEM, technological STEM, and hospitality and tourism STEM. In South Africa, STEM focus is on science and technology-related subjects, including ICT and more applied vocationally oriented subjects. In Lesotho, STEM is being taught as mathematics, science, human and social biology and/or agriculture, subjects which are traditionally regarded as softer Science than pure Biology and Physical Sciences. In Namibia, STEM is done in critical areas such as agriculture, fisheries, geology, and information technology. Botswana developed the Ministry of Tertiary Education, Science and Technology advocating for schools across the country to include STEM Clubs for the inclusion of Technology and Engineering fields. In Malawi, STEM subjects are taught using ICT. In Tanzania, STEM instructional model called iSPACES (as mentioned earlier) encompasses core principles of science, systems thinking, and entrepreneurship.

When applied to pre-service teacher preparation, individual instructors had to make the decision on the definition of STEM and on how the implementation would occur in the program and classrooms. The results of this research, interviews and policy analyses, indicate that there are barriers to STEM implementation that agree with the literature. For example, it is difficult to define STEM education and the subsequent curriculum at the tertiary science and pre-service level. There is lack of STEM preparation for students at all levels, which also means that there is lack of support and preparation for pre-service teachers. This was attributed to poor content delivery, poor learning conditions, lack of supplies, lack of support, and lack of hands-on training (Ejiwale, 2013; Kalolo, 2016).

Even though the countries in southern Africa have policy documents supporting STEM education and the implementation of STEM, curriculum and programs lacked focus for teacher education. These countries began to realize that implementation involved looking at STEM differently. Rather than a series of subjects being modified to fit a model or level (e.g., Chitate, 2016), the science instructors and teacher educators concluded that STEM also meant striving for students and teachers to obtain twenty-first century skills (ibid., 2016). These skills were most appropriately learned by students and pre-service teachers when subjects and course were interdisciplinary, transdisciplinary, and overlapped (Asunda, 2014; Czerniak & Johnson, 2014). The problem with this vision was the barriers to implementation which were more systemic than programmatic. For example, most instructors believed that they could teach and alter their courses to implement STEM ideas and content even if the programs or universities could not support them.

Ultimately, STEM implementation in teacher education supports a neoliberal perspective of the countries. The purpose and rationale for implementing STEM from policy documents is to promote the economic wellbeing of the state. If this is done properly, each country would have an educated workforce that would contribute to the economy through "manpower and infrastructure development" (Murwira, 2018). The literate citizens, through STEM implementation, would give back to the country by participating in free markets and increasing economic output, which is a neoliberal linear trajectory of thought (Gray et al., 2018; Harvey, 2005). The confluence of government policies, the culture of implementation of ideas into the curriculum of teacher education, and the culture of developing a literate workforce of citizens provides for the application and validation of neoliberalism in STEM education in the southern countries of Africa.

References

Akaygun, S., & Aslan-Titak, F. (2016). STEM images: STEM Conceptions of pre-service chemistry and mathematics teachers. *International Journal of Education in Mathematics, Science and Technology, 4*(1), 56–71.

Anderson, J., & Li, Y. (2020). *Integrated approaches to STEM education an international perspective*. Springer International Publishing.

Apple, M. (2000). Between neoliberalism and neoconservatism: Education and conservatism in a global context. In N. C. Burbles & C. A. Torres (Eds.), *Globalization and education: critical perspectives* (pp. 57–77). Routledge.

Asunda, P. A. (2014). A conceptual framework for STEM Integration into curriculum through career and technical education. *Journal of STEM Teacher Education, 49*(1), 3–15.

Badmus, O. T., & Omosewo, E. O. (2020). Evolution of STEM, STEAM and STREAM education in Africa: The implication of the knowledge gap. *International Journal of Research in STEM Education, 2*(2), 99–106.

Barrette, A. M., Gardner, V., Joubert, M., & Tickly, L. (2019). *Approaches to strengthening secondary STEM & ICT education in SubSaharan Africa*. University of Bristol.

Breiner, J. M., Harkness, S. S., Johnson, C. C., & Koehler, C. M. (2012). What is STEM? A discussion about conceptions of STEM in education and partnerships. *School Science and Mathematics, 112*(1), 3–11.

Bryman, A. (2012). *Social research methods* (4th ed.). Oxford University Press.

Carney, S. (2009). Negotiating policy in an age of globalization: Exploring educational "Policyscapes" in Denmark, Nepal, and China. *Comparative Education Review, 53*(1), 63–88. https://www.jstor.org/stable/10.1086/593152

Chitate, H. (2016). STEM: A case study of Zimbabwe's educational approach to industrialization. *World Journal of Education, 6*(5), 27–35.

Czerniak, C. M., & Johnson, C. C. (2014). Interdisciplinary science teaching. In N. G. Lederman & S. K. Abell (Eds.), *Handbook of research on science education* (Vol. 2, pp. 395–411). Routledge.

Dekeza, C., & Kufakunesu, M. (2017). Implementation of STEM curriculum in rural secondary schools in Zimbabwe: Limits and possibilities. *Journal of Emerging Trends in Educational Research and Policy Studies, 8*(1), 11–15.

Dugger, W. (2010). *Evolution of STEM in the United States.* Paper presented at the 6th Biennial International Conference on Technology Education Research Surfers Paradise Queensland, Australia. http://illios.itea/org/Research/Paradise/Australia.

Editor. (2016, February 7). Ministry of higher and tertiary education, science and technology development STEM supplement, *The Sunday Mail*, S1–S9.

Ejiwale, J. (2013). Barriers to successful implementation of STEM education. *Journal of Education and Learning, 7*(2), 63–74.

Gadzirayi, C. T., Bongo, P. P., Ruyimbe, B., Bhukuvhani, C., & Mucheri, T. (2016). Diagnostic study on status of STEM in Zimbabwe: Collaborative research by Bindura university of science education and higherlife foundation, Technical Report, 1–47. Bindura: BUSE.

Government of Zimbabwe. (2008). *National report on the status of education by Zimbabwe.* UNESCO.

Gray, J., O'Regan, J. P., & Wallace, C. (2018). Education and the discourse of global neoliberalism. *Language and Intercultural Communication, 18*(5), 471–477. https://doi.org/10.1080/14708477.2018.1501842

Harvey, D. (2005). *A brief history of neoliberalism.* Oxford University Press.

Hurley, M. (2001). Reviewing integrated science and mathematics: The search for evidence and definitions from new perspectives. *School Science and Mathematics, 101*, 259–268. https://doi.org/10.1111/j.1949-8594.2001.tb18028.x

Kalolo, J. F. (2016). Realigning approaches for successful manipulation of STEM education in today's elementary schools in developing countries' policy commitments and practices. *Journal of Education and Literature, 4*(2), 61–76.

Kandiko, C. B. (2010). Neoliberalism in higher education: A comparative approach. *International Journal of Arts and Sciences, 3*(14), 153–175.

Karras, K. G., & Wolhuter, C. C. (2019). *International handbook of teacher education* (Revised and augmented edition, pp. 234–245). HM Studies and Publishing.

Lipman, P. (2011). *The new political economy of urban education: Neoliberalism, race, and the right to the city.* Routledge.

Manteaw, B. O. (2008). When businesses go to school: Neoliberalism and education for sustainable development. *Journal of Education for Sustainable Development, 2*(2), 119–126.

MoPSE. (2015). *Ministry of primary and secondary education: Handbook on curriculum review.* Ministry of Primary and Secondary Education.

Moyo, J. (2016). Ministry of higher and tertiary education, science and technology development, Concept Note (Revised 13 January 2016). Paper presented at the 1st National Conference on Science, Technology, Engineering and Mathematics (STEM). Harare, Zimbabwe.

Mpofu, V. (2019). A theoretical framework for implementing STEM education. In G. Fomunyam (Ed.), *Theorizing STEM education in the 21st Century*. IntechOpen. https://doi.org/10.5772/intechopen.88304

Murwira, A. (2018, February). STEM way to go. *The Herald*. Harare, Zimbabwe.

Mutseekwa, C. (2021). STEM practices in science teacher education curriculum: Perspectives from two secondary school teachers' colleges in Zimbabwe. *Journal of Research in Science, Mathematics and Technology Education, 4*(2), 75–92. https://doi.org/10.31756/jrsmte.422

National Commission on Excellence in Education. (1983). *A Nation at Risk: The Imperative for Educational Reform*. Washington, D.C.: National Commission on Excellence in Education. http://edreform.com/wp-content/uploads/2013/02/A_Nation_At_Risk_1983.pdf

National Science Foundation and U.S. Department of Education. (1980). *Science and Engineering Education for the 1980's and Beyond*. Washington, D.C.: U.S. Government Printing Office.

Patton, M. Q. (2002). *Qualitative research and evaluation methods* (3rd ed.). Sage Publications.

Pimthong, P., & Williams, J. (2020). Pre-service teachers' understanding of STEM education. *Journal of Social Sciences, 41*, 289–295.

Tsupros, N., Kohler, R., & Hallinen, J. (2009). *STEM education: Project to identify the missing components*. Intermediate Unit 1: Center for STEM Education.

Tytler, R., & Self, J. (2020). Designing a contemporary STEM curriculum. In *On current and critical issues in curriculum, teaching, learning and assessment series*. UNESCO.

Tytler, R., Williams, G., Hobbs, L., & Anderson, J. (2019). Challenges and opportunities for a STEM interdisciplinary agenda. In B. Doig, J. Williams, D. Swanson, R. Borromeo Ferri, & P. Drake (Eds.), *Interdisciplinary mathematics education: The state of the art and beyond* (pp. 51–81). Springer ICME series. https://link.springer.com/book/10.1007/978-3-030-11066-6

Voogt, J., & Roblin, N. P. (2012). A comparative analysis of international frameworks for 21st century competences: Implications for national curriculum policies. *Journal of Curriculum Studies, 44*(3), 299–321. https://doi.org/10.1080/00220272.2012.668938

Zimbabwe. (2018). *Vision 2030*. Republic of Zimbabwe.

Zimbabwe, National Assembly. (2016). *Ministerial statement: Position regarding STEM*. Harare, Zimbabwe: The Minister of Higher and Tertiary Education, Science and Technology Development.

Zimbabwe National Qualifications Framework. (2018). *Ministry of higher and tertiary education, science and technology development*. MHTESTD.

CHAPTER 3

STEMifying Teacher Education: A Canadian Context

Isha DeCoito

Introduction

Improving a country's high-quality talent requires a strong educational foundation for children and youth. Globally, science, technology, engineering, and mathematics (STEM) education is viewed as essential for preparing students for competing in the economy of the twenty-first century and has become the driving-force behind many educational movements (Blackley & Howell, 2015). Be aware, STEM is not a separate education reform movement; rather, it is an emphasis that stresses a multidisciplinary approach for better preparing all students in STEM subject areas and increasing the number of post-secondary graduates who are prepared for STEM occupations (Conference Board of Canada, 2013; National Research Council [NRC], 2013).

I. DeCoito (✉)
Western University, London, ON, Canada
e-mail: idecoito@uwo.ca

S. M. Al-Balushi et al. (eds.), *Reforming Science Teacher Education Programs in the STEM Era*, Palgrave Studies on Leadership and Learning in Teacher Education,
https://doi.org/10.1007/978-3-031-27334-6_3

Prior to 2009, STEM education as an initiative did not formally exist in provincial and Canadian institutions of K-12 and higher education (Krug, 2012). The Ontario government announced an investment of $736 million more in public education in the 2020–2021 school year, with STEM programing as one of five key areas of focus (Ontario Ministry of Education, 2020). This is a significant investment, as the Programme for International Student Assessment (PISA) results over the 2003 to 2018 period show a steady decline in many countries, including Canada, where students have not demonstrated significant gains in science and mathematics (Alison & Geloso, 2021). This is concerning, as inadequate science and STEM preparation in the early grades ultimately plays a role in secondary course choices, as well as post-secondary pathways in the workplace, apprenticeship, college or university, and ultimately, career choices (DeCoito, 2015a). Thus, identifying effective strategies to ensure continuity and supports necessary for successful transition from elementary science to specialized high school STEM courses and subsequent post-secondary pathways is warranted.

Achieving the aforementioned goals will necessitate teaching in ways that inspire all students and deepen their understanding of STEM content and practices. Currently, initial teacher education programs do not prepare teachers to develop and apply STEM skills (Milner-Bolotin 2018). This is especially true with K-12 teachers as few are trained in STEM subjects and may not teach what they do not fully understand or feel comfortable teaching (DeCoito & Myszkal, 2018). Teacher education should be instrumental in imparting best pedagogical strategies and providing opportunities for teachers to develop integrated STEM knowledge and skills. Furthermore, engineering principles and technology practices are perceived as being far removed from science or mathematics teaching. Consequently, the lack of STEM pedagogical preparation is reflected in a lack of comfort by teachers in teaching the required STEM content.

Despite the government's commitment to fostering STEM-related innovation and inspiring youth to participate in STEM focused careers, a rather weak attempt was made to integrate STEM education in the revised Ontario science curriculum. In K-12 education in Ontario, integrated STEM education is not taught as a required subject and is typically introduced into a teacher education program based on faculty interests. The author reports on her development of Canada's first STEM teacher preparation program. She discusses the STEM Specialty Focus at the Intermediate/Senior (Grade 7–12) level, and accompanying courses—*An*

Introduction to STEM Education, and *Curriculum and Pedagogy in STEM Education*. In these courses, teacher candidates (TCs) are provided with opportunities to deepen their understanding of STEM concepts and enhance STEM skills while developing STEM projects aligned to provincial curriculum, digital video games (DVGs) to teach STEM concepts, digital timelines to teach nature of science (NOS), and interactive case studies focusing on contemporary socioscientific issues (SSI). As the author has conducted research on course assignments, successes and challenges within the courses are addressed, and outlines for the necessary faculty and university support for the successful implementation of a STEM program are highlighted.

Integrated STEM Teacher Education

Preparing students with global workforce skills to ensure successful careers in STEM fields will require new approaches to teaching STEM topics in K-12 classrooms. Moreover, there is a need to address equitable practices specifically related to gender and diversity in STEM education, as the under-representation of females in STEM fields has its origins in the early elementary grades (Blickenstaff, 2005; Tan et al., 2013). This is significant, as the supply pipeline for university graduates of science and engineering begins early on in elementary school when children are first exposed to and they consequently formulate opinions about mathematics and science (NSERC, 2010). The aforementioned trends highlight challenges and obstacles to developing and implementing integrated STEM curricula and instruction in teacher preparation programs; for example, ensuring adequate teacher content knowledge and development of teacher education models, as well as the specificity of school structure (Enderson et al., 2020). Most teachers have not learned disciplinary content using STEM contexts (Honey et al., 2014) nor have they taught in this manner. Hence, integrated STEM teacher education programs should promote learning experiences and skill development, incorporate curricula that integrate STEM contexts for teaching disciplinary content in meaningful ways, and develop new models of teaching that support STEM integration and meaningful STEM learning (Moore, 2010; Shernoff et al., 2017, Wang et al., 2011).

STEM Specialty Focus in Teacher Education: A Canadian Perspective

In the two-year teacher education program in Ontario, Canada, TCs enrolled in the Intermediate/Senior level stream select two teachable subjects from the Ontario Curriculum, as well as personalize their Bachelor of Education program by choosing one of five specialty areas. The STEM specialty focus was developed by the author and brings together the disciplines of science, technology, engineering, and mathematics to promote an interdisciplinary approach to teaching integrated STEM subjects. The first-year course in the STEM specialty focus *Introduction to STEM Education,* introduces TCs to the nature of STEM, including the history and philosophy of engineering, science, mathematics, and technology; science, technology, society and the environment (STSE) frameworks and STEM education; culturally relevant pedagogy with a focus on equity, diversity, and inclusion; other ways of knowing in each of the STEM disciplines; and gender disparities in STEM, with a focus on STEM educational attainment amongst minority groups and Indigenous youth. TCs are introduced to the engineering design process (EDP) and they explore inquiry practices via TC-led demonstrations and activities. In the second-year course, *Curriculum and Pedagogy in STEM Education,* TCs engage in curriculum development that deepen their understanding of concepts within each of the core disciplines and develop STEM skills while engaging in activities that enhance creative and critical thinking, problem-solving and collaborative learning, and scientific, environmental, and technological literacies.

It is important to note that all activities in the STEM courses are scaffolded and supported by guest speakers, workshops (i.e., for DVGs and STEM projects), conferencing with the instructor, course readings on STEM education, and access to specialized resources such as a 3-D printer and a drone for developing activities. Culturally responsive approaches present opportunities for curriculum development, cultural competence and knowledge construction, empowerment, transformation, and the improvement of learning and achievement outcomes of all students, more so for minoritized groups (Aikenhead & Michell, 2011; Hernandez et al., 2013; Ladson-Billings, 2009; Webb & Barrera, 2017). Culturally responsive pedagogies' (CRP) key concepts of content integration, facilitation of knowledge construction, reduction of prejudice, advancement of social justice and academic development present a framework to guide responsive education beliefs, standards, and practices that foster academic achievement (Brown et al., 2019; Calabrese-Barton & Tan, 2020). Pedagogical tenets of CRP are modeled in the STEM courses and include fostering positive teacher attitudes and expectations, integrating culturally diverse content in the curriculum, enhancing cultural communication in the classroom, and utilizing culturally congruent instructional strategies, to name a few (Hernandez et al., 2013; Ladson-Billings, 2009). In the following sections, samples of activities emanating from the course assignments are highlighted and include digital technologies (DVGs and digital timelines), case studies focusing on SSI, and project-based learning in STEM.

Digital Technologies and Digital Literacies

To support successful adaptation of technology into our lives, it is vital that education emphasize technological literacy, especially for students intending to pursue STEM focused careers, such as engineering, architecture, medicine, or information technology. To become the next generation of innovators, today's children must learn to create with technology (DeCoito, 2017, 2020b). Thus, computational thinking skills and programing skills such as coding warrant inclusion in integrated STEM curriculum given that these problem-solving methodologies can be translated across subject areas. Programing allows teachers and their students to explore concepts across the curriculum and creatively communicate learning. At more advanced stages, students can develop proficiency designing DVGs and simulations to demonstrate their understanding of STEM concepts (DeCoito & Richardson, 2016; DeCoito & Briona, 2020).

In the *Curriculum and Pedagogy in STEM Education* course, one avenue for enhancing scientific, engineering, technological, and numeric literacies, while at the same time supporting the development of global competencies, is through the implementation of DVGs within an integrated STEM education context. TCs are provided with opportunities to practice the effective integration of pedagogy, technology, and subject content often referred to as technology, pedagogy, and content knowledge (TPACK) (Koehler & Mishra, 2009). In addition to addressing a variety of STEM skills, DVGs can potentially address seven of the eight practices of science and engineering, identified in *A Framework for K-12 Science Education* (NRC, 2011) as essential for all students to learn. TCs were required to develop a DVG that incorporated three or four of the STEM disciplines to teach STEM concepts. TCs were provided opportunities to develop a variety of STEM skills, including programing, math, creative thinking, logic, and using the EDP. Storyboarding is a key aspect of the EDP, since storyboards lay the foundation for DVGs, and effectively outline characters, scenes, challenges, and gaming interface (see Fig. 3.1).

The assignment is an example of a real-world experience that engages students (both TCs and the students they teach) in STEM learning. Given the inequitable access to technological resources in schools, this assignment plays a vital role in providing opportunities for TCs to engage in the process of developing educative materials linked to curriculum, and for using and modeling technology effectively by enhancing and expanding their skill sets.

Multimedia materials embrace a wide range of products, from a PowerPoint presentation to a video game, a storybook, or a simulation, and are compatible with a wide range of pedagogies. Their power to enhance the comprehension of narrations can make them a good vehicle to aid mastery of complex skills of oral comprehension and reading (Gee, 2015). Timelines are an established method to explore the historical development of several disciplines. Unlike traditional timelines, the interactivity of online timelines allows timescales to vary substantially. Online, interactive timelines can support visually rich displays of information—text, images, multimedia, hyperlinks—using spatial arrangements, categories, and color schemes to convey meaning, which make them ideal platforms for achieving a variety of objectives. Likewise, their potential to represent and simulate different phenomena such as natural, chemical, physical, social, or historic processes means they can foster insight into different subjects across the curriculum (Muehrer et al., 2012). TCs developed digital timelines to explore the history of scientific discoveries, including the scientists and technology captured in a time period, using a variety of formats. TCs assumed dual roles—curriculum developers and co-constructors of knowledge—to inform them about the importance of NOS, which they could then, in turn, implement in their future practices. Each timeline consisted of content based on significant discoveries and inventions that occurred within an assigned era in the history of the discipline (see Fig. 3.2). This included technical/scientific information about the discovery or invention, information about the individuals and groups involved in the discoveries and inventions, relevant particulars about the inventors'/discoverers' personals lives, education, places of study and work, and so on in addition to information about the sociocultural milieu

DVG Storyboard: DNA Replication

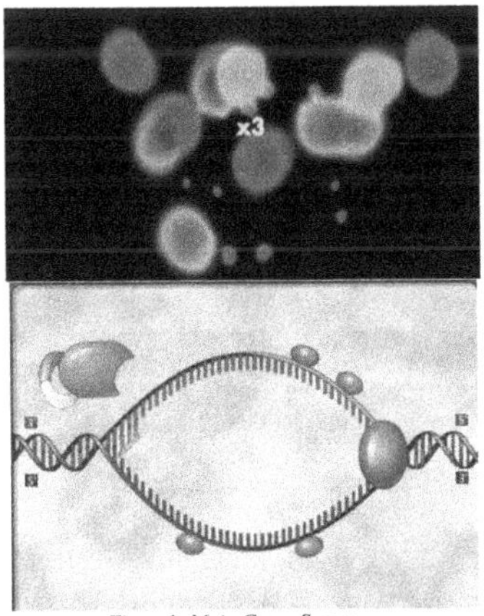

Figure1: Main Game Screen

Goal: Players will be able to identify key enzymes and landmarks involved in prokaryotic DNA replication.

Strand: Molecular Genetics

Software: Construct2 (scirra.com)

Scenario: The year is 3067: cancer has been eradicated from our species due to utilization of nanobots to assist with enzymatic placement for DNA replication. Customize your 'bot, then get to work! But be warned: DNA replication must be completed accurately and timely, otherwise cancer cells arise. Destroy the cancer cells, lest they overrun your host.

Customization: Nanobot Avatar (color, decorations)
User controls (left hand vs right hand setup)

Scenes: Welcome Screen
Setup (Avatar customization and control interface)
Teaching Module
Main Game
Game Over

Teaching Module: Walks players through steps of DNA replication and introduce them to the various key combinations to affect an action (e.g., "w" key places DNA Polymerase I on DNA).

Game interface: Employs a vertical split-screen approach (Figure 1). The top part is a petri dish of cells going through DNA replication and require player intervention to continue; magenta cells are cells that have failed to correctly complete DNA replication and are now cancerous. Magenta cells can be destroyed by clicking on them; blue cells can be clicked on to zoom in on their DNA in the lower part of the screen. If blue cell DNA replication is completed successfully, they turn green again; in the event of incorrect DNA replication they will turn magenta (cancerous).

Level 1: No cancer cells. Blue cells stay blue until DNA replication is successfully completed. Too many blue cells in the top screen (10?) = failed to complete the level. Successful completion of DNA replication for 10 cells lets the player move on to Level 2.

Level 2+: Cancer cells can now appear. Blue cells can appear faster also. If 50% of the cells in the petri dish are cancerous, then player failed to complete level (game over).

STEM: Science (Biology: DNA replication)
Technology (digital media; player is a nanobot)
Mathematics (modeling movement of interacting cell populations)

Career Options: Molecular Biology (biological processes)
Biophysics (artificial enzymes)
Analytical Chemistry (efficacy of enzymatic processes)
Biomathematics (modeling of cell populations)

Type of Game: action - strategy - simulation

Pluriversality: Western Modern Science: the various proteins and nucleotides involved in DNA replication
Ontological investment: do the cells in my petri dish live or die?

Fig. 3.1 An example of a storyboard for *Okazaki's Revenge* (DeCoito & Briona, 2020)

(including politics, the economy, art, religion, fashion, etc.) of the time period or era. The inclusion of content reflecting inventions and discoveries from all cultures and nationalities, as well as females, are mandatory.

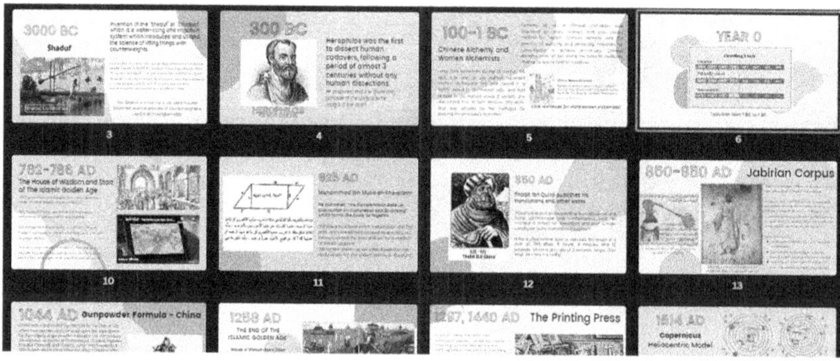

Fig. 3.2 A sample of a digital timeline, pre-1600s, developed by TCs

The primary goal of the digital timeline activity was to validate this strategy with TCs with the goal of enhancing their scientific literacy by requiring them to research and include in their timelines not only significant developments in the history of the disciplines of a specified period, but also pertinent sociocultural information related to the various discoveries and their discoverers (DeCoito, 2014, 2020a).

Case Studies

An integrative STEM curriculum is fertile ground for promoting the development of case studies focusing on SSI that are situated in science, technology, society and the environment (STSE) frameworks (DeCoito & Fazio, 2017). Important considerations when using case studies as a teaching approach include contextualizing the case in real-life scenarios to make it memorable for students (Ching, 2014), promoting peer interaction to internalize cognitive processes and gain new perspectives (Levin, 1995), and facilitating and supporting to scaffold the process by providing feedback and guidance. Central to global competencies are individuals who can examine local, global, and intercultural issues, understand and appreciate different perspectives and worldviews, collaborate with others, and take responsible action toward sustainability and collective well-being. This pedagogical approach considers equity and social justice as part of the educational experience and inspires educators to view their practices through a STSE lens. In addition, problem modeling and solving real-world scenarios encourages student participation through collaborative learning, builds communication skills, supports scientific inquiry and application of theory across STEM fields (e.g., engineering design and problem-solving), and increases student academic achievement (Kennedy & Odell, 2014; Yalçınkaya et al., 2012).

In teams, TCs collaborated to develop and conduct an interactive digital case study (including videos, images, simulations, etc.) based on an SSI around STEM education. Each team was required to complete a number of activities that comprised the research and development of the case study including lesson plans, a scenario, stakeholders' perspectives, graphic organizers, note-taking frameworks, stakeholder consequence maps, cost-benefit analysis, and a presentation (e.g., in the form of a town hall, debate, court case scenario, etc.). Examples of case studies developed by TCs include chemical warfare, global water crises, nuclear energy, historical cases (Three Gorges Dam), microplastics, COVID-19 vaccinations, and climate change, all of which can provoke students to think beyond the local contexts and into a global realm.

Inquiry and Engineering Approaches: Project-based Learning and Integrated STEM Education

Inquiry and engineering approaches when applied to the learning process are engaging for students (Gillies & Nichols, 2015; Margot & Kettler, 2019; Thibaut et al., 2018). This student-directed, teacher facilitated inquiry-based STEM instruction has the capacity to promote engagement and scientific reasoning abilities, and the development of content knowledge and transferable reasoning skills (Fischer et al., 2014; Lambie, 2020). As powerful tools in the classroom, these approaches require advanced planning of learning goals, focusing on what is important, and the scaffolding of learning experiences. Teaching STEM through inquiry can promote engineering design and problem-solving through the process of problem identification, solution innovation, prototype, evaluation, and redesign to develop a practical understanding of the designed world (Blackley & Howell, 2015; Kennedy & Odell, 2014).

Inquiry-based and engineering learning (IBEL) applied to STEM education enhances "meta-disciplinarity", that is, the integration of disciplinary, interdisciplinary and transdisciplinary knowledge enabling the learning of concepts in authentic real-world situations and the opportunity for students to investigate problems from multiple perspectives (Blessinger & Carfora, 2015). The engineering design process can be implemented across science, mathematics and technology subjects in a manner that promotes engagement, creativity, entrepreneurship, and innovation (DeCoito

& Briona, 2023). Studies comparing learning outcomes for students taught via project-based learning versus traditional instruction show that when implemented well, project-based learning increases long-term retention of content, helps students perform as well as or better than traditional learners in high-stakes tests, improves problem-solving and collaboration skills, and improves students' attitudes toward learning (Strobel & van Barneveld, 2009). This pedagogical approach has been instrumental in engaging and motivating English language learners (Florence, 2018) as well as students with special education needs (Lambie, 2020), to name a few.

In the integrated STEM program, TCs were tasked with developing a STEM project situated in a STSE framework, including opportunities for learning STEM concepts that are meaningfully integrated across the disciplines, and developing STEM skills. TCs utilized pulleys and gears in constructing an accessible playground, designed a universal coffee cup lid, and programed GPS tracking devices for pets (DeCoito & Briona, 2023), to name a few. The TC-designed integrated STEM project, *Renewable and Non-renewable Resources: Wind Turbine Blade Design* focused on power generation technologies, the environmental, economic, and societal costs of coal mining, and wind turbine blade design and optimization was successful in terms of addressing the goals of STEM education, specifically the implementation of the EDP (DeCoito, 2015b). It was necessary to divide the turbine blade design into small achievable subtasks as this allowed for timely feedback and raised the overall success of the project. More importantly, this approach provided opportunities for students to gather information through research, learn mathematical calculations, and investigate the economic costs of mining by managing a fictional Mountaintop coal mine (students were required to purchase a hypothetical coal mining site with limited start-up funds), alongside designing the wind turbine blade.

Furthermore, the process of developing the wind turbine blade afforded TCs the opportunity to assume the role of engineers, participate in knowledge construction as they amalgamated their findings in the form of a proposal to a fictional engineering firm, and engage in scientific reasoning as to why the class design was an improvement over their initial design. The infusion of design principles enhances real-world applicability and helps prepare students for post-secondary education, with an emphasis on making connections to STEM professionals and careers.

In summary, integrated STEM teacher education should stress the importance of implementing novel pedagogical approaches to support student engagement, learning, and achievement. Challenging students to solve real-world problems using approaches such as project-based learning, case studies, inquiry and engineering design approaches, computational thinking, incorporating the use of digital technologies to extend learning, and a commitment to integrate culturally relevant pedagogies have potential to enhance learning and academic achievement of all students in STEM education. The integration and representation of the experiences and knowledges of Indigenous people and other minoritized groups in curriculum and assessment are vital to the success of STEM learning and academic outcomes of these groups. Pedagogical approaches/strategies in integrated STEM teacher education should foster increased student engagement and motivation, retention of knowledge, and the development of global competencies required for participation in STEM careers and everyday life.

Conclusions and Recommendations

Integrating scientific and engineering practices, cross-cutting concepts and disciplinary core dimensions into standards, curriculum, instruction, and assessment systems provides opportunities for less fragmented and more stimulating experiences for students. In addition, it supports student-centered teaching approaches, fosters creative problem-solving, boosts critical thinking skills, improves retention, and enhances student learning and outcomes (Ajiwale, 2012; English, 2016; Kelley & Knowles, 2016; Kennedy & Odell, 2014; Stohlmann et al., 2012; Thibaut et al., 2018). Moreover, the association with project-based learning increases instructional and learning efficiency, and promotes workforce talent development (Nadelson & Seifert, 2017). There were numerous affordances noted in the integrated STEM program, especially related to curriculum-focused STEM integration, STEM-focused pedagogy, and assessment. In research studies (conducted by the author) related to the impact of integrated STEM activities, TCs reported enhanced engagement with STEM concepts, creativity and innovation opportunities, problem-solving and critical thinking skills. As well, their focus on culturally relevant resources, pedagogy, and equity, diversity and inclusion, technology literacy, STEM literacy and skills, self-efficacy and confidence in integrating STEM concepts, collaboration and belonging to communities of practice, self-realization and agency, environmental stewardship and awareness, and entrepreneurship mindsets were highlighted.

Challenges were noted as they relate to specific activities and curriculum developed by TCs in the integrated STEM specialty focus. The design and implementation of case study approaches faced some obstacles. For example, preparing cases and related teaching resources challenged TCs' research skill set, their ability to logically develop arguments to defend their stakeholder position, and selection of relevant case study topics (that address criteria and level of complexity). STEM program challenges were related to assessments around case studies (e.g., individual and group contributions), and managing TCs' expectations, as suggested in the literature (Yalçınkaya et al., 2012). Even though technological tools, when used judiciously, have the potential to impact teaching and learning in STEM disciplines (DeCoito & Briona, 2020), some TCs encountered challenges when developing DVGs as they lacked prior knowledge related to coding and computational thinking, as well as a robust TPACK framework. Moreover, these TCs were resistant to integrating and gravitated toward representing a single STEM discipline in their games. Challenges encountered with developing digital timelines were related to the plethora of resources available online, and incorporating certain aspects related to female and cultural contributions across the time periods. Overall, project-based learning in STEM elicited some challenges related to integrating engineering and mathematics content, and tensions related to self-efficacy and confidence in teaching these content areas.

The success of integrated STEM teacher education preparation programs hinges on TCs' content knowledge and pedagogical content knowledge to provide structure, support, and connections to resources aimed at facilitating and empowering students' learning and interest to innovate (Kelley & Knowles, 2016). In addition, expectations for integration must support targeted instruction and assessment by providing tasks that are measurable and observable (National Academies of Sciences, Engineering, and Medicine, 2018). Finally, quality STEM education programs require the inclusion of rigorous curriculum, instruction, and assessment, the integration of technology and engineering into the science and mathematics curriculum and promotion of scientific inquiry and the engineering design process (Kennedy & Odell, 2014, p.1).

Over the past seven years since the STEM specialty focus was developed, important barriers/challenges to the implementation of integrated

STEM were observed. This resulted in a number of recommendations by the author, including:

1. Cross-cutting connections must be explicit, as TCs can potentially miss them given their unfamiliarity with curriculum and practices aligned with integrated STEM education.
2. Integration is a complex process, which is costly and time consuming, and must be supported by administration, experts in STEM disciplines, and resources.
3. TCs' implementation of integrated STEM education must be supported by provincial curriculum.
4. Research on best practices for integrated STEM is limited. Models of best practices are essential for STEM teacher education.
5. TCs lack adequate STEM knowledge and skills and must be supported through activities that explicitly target these aspects in each of the STEM disciplines, as well as their meaningful integration.
6. Support, in the form of professional development, is needed for instructors who are new to integrated STEM education; otherwise, disciplinary integration becomes fragmented.
7. Collaboration across various disciplines, that is, Indigenous studies, mathematics, technology, engineering and science, in teacher education programs must be in place; otherwise, TCs do not connect their learnings in the integrated STEM program to these disciplines.
8. Technological tools/technology-enhanced learning should be embedded across different areas in teacher education programs; otherwise, TCs envision them as an add-on feature, only specific to the integrated STEM program.
9. Authentic opportunities must be available for TCs to practice their STEM pedagogy and skills. For example, TCs collaborate and develop curriculum for STEM outreach programs.

COVID-19 and Emergency Remote Teaching

The STEM specialty is in its seventh year, and one of the greatest challenges was presented when the teacher education program moved to emergency remote teaching (ERT) (Hodges et al., 2020) during the COVID-19 pandemic. During this time institutions were scrambling to integrate technology enhanced learning and many instructors and TCs struggled with the transition. At that time, the author was actively engaged in teaching the STEM specialty courses and pivoted the curriculum and pedagogy STEM course to a synchronous online format. TCs had not previously engaged with ERT, and it posed many challenges for them, especially related to assignments within the STEM program, which was also part of a research study. Nevertheless, it was not until after they completed the program, some TCs contacted the author to say, "Thank you. It was an invaluable experience ..."

References

Aikenhead, G., & Michell, H. (2011). *Bridging cultures: Indigenous and scientific ways of knowing nature*. Pearson.

Ajiwale, J. A. (2012). Facilitating teaching and learning across STEM Fields. *Journal of STEM Education: Innovations and Research, 13*(3), 87–94.

Alison, D. J., & Geloso, V. (2021). *Math performance in Canada*. Fraser Institute. https://www.fraserinstitute.org/sites/default/files/math-performance-in-canada.pdf

Blackley, S., & Howell, J. (2015). A STEM narrative: 15 years in the making. *Australian Journal of Teacher Education, 40*(7) https://doi.org/10.14221/ajte.2015v40n7.8

Blessinger, P., & Carfora, J. M. (Ed.). (2015). *Inquiry-based learning for science, technology, engineering, and math (STEM) programs: A conceptual and practical resource for educators* (Innovations in Higher Education Teaching and Learning, Vol. 4, p. iii). Emerald Group Publishing Limited. https://doi.org/10.1108/S2055-364120150000004027

Blickenstaff, J. C. (2005). Women and science careers: leaky pipeline or gender filter? *Gender and Education, 17*(4), 369–386.

Brown, B. A., Boda, P., Lemmi, C., & Monroe, X. (2019). Moving CRP from theory to practice: Exploring teacher' application of culturally relevant education in science and mathematics. *Urban Education, 54*(6), 775–803. https://doi.org/10.1177/0042085918794802

Calabrese-Barton, A., & Tan, E. (2020). Beyond equity as inclusion: A framework of "rightful presence" for guiding justice-oriented studies in teaching and learning. *Educational Researcher, 49*(6), 433–440.

Ching, C. P. (2014). Linking theory to practice: A case-based approach in teacher education. *Procedia—Social and Behavioral Sciences, 123*, 280–288. https://doi.org/10.1016/j.sbspro.2014.01.1425

Conference Board of Canada. (2013). *Education and skills: Percentage of graduates in science, math, computer science, and engineering*. http://www.conferenceboard.ca/hcp/default.aspx

DeCoito, I. (2014). Teaching about the nature of science through digital scientific timelines. In P. D. Morrell & K. Popejoy (Eds.), *A few of our favorite things: Teaching ideas for K-12 science methods instructors*. Sense Publishers.

DeCoito, I. (2015a). Gender differences in STEM career aspirations amongst middle school students. In *Proceedings of the STEAM International Conference*. Honolulu, HI. ISBN2333-4916.

DeCoito, I. (2015b). Developing integrated science, technology, engineering and mathematics (STEM) projects in education. In S. Nesbit & T. M. Froese (Eds.), *Proceedings of EESD15: The 7th Conference on Engineering Education for Sustainable Development* (pp. 41–48). University of British Columbia.

DeCoito, I. (2017). Addressing digital competencies, curriculum development, and instructional design in science teacher education. In *Encyclopedia of information science and technology* (pp. 1–12). IGI Global.

DeCoito, I. (2020a). The case for digital timelines in teaching and teacher education. *International Journal of E-Learning & Distance Education, 35*(1). ISSN: 2292-8588

DeCoito, I. (2020b). The use of digital technologies to enhance learners' conceptions of the nature of science. In W. F. McComas (Ed.), *The nature of science in science education: Rationales and strategies* (pp. 343–358). Springer.

DeCoito, I., & Briona, L. (2020). Navigating theory and practice: Digital video games (DVGs) in STEM education. In V. Akerson & G. Buck (Eds.), *Critical questions in STEM education* (pp. 85–104). Springer. https://doi.org/10.1007/978-3-030-57646-2

DeCoito, I., & Briona, L. (2023). Fostering an entrepreneurial mindset through digital technologies in STEM teacher education. In S. Kaya & E. Peters-Burton (Eds.), *Enhancing entrepreneurial mindsets through STEM education* (pp. 195–222). Springer International Publishing. ISBN-13: 9783031178153.

DeCoito, I., & Fazio, X. (2017). Developing case studies in teacher education: Spotlighting socioscientific issues. *Innovations in Science Teacher Education, 2*(1). Retrieved from https://innovations.theaste.org/developing-case-studies-in-teacher-educationspotlighting-socioscientific-issues/

DeCoito, I., & Myszkal, P. (2018). Connecting science instruction and teachers' self-efficacy and beliefs in STEM education. *Journal of Science Teacher Education, 29*(6), 485–503.

DeCoito, I., & Richardson, T. (2016). Focusing on integrated STEM concepts in a digital game. In M. Urban & D. Falvo (Eds.), *Improving K-12 STEM education* (pp. 1–23). IGI Global.

Enderson, M. C., Reed, P. A., & Grant, M. R. (2020). Secondary STEM teacher education. In C. C. Johnson, M. J. Mohr-Schroeder, T. J. Moore, & L. D. English (Eds.), *Handbook of research on STEM education*. Routledge.

English, L. D. (2016). STEM education K-12: Perspectives on integration. *International Journal of STEM Education, 3*(1), 1–8.

Fischer, F., Kollar, I., Ufer, S., Sodian, B., Hussmann, H., Pekrun, R., Neuhaus, B., Dorner, B., Pankofer, S., Fischer, M., Strijbos, J.-W., Heene, M., & Eberle, J. (2014). Scientific reasoning and argumentation: advancing an interdisciplinary research agenda in education. *Frontline Learning Research, 2*(3), 28–45.

Florence, S. (2018). *Decoding STEM: The impact of STEM outreach programming on English language learners.* Unpublished MA thesis, York University.

Gee, J. (2015). *Social linguistics and literacies: Ideology in discourses.* Routledge.

Gillies, R. M., & Nichols, K. (2015). How to Support primary teachers' implementation of inquiry: Teachers' reflections on teaching cooperative inquiry-based science. *Research in Science Education, 45*, 171–191. https://doi.org/10.1007/s11165-014-9418-x

Hernandez, C. M., Morales, A. R., & Shroyer, M. G. (2013). The development of a model of culturally responsive science and mathematics teaching. *Cultural Studies of Science Education, 8*, 803–820. https://doi.org/10.1007/s11422-013-9544-1

Hodges, C. B., Moore, S., Lockee, B. B., Trust, T., & Bond, M. A. (2020). The difference between emergency remote teaching and online learning. *Educase Review, 27.* https://er.educause.edu/articles/2020/3/the-difference-between-emergency-remote-teaching-and-online-learning

Honey, M., Pearson, G., & Schweingruber, A. (2014). *STEM integration in K-12 education: Status, prospects, and an agenda for research.* National Academies Press.

Kelley, T. R., & Knowles, J. G. (2016). A conceptual framework for integrated STEM education. *International Journal of STEM Education, 3*(11). https://doi.org/10.1186/s40594-016-0046-z

Kennedy, T. J., & Odell, M. R. L. (2014). Engaging students in STEM education. *Science Education International, 25*(3), 246–258.

Koehler, M., & Mishra, P. (2009). What is technological pedagogical content knowledge (TPACK)? *Contemporary Issues in Technology and Teacher Education, 9*(1), 60–70.

Krug, D. H. (2012, November 24–27). *STEM education and sustainability in Canada and the United States.* Paper presented at the 2nd International STEM in Education Conference, Beijing, China.

Ladson-Billings, G. (2009). Foreword. In M. L. Hill (Ed.), *Beats, rhymes, and classroom life: Hip-hop pedagogy and the politics of identity* (pp. vii–x). Teachers College Press.

Lambie, L. (2020). *Project-based learning (PBL) in science, technology, engineering and mathematics (STEM): Perspectives of students with special education needs (SENs).* Unpublished M.A thesis. Western University.

Levin, B. B. (1995). Using the case method in teacher education: The role of discussion and experience in teachers' thinking about cases. *Teaching and Teacher Education, 11*(1), 63–79. https://doi.org/10.1016/0742-051X(94)00013-V

Margot, K. C., & Kettler, T. (2019). Teachers' perception of STEM integration and education: A systematic literature review. *International Journal of STEM Education, 6*(2). https://doi.org/10.1186/s40594-018-0151-2

Milner-Bolotin, M. (2018). Evidence-based research in STEM teacher education: From theory to practice. *Frontiers in Education, 3*(92). https://doi.org/10.3389/feduc.2018.00092

Moore, T. J. (2010). CAREER: *Implementing K-12 engineering standards through STEM integration.* National Science Foundation (NSF) Faculty Early Career Development (CAREER) Program, Engineering Education Division, Award # 1055382.

Muehrer, R., Jenson, J., Friedberg, J., & Husain, N. (2012). Challenges and opportunities: using a science-based video game in secondary school settings. *Cultural Studies of Science Education, 7*(4), 783–805. https://doi.org/10.1007/s11422-012-9409-z

Nadelson, L. S., & Seifert, A. L. (2017). Integrated STEM defined: Contexts, challenges, and the Future. *The Journal of Educational Research, 110*(3), 221–223. https://doi.org/10.1080/00220671.2017.1289775

National Academies of Sciences, Engineering, and Medicine (NASEM). (2018). *English learners in STEM subjects: Transforming classrooms, schools, and lives.* The National Academies Press. https://doi.org/10.17226/25182

National Research Council. (2011). *Successful STEM education: A workshop summary.* Washington, DC: The National Academies Press.

National Research Council. (2013). *Monitoring progress toward successful K-12 STEM education: A nation advancing?* National Academies Press.

Natural Science and Engineering Research Council of Canada. (2010). *Women in science and engineering in Canada.* Author.

Ontario Ministry of Education. (2020, March 8). *Ontario Modernizing School Science Curriculum* [Press Release]. https://news.ontario.ca/en/release/1001722/ontario-modernizing-school-science-curriculum#content

Shernoff, D. J., Sinha, S., Bressler, D. M., & Ginsburg, L. (2017). Assessing teacher education and professional development needs for the implementation of integrated approaches to STEM education. *International Journal of STEM Education, 4*(13). https://doi.org/10.1186/s40594-017-0068-1

Stohlmann, M., Moore, T. J., & Roehrig, G. H. (2012). Considerations for teaching integrated STEM education. *Journal of Pre-College Engineering Education Research (J-PEER), 2*(1), Article 4. https://doi.org/10.5703/1288284314653

Strobel, J., & van Barneveld, A. (2009). A meta-synthesis of meta-analyses comparing PBL to conventional classrooms. *Interdisciplinary Journal of Problem-Based Learning, 3*(1). https://doi.org/10.7771/1541-5015.1046

Tan, E., Calabrese-Barton, A., Kang, H., & O'Neil, T. (2013). Desiring a career in STEM fields: Girls narrated and embodied identities-in-practice. *Journal of Research in Science Education, 50*(10), 1143–1179.

Thibaut, L., Ceuppens, S., De Loof, H., De Meester, J., Goovaerts, L., Struyf, A., Boeve-de Pauw, J., Dehaene, W., Deprez, J., De Cock, M., Hellinckx, L., Knipprath, H., Langie, G., Struyven, K., Van de Velde, D., Van Petegem, P., & Depaepe, F. (2018). Integrated STEM education: A systematic review of instructional practices in secondary education. *European Journal of STEM Education, 3*(1), 02. https://doi.org/10.20897/ejsteme/85525

Wang, H., Moore, T. J. Roehrig, G. H., & Park, M. S. (2011). STEM integration: Teacher perceptions and practice. *Journal of Pre-College Engineering Education Research (J-PEER),1*(2), Article 2. https://doi.org/10.5703/1288284314636

Webb, A. W., & Barrera, E. S. (2017). Providing equal opportunity to learn science for English language learners: The role of simulated language learner experiences in teacher preparation. *Catalyst: A Social Justice Forum, 7*(1), Article 3. https://trace.tennessee.edu/catalyst/vol7/iss1/3Catalyst

Yalçınkaya, E., Taştan-Kırık, Ö., Boz, Y., & Yıldıran, D. (2012). Is case-based learning an effective teaching strategy to challenge students' alternative conceptions regarding chemical kinetics? *Research in Science & Technological Education, 30*(2), 151–172.

CHAPTER 4

STEM in Canadian Teacher Education: An Overview

G. Michael Bowen, Dawn Wiseman, Marie-Claire Shanahan, Samia Khan, Allison Gonsalves, Pratim Sengupta, Wendy Simms, Eva Knoll, and Ashley Carter

Introduction

A recent scoping review of STEM education in Canada (DeCoito, 2016) found only one mention in research documents of STEM in teacher education despite support for expanding formal and informal K-12 STEM initiatives from various levels of government and non-governmental

G. M. Bowen (✉) • A. Carter
Mount Saint Vincent University, Halifax, NS, Canada
e-mail: mike.bowen@msvu.ca

D. Wiseman
Bishop's University, Sherbrooke, QC, Canada
e-mail: dwiseman@ubishops.ca

S. M. Al-Balushi et al. (eds.), *Reforming Science Teacher Education Programs in the STEM Era*, Palgrave Studies on Leadership and Learning in Teacher Education,
https://doi.org/10.1007/978-3-031-27334-6_4

organizations (DeCoito, 2016; Yore et al., 2014). Since emerging as a concept in the 1990's (see Shanahan et al., 2016) STEM and STEM education have really only become an area of broad interest in Canada in the past 15 years. This may have occurred as the result of increasing concerns about STEM from the perspective of future competitiveness (e.g., Science, Technology and Innovation Council, 2015) where the skills and practices of STEM disciplines are seen as essential to national economic health (Council of Canadian Academies, 2015).

To explore the question of STEM in school settings it is helpful to consider what the term means, as meaning has implications for classroom practice and teacher education (Bybee, 2013; Sanders, 2009; Breiner et al., 2012; Shanahan et al., 2016). For instance, how many of the four (or five if we consider STEAM) disciplines need to be incorporated for something to be considered a STEM activity? And to what degree should disciplines be interwoven? There are no clear answers, thus we take the position that effectively integrating as few as two disciplines can lead to rich STEM activities in schools (Sanders, 2009, p. 21; DeCoito, 2016; Moomaw, 2013).

M.-C. Shanahan • P. Sengupta
University of Calgary, Calgary, AB, Canada
e-mail: mcshanah@ucalgary.ca; pratim.sengupta@ucalgary.ca

S. Khan
University of British Columbia, Vancouver, BC, Canada
e-mail: samia.khan@ubc.ca

A. Gonsalves
McGill University, Montreal, QC, Canada
e-mail: allison.gonsalves@mcgill.ca

W. Simms
Vancouver Island University, Nanaimo, BC, Canada
e-mail: wendy.simms@viu.ca

E. Knoll
Université du Québec à Montréal, Montreal, QC, Canada
e-mail: knoll.eva@uqam.ca

Understanding the Political Context of Education and Teacher Education in Canada

Canada is a constitutional democracy comprised of 10 provinces (with 99.68% of the population) and three northern territories. Division of roles and responsibilities between the federal government and provinces/territories is stipulated in the Canadian Constitution. Education is a provincial responsibility; there is no federal role in K-12 education, although the federal government does have some shared responsibilities for Indigenous education. Consequently, Faculty of Education Bachelor of Education (BEd) programs are approved through provincial agencies with little formal collaboration between them on course requirements or content across jurisdictions. This reality, combined with the academic independence of universities, makes it challenging to discuss STEM in teacher education from a national perspective.

Some collaboration on education does occur nationally. Past initiatives include the federal government coordinating development of provincial Early Learning Frameworks (for childcare settings; see Bowen et al., 2022) and the Council of Ministers of Education (CMEC, see http://www.cmec.ca) developed the "Common Framework of Science Learning Outcomes K to 12" (1997) to provide a foundation for provincial science education curricula.

Understanding STEM in Teacher Education in Canada

Given the above, summarizing STEM practices in BEd programs in Canada is fraught with difficulties. Nonetheless, we have examined information from three sources to summarize information about the prevalence of STEM in Canadian teacher education.

(1) Publications and reports released by the CMEC for the last two decades.
(2) Academic conference presentations from the Science Education Research Group (SERG) and the Canadian Association of Teacher Education (CATE) over the last decade.
(3) BEd course descriptions that are STEM-specific or STEM-like from academic calendars for the 56 Faculties of Education cur-

rently members of the Association of Canadian Deans of Education (ACDE).

To expand on the summaries from these three sources, we also provide descriptive narratives of STEM in Teacher Education programs by faculty members representing teacher education institutions in four major political regions of the country (Atlantic, Central, Prairie, and Pacific; formal teacher education for Northern territories is accomplished through partnering with other regions). These narratives are not intended to be representative, but to portray the wide variety of STEM teacher education practices across Canada. Following each descriptive narrative is a response by its authors to questions about the narrative asked by other authors.

The State of STEM in Teacher Education in Canada

CMEC Reports and Publications

In Canada, one avenue of coordination of education across provincial jurisdictions is the CMEC which was founded in 1967. Its membership is provincial/territorial Ministers of Education and their designates. CMEC has released 294 reports or papers in the past two decades on both K-12 and post-secondary education; none have dealt with STEM other than one report that examined post-secondary STEM graduate patterns.

SERG & CATE Presentations

Annual academic conferences of the Canadian Society for the Study of Education (CSSE) include SERG and CATE presentations. CSSE includes approximately 900 papers each year. From 2013–2022, of 399 SERG presentations 56 were STEM-related; and only six dealt directly with BEd programs. In the same period at CSSE, there were 31 other papers addressing STEM, of which six dealt with BEd programs and three with professional development. There has been a higher incidence of STEM papers in recent years, but overall, those with direct relation to BEd/PD have been uncommon. CATE also holds "Working Conferences" outside of CSSE (seven in the period considered). The proceedings from those contained four STEM-related papers on teacher education (of 112 papers in total).

STEM Courses in Academic Calendars

The review of BEd course Academic Calendar descriptions revealed that ten of 56 Faculties of Education have one or more courses that are specifically STEM-focused (in either title or description); see Table 4.1. When STEM-like courses (i.e., those describing integrating two or more STEM subjects) are considered the total rises to 18. However, only six BEd programs (i.e., Memorial University of Newfoundland (MUN), Bishop's University, McGill University, Western University (WU), University of Calgary, Thompson Rivers University (TRU)) offered more than two STEM or STEM-like courses (some are electives, some for only secondary or only elementary PSTs). So, given this, it is unsurprising that only three faculties of education in Canada offered specific programs or certificates in STEM. It is worth noting that none of the Francophone teacher preparation programs had any STEM-specific courses or programs described in the calendars that met our criteria (Wiseman/Gonsalves note that at the secondary level in Québec BEd programs must address engineering and technology, so all programs may take up STEM approaches).

Table 4.1 STEM in teacher education academic calendars in Canada

	# STEM Courses @ # sites	*# STEM-like @ # sites*	*# Cohorts/ programs/ certificates*	*Total # Faculties w/STEM @ Total # Faculties*
Atlantic	6@3	1(1)[a] @1	1 (MUN)	4(1)@10(2)
Central[b, c]	8@4	10(3)@5(2)	1 (WU)	8(2)@22(5)
Prairie	2@1	4@3	0	3@15(2)
Pacific	6@2	3@2	1 (TRU)	3@9
Total	22@10	18(4)@11(2)	3	18(3)@56(9)

[a]*# of francophone that are part of the total in brackets. No brackets = no francophone*

[b]*In Quebec there is a multi-site university (6), documents from 1 was examined as representative*

[c]*Ontario's elementary science curriculum is "Science & Technology" which has minor similarities to STEM. Most Ontario Fac-ed methods courses refer to both, but they were not counted as part of STEM since the 2007 curriculum pre-dates STEM and the degree of integration is unclear.*

Narrative Descriptions of STEM-oriented BEd Courses

Pacific Region: Approaching STEM through Modeling Practices

In this section, we describe a pre-service teacher (PST) science methods course developed and taught by Khan at UBC, from which the largest proportion of new teachers in the province graduate (BCTC, 2015). This course offers an integrated STEM education that aligns with Martín-Páez et al. (2019) and Kelley and Knowles (2016); that is, a STEM education contributes to socio-scientific debate, open inquiry, and innovative solutions to personal, local and global problems. By presenting an integrated, cyclical, and collaborative merger of science, technology, engineering, and math, course activities aim to foster teacher capacity to engage youth in solving problems using a wider array of practices.

A main feature of the course is modeling and model-based teaching and learning (MBTL). Other topics include the nature of science, big ideas in the science curriculum, diagnosing students' ideas, lesson planning, questioning strategies, integrating digital technologies, and how to teach about socio-scientific issues such as climate change. Guest speakers contribute different perspectives and expertise in STEM, and teaching videos, from a local STEM academy, provide authentic exemplars of classroom-based STEM education. The course also introduces PSTs to the engineering design cycle and how it involves modeling. Outreach groups present STEM design challenges (e.g., coding microbits) and stations using different technological tools such as Merge Cubes. Finally, the class delves more significantly into mathematics with guest scientists. Using Sage Modeler and En-Roads simulations, PSTs run dynamic models about climate change and socio-scientific debates ensue.

Modeling serves an integrative function in science, technology, engineering, and math. It is a central practice in STEM as models act as representations that offer explanations of the target system. Relatedly, modeling is a primary means by which theories are rendered and developed by scientists (Nersessian, 2010). The pedagogical approach associated with MBTL was based on GEM or (G)enerating ideas about a model, (E)valuating the model using hands-on activities or simulations, and (M)odifying the model (Khan, 2011). GEM is different from the inquiry cycle, Predict, Observe, Explain sequences (see Haysom and Bowen, 2010), and 5E approaches that are often employed because learners are prompted to actively address prior models.

The course has three main assignments: (i) For the "un-demonstration"—the opposite of traditional demonstrations—PSTs are required to work across disciplines and ask questions about what they are showing. An example is "Biological Speed Up" where PSTs used yeast and hydrogen peroxide to change the speed of chemical reactions and discuss the digestive system. (ii) PSTs design a MBTL lesson based on a big idea that can traverse subject areas. They have to do so by integrating digital technology within a GEM cycle (e.g. PheT simulations, Gizmos, Biointeractive software). (iii) The final assignment is a reflective "personal pedagogical statement" responding to three questions: What is science? What are my ideas on how people learn science well, and how can people be taught science? A self-assessment rubric emphasizes science as an interdisciplinary problem-solving endeavor and modeling as a common "practice" that can be found across STEM fields.

Pacific Region Discussion

Questions (from other narrative authors): (i) How is your course using models in relation to the BC curriculum? (ii) How do you discuss modeling, especially the manner in which teachers attend to the various ways students represent and talk about their developing ideas in STEM?

Reply: (i) Models are found throughout the 2018 BC K-12 curriculum. This curriculum outlines what students need to know (content), do (competencies), and understand (big ideas) to become educated citizens. The science competencies, which are the focus of assessment in BC, speak directly to modeling as a scientific practice. From grade 7 onward, modeling is directly assessed. By middle school, students are assessed on their ability to, "*Evaluate the validity and limitations of a model or analogy in relation to the phenomenon modelled*" and, "*Construct, analyze, and interpret graphs, models, and/or diagrams.*" By high school, students must be able to, "*Formulate physical or mental theoretical models to describe a phenomenon.*" (ii) Models are discussed in various ways in the course, including scientific models, students' mental models, students' expressed models, and even curricular models. PSTs become adept at using the term models in different contexts within the course. Modeling is described as a practice that involves the generation, evaluation, and modification of models in STEM fields.

Prairie Region: Heterogeneities in Design and STEM Education

The Werklund School of Education BEd program at the University of Calgary has included a mandatory STEM Education course for all students since 2014. Through the course, BEd students in all specialty and disciplinary areas are encouraged to think about how they could build collaborations between math, science and other disciplinary areas in their future classrooms. Approximately 300 BEd students take this course each year (in sections of 30–40 according to specialization level; early childhood, elementary or secondary).

When first designed, the course had an explicit focus on programming education—students' major projects involved creating robotic solutions to societal and community issues using LEGO Mindstorms. Since then, the course has developed to take a broader view of STEM as one meaningful way to engage K-12 students in transdisciplinary experiences focusing on developing future teachers' understanding of disciplinarity, mathematization, and computational thinking. Students are encouraged to re-examine meaningful concepts from their own disciplinary specialties through the lens of mathematization, exploring how computational thinking processes—such as agent-based modeling (both with and without digital technologies)—can open new ways to understand and explore concepts in history, music, literature and beyond. Students are introduced to different types of programming/modeling experiences (e.g., through Minecraft, NetLogo, Scratch block coding) and encouraged to analyze how these environments support different kinds of learning. The course emphasizes a less technocentric approach and creates spaces for teachers across disciplines to consider STEM experiences as part of their practice.

To complement the STEM course, in 2017–2018 a required Design-based Thinking course for all pre-service teachers was introduced. This course focuses on formal design methods and concepts, not as a topic for K12 education but as an approach to teaching and addressing issues such as learning, social relationships, and equity in school and classroom communities. The course introduces students to formal human-centered design practices and emphasizes the under-appreciation of problem setting as the most crucial aspect of design, while recognizing that it is important to avoid creating a sense of solutionism among pre-service teachers. Solutionist approaches suggest that following a design algorithm should always lead to ways to fix a problem. These fixes are typically one-way (someone applies a fix and solves the problem) and reductionist, ignoring the complexity, inter-relatedness, and multi-faceted nature of any real problem (Milan, 2020). Similarly, in the Design Thinking course, it is important that teachers are encouraged to use design methods and processes but to think carefully about applying them to on-the-ground issues that are meaningful and embedded in their everyday lifeworlds as teachers. Consequently, their term projects engage them in problem setting and frame creation to rethink common issues experienced during their field placements.

Critical scholars remind us that technocentrism and techno-solutionism are explicit dangers in design, computing, and STEM education. Our classrooms and BEd programs must reflect our struggles with technology as a society, center views from the margins and advance a more aesthetic and creative agenda (e.g., Sengupta et al., 2021, 2022; Shanahan & Nieswandt, 2009). It is this essential heterogeneity that defines our critical engagement with design and STEM education in our BEd program.

Prairie Region Discussion
Questions: (i) Does the Alberta public-school curriculum have any STEM-focused courses? (ii) What is human-centered design? (iii) What is design-based thinking and does it depart from a STEM course?

Reply: (i) Currently, the K-12 curriculum documents have no explicit STEM courses, but it has curriculum connections to design, engineering and digital technology in K-12 math/science. For example, each Grade 1–6 year includes a "Problem solving through technology" Science unit. (ii) Human-centered design typically refers to the practice of centering any design activities on what might actually work for people to meet their real needs and desires rather than being driven by new technology, competition, or just novelty. It is important to engage PSTs with both understanding and grappling with the application of these practices in education as well as critically examining how they intersect with technocentrism and solutionism which can re/create bias and inequity. (iii) Design thinking is typically a term for describing the complex set of processes and practices—characterized by creativity, iteration, and reflection—used to find new ways to address commercial, social, technological, and community challenges. The Stanford Design school is well known for promoting the idea that design thinking can be applied in any kind of problem solving across lifeworlds and by anyone. Design practices and orientations are prominent in both courses. For instance, the first-year BEd STEM course has a focus on engineering design practices.

Central Region: STEM through Ambitious Science Teaching

Understanding education in Québec requires consideration of culture, language, and ongoing colonialism. Among school going children, 90% attend school in French—Québec's official language, 8.6% in English, and under 1% in an Indigenous language (e.g. Inuktitut, Kanien'kéha) (MEQ, 2021). Most schools follow the Québec Education Program (QEP). Teachers are certified primarily in four-year BEd programs (Rahm, et al., 2019) at 13 institutions. Three are English; of those, only Bishop's and McGill (B&M) certify both elementary and secondary teachers. Here we discuss B&M's BEd certification programs.

The QEP is competency-based (MELS, 2006), focused on "the capacity to act effectively by drawing on a variety of resources" (p. 7). There are three Science and Technology (S&T) disciplinary competencies:

- investigating scientific/technological problems
- using critical judgment to gather and analyze data to formulate explanations;
- developing appropriate scientific language.

S&T emphasizes exploring interesting problems/phenomena that may have no singular answer via four "worlds"—the Material World, the Living World, Earth & Space, and the Technological World—where all elements of STEM may be enacted.

At B&M, S&T BEd programs use a practice-based pedagogy aligning with both QEP and integrated STEM. We build from Windschitl et al.'s (2018) Ambitious Science Teaching (AST) where the processes of S&T teaching fall into four practices:

(1) Planning for engagement with big S&T ideas;
(2) Eliciting student ideas/prior knowledge;
(3) Supporting ongoing changes in student thinking through engagement with data;
(4) Building evidence-based explanations based on data.

AST practices focus on student and teacher discourse, written and oral expression, reasoning, modeling, and ongoing assessment building learning around complex anchoring phenomena (and related essential questions) observable in the real world but which require developing explanations at both macro- and micro- levels across disciplines. Phenomena should be sufficiently complex to address multiple related curricular requirements that connect the four S&T "worlds."

For example, for a video of a singer breaking a glass using their voice, the related essential question might be "How is it possible for a human to break a glass with their voice?" To explain the phenomenon, students need to pull together understandings about how matter and energy interact both internally and externally to a person's body. Over several lessons, students collect data moving toward evidence-based explanations bridging the "worlds" (e.g., structure of matter; how particles interact; structure and strength of materials; transmission/transformation of energy; how sound is produced, experienced, and interpreted by the human body) to develop conceptual understandings of vibration, resonance, frequency, and so on across multiple scientific disciplines, but can also connect these "big ideas" to explain related phenomena, such as a bridge collapse.

The practice-based pedagogy approach requires that practices are modeled by teacher educators then rehearsed and enacted by novice teachers to approximate the look and feel in a classroom (e.g., Kazemi et al., 2009). Novice teachers may also have opportunities to try out S&T practices during their 700 hour practicals. These enactments support understandings of how approximations of practices modeled and rehearsed in methods classes may be imprecise (Jao et al., 2018; Gonsalves et al., 2021).

Central Region Discussion

Question: (i) In what way do your certification programs incorporate Indigenous perspectives? (ii) Is there movement in making Indigenous perspectives more prominent in BEd programs in Quebec?

Reply: (i) One of us has worked alongside Indigenous peoples and communities quite extensively. This helps inform our S&T course development. Our PSTs learn to question the epistemological and ontological stance of school-presented STEM, examine what might be termed STEM in historical and contemporary Indigenous contexts, and understand the complicity of STEM and STEM practitioners in residential schools and colonization. Local Indigenous STEM teachers visit methods courses. We also have conversations about the limits on understanding solely based on Western/Enlightenment conceptions of STEM.

(ii) Unlike ALL other provinces and territories, Quebec has no provincial curricular mandate to engage with Indigenous ways of knowing, being, and doing. It's embarrassing. It is essentially up to the discretion of the instructor how to accomplish this (even though both faculties have signed onto the ACDE Accord on Indigenous Education, and the Truth and Reconciliation Commission Calls for Action). Despite nearly all universities noting that a teacher education competency specific to the understandings, histories, contributions, and contemporary contexts of Indigenous peoples was needed, the 2021 update to these competencies added but a glancing reference. To address the absence, the First Nations Education Council of Quebec, developed and released "Competency 15" (https://cepn-fnec.ca/en/competence-15/), which has been adopted by some Faculties of Education which are figuring out how to integrate and operationalize it.

Atlantic Region: Stepping into the Technology and STEM Pool

In 2015/2016 the Nova Scotia education department (NSDE) introduced several technologies into elementary schools (e.g., Bee-Bots, Sphero SPRKs, Makey-Makeys, Scratch), announced that coding would be a cross grade/curriculum outcome (Casey, 2015), and work-shopped all elementary teachers on the new curriculum. Organizations supporting K-12 education also had a workshop opportunity, although the invitation made no mention of technology or coding, merely mentioning that there was a new curriculum.

G. Michael Bowen attended as his faculty's sole representative (and the only Faculty of Education science/STEM educator) learning that some subjects had little weekly scheduled time (e.g., science, social studies) so taking an integrated approach with those subjects having more scheduled time (e.g., mathematics, language arts) was promoted. Although STEM was not specifically mentioned, the described integration approach had many parallels (see Haverly et al., 2022). A demonstrated example integrated language arts, music, and science, although GMB had some concerns that the science was conceptually misrepresented. Workshop time was spent using the technologies, and discussions suggested that NSDE saw them as the "focal point" for subject integration.

In Nova Scotia (NS), teacher certification is mostly two-year post-baccalaureate programs. To address the new curriculum (with technologies) Mount Saint Vincent University (MSVU) modified its second elementary science methods course into one using the technologies in an integrated subject fashion—essentially STEM—providing the "core" NSDE technologies and those in local schools (e.g., Ozobots, 3D printers, Microbits). Students were first introduced to the technologies, engaged in basic non-computer coding activities (e.g., weaving as coding), and course assignments were described. Next, they participated in a 3h Scratch coding workshop.

Thereafter, in weekly assignments student pairs selected one of the technologies and completed a report for which they each:

- identified what they wished to learn about it,
- described learning to use it,
- described how classroom teachers used it, and
- designed a classroom activity with subject-based learning outcomes using the technology.

Nine reports were required—five for NSDE "core" technologies, four others with "core" or enrichment technologies—encouraging mastery learning for at least the "core" technologies. GMB supported the students by using a modeling-coaching-fading sequence (see Roth & Bowen, 1994).

There were also three major individual assignments. Two were detailed lesson plans which used a technology with two or three different subjects integrating the learning outcomes. The third was building a tin foil "switch circuit board" which was used with a Makey-Makey to control an integrated subject "educational program" each student created using Scratch.

Most students were enthusiastic about the course and structure. Those who considered themselves "weak" using technology (Nova Scotia is rural with little technology availability) usually reported strong gains in knowledge (evaluations mostly confirmed this). Subject integration was new and challenging but usually well implemented by the second lesson plan. A very few students indicated that they wanted more direct instruction at a class-wide level.

Coda: MSVU's "new" BEd program has replaced this course with one having much less of a technology focus and no explicit science/math focus.

Atlantic Region Discussion

Questions: (i) How was disciplinary integration discussed with students from a theoretical or meaning making perspective and how did students come to understand disciplinary integration? (ii) What is the uptake of robotics and coding in elementary classrooms?

Reply: (i) BEd programs in NS do not have courses on learning or curriculum theory and these seem little explored in the 50–75% of courses taught by sessional instructors from a practitioner perspective. However, with many technology-inexperienced students it was considered more important to first develop reasonable competency using the technologies. There was one discussed reading on "integrating subjects" used explicitly as part of the integrated lesson planning activities. Subject teaching in NS has been very siloed across all grades. Students tell me that these lesson plans are the first time they've ever thought about integrating across subjects. The resources students provided to me suggest that they see few examples of teachers using technology where a cross-subject approach was adopted. (ii) I hear mixed stories about technology adoption. Seven years after the technologies were put into schools some elementary PSTs have classroom mentors who use the technologies frequently. Others tell me that they're told that the school doesn't have the technologies and they find them buried in a closet, never unpacked. This despite NSDE's yearly conference for K-12 teachers on integrating these technologies into classrooms. So, uptake is mixed.

Discussion and Conclusions

It is notable that there appears to be low availability of STEM-related courses, and even fewer STEM "certificate" programs, across Faculties of Education in Canada. This possibly reflects a lack of STEM being explicit in K-12 schooling documents. As authors, we have each noted in our own provinces the lack of explicit STEM references in provincial curriculum documents and this could be influencing STEM-specific offerings in teacher education.

The regional narratives describe a broad range of approaches used with STEM in teacher education in Canada, ranging from those that emphasize interdisciplinarity and cross-subject integration to those that adopt a more transdisciplinary perspective on schooling (and therefore STEM). Transdisciplinary approaches extend beyond subject integration to encompass experiences that value cultural and personal knowledges and prompt rethinking of disciplinary assumptions.

DeCoito's wide-ranging review of the state of STEM education in Canada (2016) supports the need for greater attention to STEM education in K-12 schools, particularly the importance of laying the foundations for STEM interest in early grades. Anecdotally, there is some evidence this may be happening at the elementary level. Nonetheless, there also seems to be a need for more explicit STEM education in teacher education, which our review of academic calendars suggests is uncommon (Table 4.1).

The review of conference presentations, the Atlantic narrative, and the regional discussions suggest that STEM is approached implicitly if not explicitly in many other faculties than the academic calendar review suggests.

It is also worth asking in what manner we should be addressing STEM in teacher education. In their narrative, Shanahan and Sengupta describe the reflective discussions they have with their PSTs on issues of technocentrism and solutionism, whereas in other narratives these critical discussions were a lesser concern. In all of the narrative settings, however, commonality can be found in attention to collaboration and group work toward the goal of understanding integrated STEM subjects and practices, better reflecting the actual work of STEM practitioners (see Roth & Lee, 2002).

So, how could a broader STEM agenda in teacher education be developed in Canada? One potential exemplar is found in a 2016 initiative to develop Environmental Education in Canadian teacher education initiated by Paul Elliot at Trent University (see https://eseinfacultiesofed.ca/; Kool et al., 2021). Additionally, the Association of Canadian Deans of Education (https://csse-scee.ca/acde/) has released reports and signed accords in the past to encourage particular practices at member faculties. A STEM education accord from ACDE could lead to a more coordinated offering in Canadian teacher education.

Finally, any forwarding of a broader agenda in STEM in teacher education needs to account for the concerns and proposals of Shanahan et al. (2016) who suggest that a Canadian-oriented STEM perspective needs to be contextual to local educational values and needs, focused less on an economic purpose (as in many other jurisdictions) and more on STEM teaching as a way of re-understanding disciplinary knowledge in a more authentic fashion—as gathering points of activity, creation, investigation, and inquiry by like-minded individuals with common or synergistic purposes. Shanahan and co-authors propose STEM be viewed as a boundary object, "pragmatic entities valued for their ability to bring collaborators together and facilitate projects and outcomes that might be impossible otherwise" (p. 134), which we note also happens to be an outcome of this coming together of authors to write this chapter on STEM in teacher education in Canada.

References

BC Teacher's Council. (2015). *New Teacher Survey Results—BC Teacher Education Program Graduate Report.*

Bowen, G. M., Knoll, E., & Willison, A. M. (2022). Bee-Bot robots and their STEM learning potential in the play-based behaviour of preschool children in Canada. In S. D. Tunnicliffe & T. J. Kennedy (Eds.), *Play and STEM education in the early years: International policies and practices.* Springer.

Breiner, J. M., Harkness, S. S., Johnson, C. C., & Koehler, C. M. (2012). What is STEM? A discussion about conceptions of STEM in education and partnerships. *School Science and Mathematics, 112*(1), 3–11.

Bybee, R. W. (2013). *The case for STEM education: Challenges and opportunities.* National Science Teachers Association Press.

Casey, K. (2015). *Minister announces coding as a priority during education day.* https://novascotia.ca/news/release/?id=20151021002

Council of Canadian Academies. (2015). *Some assembly required: STEM skills and Canada's economic productivity.* Author.

Council of Ministers of Education, Canada. (1997). *Common framework of science learning outcomes K to 12.* Author.

DeCoito, I. (2016). STEM education in Canada: A knowledge synthesis. *Canadian Journal of Science, Mathematics and Technology Education, 16*(2), 114–128.

Gonsalves, A., Sprowls, E., & Wiseman, D. (2021). Teaching novice science teachers online: Considerations for practice-based pedagogy. *LEARNing Landscapes, 14*(1), 111–123.

Haverly, C., Lyle, A., Spillane, J. P., Davis, E. A., & Peurach, D. J. (2022). Leading instructional improvement in elementary science: State science coordinators' sense-making about the Next Generation Science Standards. *Journal of Research in Science Teaching., 59,* 1–32.

Haysom, J. & Bowen, G. M. (2010). *Predict, Observe, Explain: Activities enhancing scientific understanding.* Arlington, VA: National Science Teachers Association Press.

Jao, L., Wiseman, D., Kobiela, M., Gonsalves, A., & Savard, A. (2018). Practice-based pedagogy in mathematics and science teaching methods: Challenges and adaptation in context. *Canadian Journal of Science, Mathematics and Technology Education, 18*(2), 177–186.

Kazemi, E, Franke, M., & Lampert, M. (2009). Developing pedagogies in teacher education to support novice teachers' ability to enact ambitious instruction. In Hunter, R., Bicknell, B., & Burgess, T. (Eds.). *Crossing divides: Proceedings of the 32nd annual conference of the Mathematics Education Research Group of Australasia* (Vol. 1, pp. 12–30). Wellington, NZ.

Kelley, T. R., & Knowles, J. G. (2016). A conceptual framework for integrated STEM education. *International Journal of STEM Education, 3*(1), 1–11.

Khan, S. (2011). What's missing in model-based teaching? *Journal of Science Teacher Education, 22*(6), 535–560.

Kool, R., Karrow, D. D., & DiGiuseppe, M. (2021). Environmental and Sustainability Education in Canadian Faculties of Education, 2017–2018: A research report for the EECOM Standing Committee on Environmental and Sustainability Education in Teacher Education.

Martín-Páez, T., Aguilera, D., Perales-Palacios, F. J., & Vílchez-González, J. M. (2019). What are we talking about when we talk about STEM education? A review of literature. *Science Education, 103*(4), 799–822.

Milan, S. (2020). Techno-solutionism and the standard human in the making of the COVID-19 pandemic. *Big Data & Society, 7*(2), 1–7.

Ministère de l'éducation (MELS). (2006). *Québec Education Program. Secondary School Education, Cycle One.* http://www.education.gouv.qc.ca/fileadmin/site_web/documents/PFEQ/qepsecfirstcycle.pdf

Ministère de l'Éducation du Québec (MEQ). (2021). *Prévisions de l'effectif scolaire à l'éducation préscolaire, à l'enseignment primaire et secondaire, par centres de services scolaires et commissions scolaires et pour l'ensemble du Québec. Faits saillants.*

Moomaw, S. (2013). *Teaching STEM in the early years: Activities for integrating science, technology, engineering, and mathematics.* Redleaf Press.

Nersessian, N. J. (2010). *Creating scientific concepts.* MIT Press.

Rahm, J., Potvin, P., & Vásquez-Abad, J. (2019). Science education in Québec: La science et la technologie port tous. In C. D. Tippett & T. M. Milford (Eds.), *Science Education in Canada* (pp. 129–150). Springer.

Roth, W. M., & Bowen, G. M. (1994). An investigation of problem framing and solving in a grade 8 open-inquiry science program. *The Journal of the Learning Sciences, 3*(2), 165–204.

Roth, W. M., & Lee, S. (2002). Scientific literacy as collective praxis. *Public Understanding of Science, 11*(1), 33–56.

Sanders, M. (2009). STEM, STEM education, STEMmania. *Technology Teacher, 68*(4), 20–26.

Science, Technology and Innovation Council. (2015). *State of the nation 2014. Canada's innovation challenges and opportunities.* Ottawa, ON, Canada.

Sengupta, P., Chokshi, A., Helvaci Ozacar, B., Dutta, S., Sanyal, M., & Shanahan, M. C. (2022). Language and symbolic violence in computational models of ethnocentrism: A critical phenomenology and Southern re-orientations. *International Journal of Qualitative Studies in Education*, [35?], 1–20.

Sengupta, P., Dickes, A., & Farris, A. V. (2021). *Voicing code in STEM: A dialogical imagination.* MIT Press.

Shanahan, M. C., Burke, L. E. C.-A., & Francis, K. (2016). Using a boundary object perspective to reconsider the meaning of STEM in a Canadian context. *Canadian Journal of Science, Mathematics and Technology Education, 16*(2), 129–139.

Shanahan, M. C., & Nieswandt, M. (2009). Creative activities and their influence on identification in science: Three case studies. *Journal of Elementary Science Education, 21*(3), 63–79.

Windschitl, M., Thompson, J., & Braaten, M. (2018). *Ambitious science teaching.* Harvard Education Press.

Yore, L. D., Pelton, L. F., Neill, B. W., Pelton, T. W., Anderson, J. O., & Milford, T. M. (2014). Closing the science, mathematics, and reading gaps from a Canadian perspective: Implications for STEM mainstream and pipeline literacy. In J. V. Clark (Ed.), *Closing the achievement gap from an international perspective* (pp. 73–104). Springer.

CHAPTER 5

Science Teacher Education in Chile: On the Verge of a Turning Point toward STEM-Oriented Science Education

Cristian Merino, Ainoa Marzabal, Brant G. Miller, and Ximena Carrasco

C. Merino (✉)
Instituto de Química, Pontificia Universidad Católica de Valparaíso, Valparaíso, Chile
e-mail: cristian.merino@pucv.cl

A. Marzabal
Facultad de Educación, Pontificia Universidad Católica de Chile, Santiago, Chile
e-mail: amarzabal@uc.cl

B. G. Miller
Department of Curriculum and Instruction, University of Idaho, Moscow, ID, USA
e-mail: bgmiller@uidaho.edu

X. Carrasco
Programa de Doctorado en Didáctica de las Ciencias, Pontificia Universidad Católica de Valparaíso, Valparaíso, Chile

S. M. Al-Balushi et al. (eds.), *Reforming Science Teacher Education Programs in the STEM Era*, Palgrave Studies on Leadership and Learning in Teacher Education,
https://doi.org/10.1007/978-3-031-27334-6_5

Introduction

In the STEM era citizens are expected to apply both the key knowledge, ways of doing, reasoning, and communicating of science, technology, engineering, and mathematics, in an integrated way (Izquierdo & Adúriz-Bravo, 2003; Merino & Izquierdo, 2011). This set of knowledge and skills enable citizens to address complex problems by building creative and innovative solutions in a critical, reflective, and value-based way (Couso, 2017).

In the last decades, new social demands have challenged schools to move toward more flexible and interdisciplinary approaches. However, in most countries, the rigid structure of the curriculum and teaching practices have hindered the transformation of the school experience for students. Thus, despite the consensus on the need to move toward a STEM oriented education, traditional practices persist (Bybee, 2011).

Given the key role of teachers to incorporate STEM perspectives in schools (Shernoff et al., 2017), educational policies have focused on reforming the initial and continuing education of secondary science teachers. This is the case for Chile, where this chapter is framed. Recent educational policies regarding the school science curriculum and science teacher education have placed Chile on the verge of a turning point toward STEM oriented science education.

In this chapter, we present the most recent national policies and how they have reshaped secondary science teacher education. We believe that the processes of the two higher education institutions presented in this chapter exemplify the changes undertaken by many institutions in Latin America. We hope that this chapter will be of interest to teacher educators who, like us, face the challenge of rethinking science teacher education to move toward STEM-oriented science education.

Science Teacher Education in Chile

Chilean National Policies for Teacher Education Improvement (2002–2022)

Improving the quality of teachers has been a priority of the Chilean Ministry of Education in the last 20 years. The unregulated opening of new teacher education programs as of 2002 led to an explosive increase of pedagogy programs with the main consequence being a decrease in the quality of school teaching practices and an unequal distribution of teachers in the school system (Avalos, 2011).

In response to these issues, educational policies have been developed to attract high quality candidates to teaching careers, improve teacher education processes, and establish conditions to retain teachers in school settings. Five initiatives are currently being implemented nationwide (MINEDUC, 2021): (a) a progressive increase in the requirements to access pedagogy careers, (b) teacher vocation scholarships, (c) initial teacher education standards, (d) projects to strengthen initial teacher education programs, and (e) evaluation of pedagogy graduates.

The set of policies implemented for greater control and regulation of initial teacher education has effectively managed to progressively improve the quality of teaching and learning processes in Chilean schools. However, they have been considered as an interference on higher education autonomy and teacher education innovations (Ell & Grudnoff, 2013).

Although teacher education programs are currently oriented toward the achievement of the initial teacher education standards, each institution offers programs with distinctive features that respond to their own vision of the knowledge and practices Chilean teachers require. Those programs are evaluated and adjusted on an ongoing basis, in accordance with changes in public policies, curriculum, and the school system, as well as feedback received from students, graduates, employers, accreditation processes, and evaluations.

Science Teachers' Education in Chile

In Chile, there are 37 science teacher education programs. In total, approximately 800 students are enrolled to become science teachers every year. The current offering of science teacher education programs in Chile is quite diverse. The educational applications can be characterized based on the curricular areas in which the graduates are qualified to teach.

The Chilean compulsory school trajectory is structured in two stages: primary education (from 6 to 13 years old) and secondary education (from 14 to 18 years old). During primary education, the curriculum presents a single subject of natural sciences, which later, in secondary education, is divided into three subjects: physics, chemistry, and biology.

Most universities offer programs focused on one of the three scientific areas for secondary education, opting for educating teachers with in-depth knowledge of a scientific discipline and its teaching and learning processes. Pedagogy in Biology careers are the ones that offer more annual positions

(280), followed by Pedagogy in Chemistry (170) and Pedagogy in Physics (130). Other institutions have opted for programs that enable teachers to oversee two disciplines of the science curriculum, opting for an interdisciplinary approach that has a positive impact on graduates' employability. Two programs of this type can be found with a similar number of annual positions: Pedagogy in Biology and Chemistry (120), and Pedagogy in Physics and Mathematics (100).

In their review of science teacher education programs in Chile, Cofré and collaborators found that even when the latest reforms have been constructivist and inquiry-oriented, most programs maintain traditional visions of science education (Cofré et al., 2010; Vergara & Cofré, 2014). According to Cofré and Vergara, science teacher education programs focus on the disciplinary domain rather than developing science practices or fostering an understanding of science activity related to the historical and epistemological aspects of science. Gaete et al. (2017) confirmed that Chilean beginning science teachers presented traditional teaching practices that are barely innovative and scarcely aimed at educating citizens. Socio-scientific, environmental, or socio-cultural issues were mostly absent, even in those who graduated from careers whose study plans tried to promote those approaches (Gaete et al. 2017).

A New Science Curriculum as a Turning Point for Secondary Science Teacher Education

Initial teacher education standards have been a key component for the regulation of science teacher education programs, providing a shared definition of the learning outcomes expected from education processes (Sotomayor & Gysling, 2011). However, initial teacher education standards have not yet had a significant impact on secondary science teacher education programs. Traditional teaching practices persist, and therefore, innovative science learning processes in schools are limited (Camacho & Gaete, 2017).

Given the relevance of science education for citizenship, a new subject called "science for citizenship" has been recently incorporated into the secondary national curriculum for scientific-humanistic, vocational education and training, and artistic itineraries. The new subject seeks to promote an integrated understanding of complex phenomena and problems that occur in our daily work, to train a scientifically literate citizenry with the ability to think critically, participate and make decisions in an informed manner based on the use of evidence (MINEDUC, 2019).

The subject "science for citizenship" is structured in four modules to be developed during the last two years of secondary education: (a) environment and sustainability, (b) welfare and health, (c) safety, prevention, and self-care, and (d) technology and society.

In this new curriculum, it is recommended that a STEM approach support students to learn that mathematics and science, along with technology, are necessary tools to identify problems, collect, and analyze data, model phenomena, test possible solutions, and solve problems, both in professional and everyday life (MINEDUC, 2021). The STEM approach perspective makes visible the diverse processes that relate scientific and technological knowledge with the construction of society and allows students to engage with critical thinking in everyday life and contribute to the exercise of participatory and conscious citizenship.

The implementation of this new curricular subject has pushed important processes of evaluation and adjustment of the current secondary science teacher education programs. For most institutions, this has meant that teacher educators have had to redefine the expected outcomes of science teacher education, resulting in important changes in the nature of the offered programs. It has taken years of collaborative work to build a common vision of the school science education we expect for the coming decades. The new proposals do seem promising in transforming science education in Chile for the upcoming years.

Rethinking Secondary Pre-service Science Teacher Education

Moving toward secondary science education with a STEM orientation requires rethinking the pre-service education of science teachers in four key areas of professional teaching knowledge: (a) disciplinary knowledge, (b) pedagogical knowledge, (c) didactic knowledge, and (d) practical training.

Concerning disciplinary knowledge, besides the development of the core ideas and practices of science, the STEM approach requires to articulate knowledge from various disciplines to build interdisciplinary visions and engage in science and engineering practices.

In terms of pedagogical knowledge, there is a need to strengthen the inclusive approach to provide learning opportunities for all students in an increasingly diverse and complex school system. This requires greater attention to classroom management, teacher monitoring, and feedback practices in STEM-oriented science learning processes.

Regarding didactic knowledge, it is necessary to incorporate active learning strategies, with special emphasis on inquiry, modeling, and argumentation, designing innovative teaching and learning sequences using technology for citizen training. It is also desirable to explore possible articulations between teaching strategies and school science/science topics in the school science curriculum.

Disciplinary, pedagogical, and didactic knowledge converge in the practical training of future science teachers. The collaborative work between the pre-service teachers and the school system actors constitutes opportunities to design, apply, evaluate, and reflect on the "implementation" of instructional practices with a STEM orientation. Practical training is a key experience for exploring new possibilities for science teaching, which pre-service teachers can test in school settings.

Below, we present two experiences on how secondary science teachers are being trained in two Chilean higher education institutions within a STEM oriented framework, with two different approaches: (a) Focusing on the development of STEM pedagogical content knowledge (PCK), and (b) Focusing on reflection, practice and action. From both experiences, we will present some ideas that align with promoting scientific practices and STEM.

Developing Secondary Pre-service Teachers' STEM Pedagogical Content Knowledge

At the Pontificia Universidad Católica de Chile (PUC), the pedagogy careers focused on secondary education in chemistry, physics, and biology were created in 2012. The main purpose was to develop secondary science teachers with a comprehensive vision of the human being, profound disciplinary and pedagogical knowledge, extensive practical work experience in schools, and high motivation to improve the quality of learning for students.

The training program was designed based on a secondary pre-service science teacher training model based on four guiding principles: (a) develop a robust knowledge of the disciplinary content (Wallace & Loughran, 2012), (b) visualize learning as a psychological and socially mediated process, (c) integrate disciplinary and pedagogical knowledge, building pedagogical content knowledge (PCK) (Loughran et al., 2012), and (d) put into play the fundamental teaching practices that would enable them to guide students' learning processes effectively (Ball & Forzani, 2010; Grossman et al., 2009). This training model took the form of three

8-semester programs for pedagogy in biology, pedagogy in chemistry, and pedagogy in physics, which has enrolled some 600 students in the last 10 years.

In 2019, an evaluation of the training plan was carried out to adjust it to the new demands that emerged from the feedback received from teacher trainers, pre-service teachers, graduates, and employers in the first years of the program. One of the main results of this evaluation was to recognize the potential of developing PCK during pre-service teacher training as a strategy to promote teaching and learning processes with STEM orientation (Shulman, 1986, 1987; Uzzo et al., 2018).

The teacher trainers of the institution agreed that the axis of training focused on the development of PCK intentionally and explicitly, providing a set of knowledge, valuable tools, achievements, and beliefs for the insertion of new secondary science teachers in the field of work. In addition, we valued the opportunity for collaboration across disciplines (cross-disciplines) generated in the dialogue between disciplinary, pedagogical, and contextual knowledge that allowed us to build the pedagogical content knowledge (PCK) (Magnusson et al., 1999).

In the evaluation process, the existing PCK courses in the curriculum were redesigned, taking into consideration the following statements:

- During the design, implementation, and evaluation of teaching, teachers use their PCK to make decisions that impact their students' learning (Park et al., 2011).
- Science teachers who have pedagogical knowledge of STEM content can engage in teaching and learning processes of sciences responsive to diversity in the classroom.
- The development of PCK requires that the secondary pre-service science teachers focus on deepening the disciplinary knowledge integrated into the practice of teaching in an environment of continuous reflection and collaboration (Chung Wei et al., 2010).
- This disciplinary knowledge should be interrelated with other STEM disciplines, merging separate disciplines to solve real-world problems (Sanders, 2012).
- Integrating disciplinary, epistemological, pedagogical, and contextual knowledge into a coherent structure requires opportunities for classroom practice and high levels of critical reflection (Marzábal et al., 2016).

- During training, strategies are needed to extract this professional knowledge from pre-service teachers, reflect explicitly on it, and assess how it is transformed along this axis of initial training (Loughran et al., 2012).
- These training spaces are opportunities for pre-service teachers to experience first-hand the active methodologies they are expected to implement in the school context and reflect on them collaboratively (Martínez-Chico et al., 2015).

Finally, the programs of the four courses of PCK were specified, with the main characteristics presented in Table 5.1 below:

The *chemistry/physics/biology and its relationship with other sciences* course is the one that incorporates more STEM-based experiences, providing opportunities to merge knowledge from various scientific disciplines. For example, in the case of secondary chemistry teachers, preparation the course is structured around the chemistry of soil, water, air, food, health, and materials. Throughout the course, scientists, and engineers from each of these areas share their knowledge and experiences with secondary pre-service teachers and engage them in their research projects. Through these experiences, knowledge from various scientific disciplines is not only brought together but the practices of scientific and engineering activity are enacted. In addition, the potential of these experiences for their application in school contexts is evaluated, considering their accessibility and relevance, and their possible curricular alignment.

In summary, the curricular redesign of secondary science teacher training programs at PUC strengthened the curricular activities associated with PCK, providing greater opportunities to merge the knowledge and practices of science, engineering, and mathematics for a STEM approach.

Secondary Pre-service Science Teacher in Reflection, Practice, and Action

The Pontifical Catholic University of Valparaiso (PUCV) has over 60 years of experience training teachers in all areas. Over the years, different processes of reflection, updating, and innovation have led PUCV to consolidate the conceptual framework for pre-service teacher training, which is located at the center of the values of the university. In this way, the educator is seen as responsible for the formation of the human person, who promotes the integral development of students and their dignity as participants in a democratic society. This vision materializes in the commitment

Table 5.1 PCK four courses: main characteristics

Course name	*Development of scientific practices for the teaching of chemistry/physics/biology*	*Challenges in teaching and learning chemistry/physics/biology*	*Chemistry/physics/biology and its relationship with other sciences*	*Seminar on applied research in the teaching and learning of chemistry/physics/biology*
Disciplinary knowledge	Science practices	Knowledge of the scientific discipline	Knowledge of STEM disciplines merged	Knowledge and practices of STEM disciplines merged
Knowledge for teaching	Inquiry	Modeling	Argumentation	Inquiry, modeling, argumentation or project-based learning
Proximity to real teaching contexts	Simulated	Real students' written evidence	Real science classroom recordings	Real school settings
Learning outcome	Teachers in training repeatedly experience the investigative model. The aim is to consolidate scientific practices and begin didactic reflection.	Teachers in training face simple teaching challenges, which develop their ability to identify learning challenges and propose appropriate pedagogical responses.	Teachers in training face complex teaching challenges situated in real contexts, which develop their ability to identify teaching challenges, break them down, and propose appropriate pedagogical responses.	Teachers in training face real teaching challenges, design and implement pedagogical responses, and assess them.

to train teachers who in their professional practice demonstrate the values, skills, and knowledge needed to promote academic, social, and value-based learning for all their students in an environment characterized by solidarity, equity, respect, and appreciation for social and cultural diversity (PUCV, 2014).

Pre-service teachers for competence in the sciences, with a vocation of service, requires collaborative work between different academic units inside the university (i.e., biology institute, chemistry institute, physics institute, math institute, school pedagogy) as well as with the school system, aimed at the simultaneous improvement of pre-service teacher training and learning outcomes in the school system (PUCV, 2014). From this collaboration, a common axis of subjects emerged that is linked to the teaching of natural sciences for the 3 pedagogies of the faculty of sciences (physics, biology and chemistry) that include: mathematics, physics, biology, chemistry, statistics, integrated sciences, design of school scientific projects, technologies for the teaching of sciences and sciences education. Based on these subjects, the development of learning activities that favor a vision of STEM integrated into the training of our pre-service teachers is intended.

The above implies that the process of learning to teach involves developing the capacity to think and act as a teacher, mobilizing professional knowledge to meet the learning needs of all students (Hammerness et al., 2005). This involves, (a) disciplinary knowledge and didactic and pedagogical knowledge of the content; (b) competencies associated with the psychological dimension of teaching, such as knowing how to motivate, develop self-esteem and self-efficacy of their students; and (c) the moral dimension related to professional integrity, building relationships of respect, compassion, justice, and solidarity between students and other members of a school community (Fenstermacher & Richardson, 2005).

To prepare competent teachers who promote the learning of all their students in science from a STEM perspective, the pre-service teacher training program in chemistry and natural sciences at PUCV is aligned with the following principles:

- STEM training experiences need to encourage pre-service teachers to develop much more extensive disciplinary knowledge than they need to teach, allowing them a high and up-to-date command of the discipline to work in the classroom. However, didactic knowledge refers to knowing how to organize STEM teaching so that all students learn actively, designing innovative teaching, and learning sequences using technology to address diversity, enabling students to relate units to everyday life.

- The promotion of equitable, supportive, and democratic pedagogical and social interactions fosters the learning and well-being of all students. Practical training in STEM requires collaborative work with the school system to jointly design opportunities for pedagogical interactions between future teachers and students in the school system. These interactions are designed to support, for example, projects that reflect in some dimension the improvement in schools.
- The systematic reflection and research of their pedagogical practice, in dialogue with their community and updated knowledge, strengthen their professional work. The transformation of STEM practices to offer equal opportunities to all its students considers the teacher a researcher of their reality to improve their decision-making, which shows the intellectual humility of those oriented to continuous learning. A teacher with research capacity knows how to look for research done by others, read scientific articles, and transfer the results of that research to the classroom, to recreate this knowledge in the localized context.

Consequently, practical training is an integrative curricular formation where theory is linked with reality and in which the formative triad participates actively and coordinates with (a) tutors' teachers (of the university), (b) mentors (classroom teachers of schools of practice), and (c) pre-service teachers, joining the managers of the school, in our case, to promote the best practices of STEM. Through a reflective accompaniment, understood as a mediated analysis built through conversations with peers and teachers and the interrogation of the practice itself, the mentor promotes the reflection on his/her practice with the pre-service teacher. In this way, a transformative process is carried out through the critical analysis of situations observed and experienced in the actual exercise of teaching through three practicums during the career, in which the development of STEM projects is intended to:

(a) *Initial teaching practicum*, located in the fourth semester aligned with subjects of learning psychology, diversity, and didactics of the specialty. The main focus is to bring the pre-service teacher closer to the knowledge and dynamics of the classroom, based on experiences of interaction with students in the STEM field. Initial teaching practice focuses on how students learn in the school system. To this end, it collaborates with the classroom teacher through the implementation of learning activities designed by the classroom teacher with small groups of students;

(b) *Intermediate teaching practicum*, which corresponds to the second experience in the seventh semester, aligned with the subjects of planning, assessment, and the second subject of didactics of the specialty. The main focus is the didactics of disciplinary content and STEM teaching. Therefore, it is of vital importance that the pre-service teacher has formative experiences that allow them to know and understand the students' contexts, knowledge, and previous experiences. This will allow the pre-service teacher to formulate goals and design learning sequences and didactic resources for student diversity, consistent with the institutional project and curriculum framework, and finally,

(c) *Final teaching practicum,* in the tenth semester aligned with their degree seminar where they apply the research of the educational practice in sciences designed in the previous semester and aligned with the third subject of didactics of the specialty, formulation of scientific projects, chemistry and citizenship, and technologies for science education. The final teaching practice's main focus is the completion of professional development for pre-service teachers. Therefore, the pre-service teacher must have STEM training experiences that allow them to know and understand the students' contexts, knowledge, and previous experiences. This will allow them to formulate goals and design learning sequences, teaching resources and activities, and assessment tools for student diversity and be consistent with the institutional project and curriculum framework.

In summary, to develop appropriate STEM practices, the model of collaborative reflexive accompaniment requires providing criteria for discernment and action and not rigid rules or techniques to be applied mechanically. This is complemented by:

(a) The evaluation system of teaching practices (SEPRAD http://seprad.ucv.cl/) is a virtual platform that allows evidence of the processes linked with each practice and, in our case (PUCV), expected performances in scientific practices and STEM. It is a tool that facilitates evaluation processes, feedback, follow-up, and monitoring, both for pre-service teachers and their respective mentors and tutors. On this platform, pre-service teacher uploads their work and reports corresponding to each "evaluation body" that considers teaching practice, according to the dates established and informed at the beginning of the semester. In addition, the progress of pre-service teachers can be monitored during their three practicum experiences and identify the center in which they are located and who their tutors and mentors are, and

(b) Compensation system for mentors who have access to continuous training in different subjects and specific training in mentoring, workshops, graduates, English courses, and other courses that the institution offers as a form of permanent linkage.

Final Remarks

The inclusion of the STEM focus in secondary science teacher education in Chile is a challenge but also an opportunity. The experiences that we present constitute the first attempts to respond to the new educational policies.

Changes in the curricular approach entail new demands for teachers, among which we can highlight the need to integrate various disciplines and overcome traditional teaching models to move toward scientific education for citizenship. According to the current state of science teacher education in Chile, this implies questioning the current training models, focused on the conceptual learning of a single scientific discipline in which the teacher specializes. Advancing toward a new science teacher education implies incorporating new scientific and technological aspects, offering opportunities to value the potential of integrating this knowledge for the understanding of the current socio-scientific dilemmas. By placing teacher training in the application of scientific disciplines in socially relevant contexts, aspects associated with the knowledge and appreciation of science are strengthened. In addition, these teacher training spaces can constitute models that configure the teaching of future teachers, when they are inserted in schools. Even when policies may limit the transformation of science teacher education programs, they leave enough room to innovate in this direction.

These innovations will occur in accordance with the potential spaces for collaboration between disciplines in the faculties involved in secondary science teacher education. Even when higher education institutions declare their intention to promote interdisciplinary academic work, this implies a cultural change that we are just beginning. However, discussions held so far that led to the reconfiguration of pre-service teacher programs are promising, since they open fruitful spaces to move toward a common vision of what we understand by STEM-oriented science education.

Existing literature in the area provide solid foundations to move toward a STEM-oriented science education but further research is needed to inform the changes to come. In the coming years, we expect to continue enriching these proposals with evidence of teacher training processes and their impact once they enter the professional field. Our intention is that, through this process of continuous transformation, the training of secondary pre-service science teachers improves and, with it, the teaching and learning processes of science in Chilean schools.

Acknowledgments This work has received funding from the National Agency for Research and Development (ANID) through FONDECYT Programs 1180619 and 1211092.

References

Avalos, B. (2011). Teacher professional development in teaching and teacher education over ten years. *Teaching and Teacher Education.*, *27*(1), 10–20.

Ball, D., & Forzani, F. M. (2010). Teaching skillful teaching. *Educational Leadership.*, *68*, 40–45.

Bybee, R. (2011). Scientific and engineering practices in K-12 classrooms: Understanding "A framework for K-12 science education.". *Science Teacher*, *78*(1), 34–40.

Chung Wei, R., Darling-Hammond, L., Andree, A., Richardson, N., & Orphanos, S. (2010). Professional learning in the learning profession. A status report on teacher development in the u.s. And abroad. *Technical Report. School Redesign Network*, Stanford University

Cofré, H., Camacho, J., Alberto, G., Jiménez, C., Santibáñez, D., & Vergara, C. (2010). La educación científica en chile: debilidades de la enseñanza y futuros desafíos de la educación de profesores de ciencia [Science education in Chile: Teaching weaknesses and future challenges of science teacher education]. *Estudios Pedagógicos (Valdivia)*, *36*, 279–293. https://doi.org/10.4067/S0718-07052010000200016

Couso, D. (2017). Per a què estem a STEM? Un intent de definir l'alfabetització STEM per a tothom i amb valors [Why are we in STEM? An attempt to define

STEM literacy for all and with values]. *Ciències Revista del Professorat de Ciències de Primària i Secundària, 34*, 22–30.

Ell, F., & Grudnoff, L. (2013). The politics of responsibility: Teacher education and "persistent underachievement" in New Zealand. *The Educational Forum, 77*(1), 73–86.

Fenstermacher, G. D., & Richardson, V. (2005). On making determinations of quality in teaching. *Teachers' College Record, 107*(1), 186–213.

Gaete, M. & Camacho, J. (2017). Life experiences of pre-service teachers undertaking a bachelor of sciences and education program. *Educaçao e Pesquisa. 43*(2), 341–356. https://doi.org/10.1590/S1517-9702201609146976

Gaete, A., Castro Navarrete, M., Pino Conejeros, F., & Mansilla Devia, D. (2017). Abandono de la profesión docente en Chile: Motivos para irse del aula y condiciones para volver [Leaving the teaching profession in Chile: Reasons for leaving the classroom and conditions for returning]. *Estudios Pedagógicos (Valdivia), 43*(1), 123–138. https://doi.org/10.4067/S0718-07052017000100008

Grossman, P., Compton, C., Igra, D., Ronfeldt, M., Shahan, E., & Williamson, P. W. (2009). Teaching practice: A cross-professional perspective. *Teachers College Record, 111*(9), 2055–2100. https://doi.org/10.1177/016146810911100905

Hammerness, K., Darling-Hammond, L., & Bransford, J. (with Berliner, D., Cochran-Smith, M., McDonald, M., & Zeichner, K.). (2005). How teachers learn and develop. In L. Darling-Hammond & J. Bransford (Eds.), *Preparing teachers for a changing world: What teachers should learn and be able to do* (pp. 358–389). Jossey-Bass.

Izquierdo, M., & Adúriz-Bravo, A. (2003). Epistemological foundations of school science. *Science & Education, 12*(1), 27–43.

Loughran, J., Berry, A., & Mulhall, P. (2012). *Understanding and developing science teachers' pedagogical content knowledge*. Sense Publishers.

Magnusson, S., Krajcik, J., & Borko, H. (1999). Nature, sources and development of pedagogical content knowledge for science teaching. In J. Gess-Newsome & N. G. Lederman (Eds.), *Examining pedagogical content knowledge* (pp. 95–132). Kluwer Academic Publishers.

Martínez-Chico, M., Jiménez-Liso, M., & López-Gay, R. (2015). Efecto de un programa formativo para enseñar ciencias por indagación basada en modelos, en las concepciones didácticas de los futuros maestros [Effect of a training course to teach science through model-based inquiry on prospective teachers' didactic conceptions]. *Revista Eureka sobre Enseñanza y Divulgación de las Ciencias, 12*(1), 149–166.

Marzábal, A., Moreira, P., Delgado, V., Moreno, J., & Contreras, R. (2016). Hacia la integración del conocimiento disciplinar y pedagógico: desarrollando el conocimiento pedagógico del contenido en la formación inicial de profesores de química [Towards the integration of disciplinary and pedagogical knowledge: Developing pedagogical content knowledge in the training of pre-service chemistry teachers]. *Estudios pedagógicos (Valdivia), 42*(4), 243–260. https://doi.org/10.4067/S0718-07052016000500014

Merino, C., & Izquierdo, M. (2011). Aportes a la modelización según el cambio químico [Contribution to modelling in chemical change]. *Educación Química, 22*(3), 212–223. https://doi.org/10.1016/S0187-893X(18)30137-X

MINEDUC. (2019). Bases Curriculares 3° y 4° Medio [Curricular Bases 3rd and 4th grade]. Unidad de Currículo y Evaluación. Gobierno de Chile. https://www.curriculumnacional.cl/portal/Secciones/3-y-4-medio/133992:Curriculum-3-y-4-medio

MINEDUC. (2021). Programa de Estudio, Ciencias para la Ciudadanía [Program of study, sciences for citizenship]. Unidad de Currículo y Evaluación. Gobierno de Chile. https://www.curriculumnacional.cl/estudiantes/Formacion-General/Plan-Comun-de-formacion-general/Ciencias-para-la-ciudadania/140116:Programa-FG-Ciencias-para-la-ciudadania

Park, S., Jang, J. Y., Chen, Y. C., & Jung, J. (2011). Is pedagogical content knowledge (PCK) necessary for reformed science teaching? evidence from an empirical study. *Research in Science Education, 41*, 245–260. https://doi.org/10.1007/s11165-009-9163-8

PUCV. (2014). Manual de Prácticas y Campos Pedagógicos: Carreras de Pedagogía [Manual of pedagogical practices and fields: Pedagogy careers.] Pontificia Universidad Católica de Valparaíso, Chile. https://www.pucv.cl/uuaa/site/edic/base/port/formacion_inicial_docente.html

Sanders, M. (2012). Integrative STEM education as 'best practice'. *Explorations of best practice in technology, Design and Engineering Education, 2*, 102–117.

Shernoff, D. J., Sinha, S., Bressler, D. M., & Ginsburg, L. (2017). Assessing teacher education and professional development needs for the implementation of integrated approaches to STEM education. *International Journal of STEM Education, 4*, 13. https://doi.org/10.1186/s40594-017-0068-1

Shulman, L. (1986). Those who understand: Knowledge growth in teaching. *Educational Research., 15*(2), 4–14.

Shulman, L. (1987). Knowledge and teaching: Foundations of the new reform. *Harvard Educational Review., 57*(1), 1–22.

Sotomayor, C., & Gysling, J. (2011). Estándares y regulación de calidad de la formación de profesores: discusión del caso chileno desde una perspectiva comparada. *Calidad en la Educación, 35*, 91–129. https://doi.org/10.4067/S0718-45652011000200004

Uzzo, S. M., Ba, H., & Umer, L. (2018). Collaborative PCK in practice: Bringing together secondary, tertiary, and informal learning in a stem residency program. In S. Uzzo, S. Graves, E. Shay, M. Harford, & R. Thompson (Eds.), *Pedagogical content knowledge in STEM. Advances in STEM education*. Springer. https://doi.org/10.1007/978-3-319-97475-0_12

Vergara, C., & Cofré, H. (2014). Conocimiento Pedagógico del Contenido: ¿el paradigma perdido en la formación inicial y continua de profesores en Chile? [Pedagogical Content Knowledge: The lost paradigm in the initial and continuous training of teachers in Chile?]. *Estudios Pedagógicos* (Valdivia), 40(Especial), 323–338. https://doi.org/10.4067/S0718-07052014000200019.

Wallace, J., & Loughran, J. (2012). Science teacher learning. In B. Fraser, K. Tobin, & C. McRobbie (Eds.), *Second international handbook of research in science education* (Vol. 1, pp. 295–306). Springer.

CHAPTER 6

To STEAM or Not to STEAM: Is It a Matter of Professional Development or Professional Creation?

Heba EL-Deghaidy and Mohamed El Nagdi

Introduction

When science, technology, engineering, and mathematics (STEM) (later STEAM education with the Arts included) was first introduced in Egypt through the Ministry of Education and Technical Education (MoE&TE) and supported by the United States Agency for International Development (USAID, 2011, 2017; Rissmann-Joyce & El Nagdi, 2013), STEM education had not even reached its infancy stage in Egypt. Teachers and leaders were transferred from mainstream schools to the newly established STEM schools with limited knowledge and professional experience in STEM settings. The USAID sponsored program led by the World Learning group started providing this urgently needed support at both the curriculum and

H. EL-Deghaidy (✉) • M. El Nagdi
Department of Educational Studies, The American University in Cairo, Cairo, Egypt
e-mail: H.eldeghaidy@aucegypt.edu; mohamedelnagdi@aucegypt.edu

S. M. Al-Balushi et al. (eds.), *Reforming Science Teacher Education Programs in the STEM Era*, Palgrave Studies on Leadership and Learning in Teacher Education,
https://doi.org/10.1007/978-3-031-27334-6_6

professional level (El Nagdi & Roehrig, 2020). However, the need for more teachers in the increasing number of STEM schools in Egypt necessitated that higher education institutions look into this by providing programs to help prepare teachers for the MoE&TE STEM schools. Other schools too adopted the idea of STEM for either providing a better learning environment or for marketing reasons, attracting students to their schools.

A not-for-profit university in Egypt was so vigilant to this need. In 2012, the Graduate School of Education (GSE) included in its strategic plan a new track driven by state-of-the-art pedagogies aligned with international recognition for interdisciplinary learning and the introduction of STEM education in the United States and elsewhere. There was a deliberate decision to expand on the new buzz word of 'STEM' that only includes the 'sciences' to go beyond that and include the liberal arts, social science and Arts in its well-known field of fine arts and visual arts. These non-scientific disciplines would represent the additional 'A' and form the 'STEAM' acronym. GSE introduced a Professional Educator Diploma (PED) program focusing on preparing and developing teachers for STEM schools. STEAM-PED track was the first of its kind in the country and the MENA region. In this chapter, STEAM is used when referring to the PED program while STEM/STEAM presents the interdisciplinary nature of the concept used interchangeably.

Since teachers in Egypt, as in many countries, are only prepared to teach one subject in its silo with limited opportunities to expand to other disciplines in the sciences or humanities, the STEAM track aimed to fill one of the gaps found in the Egyptian teacher education system, especially with the increasing number of STEM schools. The program aimed to support the idea of crossing discipline boundaries by providing teachers with innovative teaching and learning practices. With that in mind, the PED program was to help in achieving Egypt's aim to attract students in the science areas and enabling them to meet job market requirements, both locally and globally. Moreover, it is a means to provide teachers and those interested in STEM/STEAM education with opportunities to understand and implement this innovative interdisciplinary practice, thus increasing teacher efficacy and self-confidence (Nadelson et al., 2013).

As STEM schools increased and both private and international schools started to recognize the need to infuse such philosophy, schools started to hire teachers from two pools. One was from current on-the-job working teachers, while the other was from newly fresh graduates or prospective teachers. With this in mind, the design of the STEAM-PED has been providing both professional development for in-service teachers from MoE&TE aspiring or actually teaching in a STEM school as well as those with no previous professional experience in STEM-teaching or teaching in general. Therefore, the STEAM-PED is a means to offer 'professional development' (PD) directed to existing teachers to assume the role of STEM teachers in addition to 'professional creation' (PC) to prospective teachers to work at STEM schools or undertake STEM related roles by starting a new career path. By that, the STEAM-PED is unique through its flexibility and openness to be offered to current as well as prospective teachers (Nowikowski, 2017).

Although PD is a well-established means in various professions, including teaching, when it comes to STEM/STEAM there are variations related to who, what, how and when (Baxter et al., 2014; Roehrig et al., 2012). Such variations entail not only the main principles underlying PD, but include the means and strategies used to execute such plans. With such attention, there is a further need to understand how teacher PD programs can align with local, regional, and global interest to reform educational systems. However, with the contentious discourse around STEM/STEAM and its implementation (Moore et al., 2020; National Academies of Sciences, Engineering, and Medicine, 2016) questions related to the content and nature of teacher PD programs are warranted (Robinson et al., 2005). This study explores the STEAM-PED program and explores its impact on its current and former students, professionally and academically, guided by the following research questions:

1. What is the impact of the STEAM-PED on teachers' practices and professional growth?
2. How has the STEAM-PED assisted in creating a unique professional identity?
3. What are the proposed suggestions to improve the STEAM-PED?

Background and Conceptual Framework

Description of the Program

The STEAM-PED track provides teachers and those interested in STEM/STEAM education with opportunities to understand and implement innovative practices. The program includes learning theories, alternative assessment, interdisciplinary methods of teaching, utilizing engineering design in STEAM teaching, integrating technology and arts, and finally a clinical practicum course. The six-course 18-credit program spans from 18–24 months for completion.

The demand for the STEAM track increased with the expansion of STEM schools in Egypt that started with one school in 2011 then expanded to 19 schools in 2021. The STEAM-PED is seen as an opportunity to provide a better understanding of the interdisciplinary nature of STEAM's philosophy and impact. Since its start, the program has attracted over 1500 teachers showing a demand in this new state-of-the-art track. The program attracts both teachers with previous experience and others interested in pursuing a teaching career. This variation and the impact of the program on both career paths is the main focus of the chapter. It is worth noting that teachers come from different disciplines. Such variation provides richness and diversity to the program as teachers come together to design lesson plans and curricula units that address STEAM based problems. The educational goal is to enable educators in the development of STEAM literacy and with it, students' ability to innovate and become leaders of tomorrow's industry.

Teachers' Professional Development and Creation

Teachers are seen as the cornerstone for the success of any education reform initiative (Wilson, 2011). However, becoming a teacher is not an easy task; the recipe to become an effective teacher is a complex one: rigorous planning, induction and retention of the best, capacity building and continuing learning to cope with the different trends in the education arena especially the twenty-first century skills integration in the teaching practices (Nguyen et al., 2021). Teachers on top of their jobs as well as fresh graduates need different kinds of support to start or switch roles in the teaching profession. These include changes at the professional, attitude and beliefs levels. That change in professionalism is what we mean by 'professional creation' in this study. Sutherland et al. (2010) describe the process of transitioning from a preservice teacher to a full member of the professional community that needs not only to acquire the knowledge and skill-base of a teacher; but also, to refine their understanding of pedagogical practices and develop their professional knowledge. As part of this transition process, preservice teachers create and recreate the image of themselves as members of a community as they start building their professional identity. Robinson et al. (2005) discussed two major aspects of potential transformation for professional teams: knowledge creation and professional identity transformation that are key to their continuing professional education within the framework of Wenger's (1998) community of practice theory and Engestrom's (1999) activity theory. Both present alternative pathways to better build and develop professional expertise. While Wenger (1998) argues that knowledge, and subsequently professional creation is done within communities of practice through participatory processes in situated interactions with people of the community toward common goals, Engestrom (1999) highlights that conflict is inevitable. Admitting and working toward resolving this conflict takes place through being committed to real actions within the professional communities. For these communities/teams to bring about change, they must work through processes of articulating differences, exploring alternatives, modeling solutions, examining an agreed model and implementing activities (Engestrom, 2001). Building a STEM teacher identity is, therefore, a sophisticated and complex process that takes time, flexibility, and understanding what STEM really offers for both teachers and students (El Nagdi et al., 2018). Therefore, building a program designed to prepare teachers ready to work in STEM settings and/or adopt progressive education practices within the framework of the activity and the community of practice theories can be seen as a proactive step toward building an emerging STEM community of practice in Egypt (Engestrom, 2001; Wenger, 1998). Therefore, in this study, the concept of professional creation (PC) is akin to professional identity creation. 'Professional creation' here refers to prospective teachers (first time teachers) or on the job teachers wanting to take new and divergent career trajectories than teaching (e.g., leadership roles, curriculum developers) whether teachers are in STEM or a semi-STEM schools. Therefore, the context of where such identity is created is of importance.

Research Design

This study explores and probes how the STEAM-PED program contributed to the professional growth of teachers on-the-job and fresh graduates, through the concepts of 'professional development' and 'professional creation', respectively. For these reasons utilizing a case study research design seems to match (Merriam, 1988).The time span for the case study encompasses cohorts as old as graduating in 2015, when the program was first initiated, to the graduating cohort of Fall 2021 through qualitative semi-structured interviews for in-depth understandings of the case at hand (Creswell, 2014). One of the authors was an instructor in the STEAM-PED with expanded direct experiences with the participants while working in STEM schools.

Instruments

Preliminary Online Survey

An online survey seeking to explore the impact of the STEAM-PED experience was sent to graduates and current students in the program. The results served as an initial source of data that was utilized in developing the semi-structured-interviews.

Semi-structure-Interviews

For deeper understanding of the impact of the program on teachers, individual semi-structured-interviews were conducted with 18 participants ranging from the first cohort to the last cohort of the program based on results received from the online survey. The interviews were intended to qualitatively probe teachers' experiences, professional growth and development, and their insights on how to improve the program. The individual interviews were audio recorded zoom calls, analyzed later by the research team. Interview questions related to why they joined the PED, their expectations when joining, teaching methods before/during/after, extent of student autonomy, examples of designed STEAM lesson plans, integrating engineering and technology in their plans, and means of assessment. A final question aimed to elicit their recommended changes for an effective PED program based on their experience.

Participants

Eighteen teachers working in STEM schools/semi-STEM schools (4 male and 14 female teachers) graduated from the STEAM-PED responded to invitations to take part in the individual interviews. Due to the fact that the second author was directly involved in their STEM schools and PED diploma, the participants were purposively selected. Teachers' age ranged from 27–51 with 2–27 years of teaching experience. Teachers represented disciplines from Science, English, Math, Home economics and Computer science (n = 6,6,4,1,1) respectively who graduated in 2015, 2016, 2019, 2020 and 2021 (n = 4,1,1,4,8) respectively. The interviewed teachers were from different types of schools: MoE&TE STEM schools; international private schools adopting some aspects of STEM/STEAM education in their programs referred to as semi-STEM schools and public or private schools with no STEM program but with STEM/STEAM efforts.

Qualitative Data Analysis

During each interview, notes were taken. All interviews lasted between 30 to 55 min. Interviews were carried out in English. The authors reviewed and analyzed the responses by looking at patterns in the data that would indicate major themes that could be developed (Cohen et al., 2011). The authors discussed the codes and themes together until they reached agreement, after which the list of codes compiled in the findings was revised again and then examined in order to look for meaningful clusters around these themes (Coffey & Atkinson, 1996).

Findings

Findings are discussed to offer insights on the impact of the program on teachers' practices and professional growth in additional to recommendation to improve PD programs in as stated in the research questions. Findings below are based on teachers' self-reported data, a limitation this study acknowledges despite the direct interaction of the one of the authors with the STEM teachers as previously explained.

Emerging Themes from the Semi-structured-Interviews

Transformational Experience in Teaching and Understanding STEM

Data analysis from teachers' interviews indicated that the STEAM-PED impacted their practices and professional growth positively. All teachers during the interviews mentioned that their teaching practices transformed one way or the other. Reference was made to changes from traditional teacher-led pedagogies to those that were student-centered linked to real life situations for meaningful learning. Although three teachers mentioned that their teaching experiences before joining the program was somehow innovative when compared to others, yet after the program there were still major changes that were visibly identified. The following quotations highlight pedagogical changes as stated by the respondents. Amira explained that

> Prior to the diploma I was feeling as if I was doing activities just looking after a final product from the students but not the process. Yet after the diploma things are so different as I plan the curriculum—alignment is crucial between objectives, activities—not just making a project but the considering target of the project as students now have more independence ... previously we had to make it more beautiful .... Just give instructions and leave them on their own. The projects now are so different: more emphasis on rubrics and the process.

Deema took it a step further; she looked at the STEAM track experience as a preparation for the future: "I see STEM as the future of education. I also wanted to prepare myself for that—it helped me with the new education 2.0. I got many ideas, especially in game-based learning." Dalia explained how the program helped her grow as a teacher; "I became a more confident, different teacher. I used to think of effective teaching methods intuitively before, but now my understanding is based on knowledge and learning. Here I have some evidence for my assumptions." Mary described the change that happened to her as "radical change: it was the first time to create a written lesson plan, to employ engineering concepts and use interactive teaching apps, hands on activities: learned to facilitate not to tell students what they have to do—How to work in an interactive group—build on others' work." Sally described the transformative experience she had gone through during the program as an introduction to a new "era of education—STEM is the future of education and I needed to learn about it. It allows us to be creative, think outside of the box....as a math teacher before joining the diploma I used traditional methods like using white board and explaining examples—students answering the math problems." After the diploma my teaching is "totally different—changes the method of teaching: watching videos—platforms for assessment—formative assessment—discussions—games—utilizing apps to increase collaboration among students". She added that STEM

> fosters creativity and things become more connected than before. The class has become totally different than before. My supervisor visited my class and she was so amazed by the teaching and wrote an excellent evaluation of it.

As a fresh graduate, Yara described how this initial introduction to education was an eye opening one: "I have never worked in a school before the diploma. It opened the gates for me. As I started teaching and in a short-time I was asked to orient fellow teachers about STEM. Based on my learning in the diploma, I get students to link everything with real-life. I created a market day activity where all teachers prepare and integrate things: science, math, Computer Science, English, to be integrated on that day. I emphasize hands-on activities and projects." Similarly, Jasmin reiterated the same view,

> I have only two years of teaching experience which actually started after the diploma. I now know how to plan lessons—develop assessment—use technology—project-based—understanding by design—I worked in the national section of this international private school where we applied some features of STEM.

Professional Development and/or Identity Creation

What drove teachers to transform their teaching practices was their passion for teaching, will to change, interest in finding new learning experiences for their professional development and for new job openings. While acknowledging that the STEAM-PED program experience may not be the sole reason for teachers to progress and find different pathways or change roles later, it is clear from the participants' responses how this experience has opened gates and horizons for them to pursue. They definitely have developed skills beyond what the degree program provided. However, joining the program was mainly driven by passion, need for change, and new learning experience for their professional development or better learning opportunities for their own students.

Amira was a science teacher and has become a STEM coordinator in her school based on her experience in the program; she explained that leading the STEM team has become clearer and the purpose of doing a STEM project has changed toward "the process not the product." She now has, what she described, as "the tools to plan and lead a STEM project." While Mary joined the diploma as a public-school IT teacher, the PED experience gave her a chance to realize how technology can be of great importance to enhancing education. She engaged in different ventures in using technology in classrooms and is now an expert and an influencer in designing and using technology tools in teaching and learning. She has created and led a digital literacy platform to increase people's awareness about technology not only in education but in life, in general. Rokia was promoted from a math teacher to deputy principal, principal, and then STEM unit head and is currently technical education consultant at USAID. She described her experience in the program, especially the practicum course as very beneficial and gave her a practical way to apply the philosophy of STEAM in teaching in addition to the experience she had from other teachers on how to integrate different concepts from different subjects. As a leader, "I was able to understand the mechanism of how things happen in the STEM schools I was overseeing as a MoE&TE STEM unit leader." Yara and Jasmin were real examples of how to develop a new teacher as fresh graduates from higher education. Yara has a degree in political science and economics and works as a math teacher. The PED was her first teaching experience. Not only did she teach but was offered a leadership position as she was asked to lead an orientation for the teachers on STEM. Jasmin had a degree in pharmacy and decided to pursue a teaching career. She described her experience in the PED as the first experience to know what teaching is. She now develops lesson plans, designs assessment, and leads classroom discussions in a professional manner. Yasser joined the STEM department at his school and is currently developing STEM curriculum. He changed careers from an English teacher to go beyond that to benefit students the most and by including technology. Life skills and STEM was the connection that got him interested. This is after changing careers from an engineer to a teacher. Ramy took on new roles and responsibilities after the PED such as his role in an international organization. As a curriculum coordinator for 2.0, localization of Education 2.0 content and teacher coach and mentor, he too shifted from being an English teacher. Similarly, Sophia has become a capstone coordinator in her STEM school after being an English teacher. Hadeer found it to be a creative way to teach. Now in the STEM team in her school after 5 years of teaching science "I am now confident in teaching and planning using the Understanding by Design framework, creating plans and student-led activities." Ahmed is another model of ambitious changing roles. He was an English teacher in a public school. After graduating from the STEAM-PED, he became an instructional coach in STEM education. He also wanted to develop himself by joining post graduate studies, exchange experiences with other teachers, and found it an opportunity to advance his skills, know more about new trends in education, increase professional skills, and to deepen his knowledge in STEM education. "I even trained teachers in my school about STEAM and project-based learning." He also trained teachers in different schools in Cairo and Nasr city. Ahmed is now a STEAM curriculum developer and facilitator in an international organization helping with Education 2.0 in Egypt.

Teaching STEM/STEAM: Design and Implementation

Structuring the lesson in an engaging, constructive, and interesting manner is uniform across all participants. It is so evident that almost all teachers are so keen to hook the students from the start, rely on hands-on activities, use technology tools in their teaching, and utilize formative and summative modes of assessment for learning. Examples of STEAM lesson plans also included establishing connections between science, math, and sometimes English. Others emphasized the role of the essential questions when planning and designing lessons. Some mentioned coming up with a 'product' after going through the engineering design process. The exemplary lesson plans shared by almost all participants included a hook, questions to drive inquiry and guided discussions, reliance on implementing the engineering design process, usage of alternative assessment techniques and a section for reflection and feedback. Dalia's model of teaching a history lesson to her grade two kids is a good model where she emphasized thinking routines. Though Dalia is not working in a STEM school, she integrated history with science and mathematics in a lesson. "I use the GRASPS (Goal, Role, Audience, Situation/Scenario, Product/Performance, Standards) as a key concept in my teaching and in rubrics to assess all tasks."

Future Career Trajectories and Pathways

The interviewed graduates of the program showcased their diverse roles, whether academic, professional, or administrative. Examples included coaching and mentoring other STEM teachers, STEM unit coordinators, department heads, researchers and STEM material developers in addition to other roles. Despite the role, these graduates' STEAM identities seemed shaped and impacted by what the program provided and how each graduate gained strength in themselves and their careers.

STEAM-PED Program Improvements Needed

Based on both their rich experience in the program and their professional life, participants presented a number of suggestions to make improvements to the program. Suggestions were related to structure, modality, design of activities and partnering with schools for the practicum. Sally recommended that the courses should be delivered in a hybrid system that combines face to face with online sessions. Amira argued that most STEAM activities are based on group work. So, instructors should be taking care of grouping. She suggested, "depending on pair work or small groups of three is a better option to make sure that every person in the group is doing their best." Deema suggested "reducing the number of readings, improving the quality of the print and scanning, depending more on flipped classes, and using more videos." Dalia and Mary suggested that it would be great if the STEAM-PED "partners with a STEAM school to have some firsthand training there and more interaction with real STEM teachers." They (Dalia and Mary) also suggested "schools can announce job opportunities and for practical training to STEAM track students and graduates." Nafisa and Rokia went even further and asked to have "everything learned in the program in action. Students can volunteer in a STEM school as part of the practicum course or have an internship in a STEM." Recommendations showcase teachers' deep involvement in wanting to improve the program to ensure the greatest impact on their teaching.

Recommendations for Program Improvements

Based on the participants' recommendations to make the STEAM–PED Program stronger, the authors divided them into the following three themes.

1. *Nature of the program*

The program needs to be a Master's level program. It can open pathways for aspiring teachers and other candidates to assume the roles of the academic practitioners in the field. The Program can be a hybrid program where some course sessions are done through an online modality while others on campus via face-to-face teaching. The technology course may need to be extended to provide opportunities to learn how to utilize various applications with an emphasis on how the 'T' as in technology is really integrated in STEM education. This last recommendation seemed to arise especially as there were different interpretations of how the 'T' is perceived similar to what other studies have identified (Bull et al., 2019; Ellis et al., 2020; Honey et al., 2014).

2. *Establishing STEM/STEAM partnerships*

The program needs to build strong partnerships with STEM schools whether at MoE&TE public, private, and international semi-STEM schools. Semi-STEM schools are perceived as schools that have initiated STEM practices through professional development or STEM units yet with no clear reflection in the school's name. Such partnerships, despite the type of school, can provide for school based professional development (Mansour & EL-Deghaidy, 2021) for applications in authentic contexts with students, school facilities and real time application to better perceive how STEM is really done in action.

3. *Instruction (Pairing and grouping, readings)*

No wonder that the participants brought forward different ideas to improve the instruction at the STEM PED; all of them are expert educators. They referred to some class mechanisms such as grouping. For instance, in adult education getting people to work really well in a group may be challenging. Therefore, one of the suggestions is to make the tasks in the form of pairs or small groups (3 people) which sounds very practical from their perspective. Taking care of the participants' experience level, language proficiency, background knowledge is critical while designing a learning activity in class so that nobody is left behind. Last but not least, using digital tools in teaching and learning as a substitute to paperwork would be a great hands-on experience for teachers to transfer what they learn in the program to students in their schools.

Discussion

Within the framework of both the community of practice where change is activated within the situated cognition of the group (Wenger, 1998), and the activity theory where conflict within professional groups is settled through a process of admitting differences, exploring alternatives, modeling solutions, examining an agreed model, and implementing activities

(Engestrom, 2001), the STEAM-PED Track was established with the purpose of creating and professionally developing teachers for existing and aspiring STEM schools channeling the argument that teacher quality is the cornerstone for a successful STEM/STEAM reform initiative (Wilson, 2011). While the STEAM-PED program development was based heavily on the activity theory where rounds of discussions and reflections were conducted to meet the needs of the STEM teaching community, the real delivery and practice in the program depended mainly on the community of practice theory where most courses are based on a participatory teaching and learning model, where students are looked upon as participants who come to class with experience to share and lessons to learn from other colleagues. The program expanded and attracted more teachers with progressive and futuristic visions regarding the future of education other than STEM teachers. Sally, Dalia, and Reda reiterated the same view that attending the program was basically connected with the new trends in education and how to deal with students in the twenty-first century (Nguyen et al., 2021). Considering STEM education as an effective reform effort for education in Egyptian schools has been reflected in the teachers' actions not only words; lesson plans, use of alternative assessment, relying heavily on student centered approaches, designing lessons based on Understanding by Design (UbD) framework, and including engineering design processes (Roehrig et al., 2021).

As part of their professional identity creation and evolving roles within the education system both at the school and the wider organizational levels, participants demonstrated both conceptual understanding and practical application of STEM/STEAM education (El Nagdi et al., 2018; El Nagdi & Roehrig, 2020), even if the places of work are not officially recognized as STEM schools. With such understanding and application, this showcases a professional identity creation model that includes creating new knowledge and practice; enhancing professional identity; and building inter-professional communities (Robinson et al., 2005). Graduates from the PED like Rokia, Ahmed, Ramy, showed how their learning experiences in the program were so transformed in their teaching, curriculum development, and leadership careers.

Conclusion

This chapter investigated the impact of the STEAM-PED program through a qualitative inquiry based on the findings from interviewing 18 graduating teachers. Teachers discussed the impact of the program on their classroom practices and on how they perceived it as a valuable route to their professional growth. As teachers went on describing their current roles after graduation, various roles and responsibilities were highlighted other than teaching. This showed that teachers, through programs such as the PED, can either perceive it as professional development or professional creation. The latter is more related to pursuing new and divergent roles as career paths. With such new anticipated roles, different identities started to develop showing that teachers can expand their professional contributions to education. Although many teachers joined the program eager to learn, grow, and join a contemporary state-of-the-art field in STEM/STEAM, years after graduation they became coaches, mentors, curricula developers, and researchers among others. With these new identities in mind and endless possibilities of growth and lifelong learning suggestions at the program level and building partnerships with existing and potential STEM schools were provided. Despite the fact that the teachers' responses outlined in this chapter are a case study from Egypt, the insights from the findings can be replicated in similar programs.

References

Baxter, J., Ruzicka, A., Beghetto, R., & Livelybrooks, D. (2014). Professional development strategically connecting mathematics and science: The impact on teachers' confidence and practice. *School Science and Mathematics, 114*(3), 102–113.

Bull, G., Hodge, C., Mouza, C., Kinshuk, Grant, M., Archambault, L., Borup, J., Ferdig, R. E., & Schmidt-Crawford, D. A. (2019). Editorial: Conceptual dilution. *Contemporary Issues in Technology and Teacher Education, 19*(2), 117–128. https://citejournal.org/volume-19/issue-2-19/editorial/editorial-conceptual-dilution/

Coffey, A., & Atkinson, P. (1996). *Making sense of qualitative Data: Complementary research strategies*. Sage.

Cohen, L., Manion, L., & Morrison, K. (2011). *Research methods in education* (7th ed.). Routledge.

Creswell, J. W. (2014). *Research design: Qualitative, quantitative and mixed methods approaches* (4th ed.). Sage.

El Nagdi, M., Leammukda, F., & Roehrig, G. (2018). Developing identities of STEM teachers at emerging STEM schools. *International Journal of STEM. Education, 5*(36). https://doi.org/10.1186/s40594-018-0136-1

El Nagdi, M., & Roehrig, G. (2020). Identity evolution of STEM teachers in Egyptian STEM schools in a time of transition: A case study. *IJ STEM Ed., 7–41*. https://doi.org/10.1186/s40594-020-00235-2

Ellis, J., Wieselmann, J., Sivaraj, R., Roehrig, G., Dare, E., & Ring-Whalen, E. (2020). Toward a productive definition of technology in science and STEM education. *Contemporary Issues in Technology and Teacher Education, 20*(3), 472–496.

Engestrom, Y. (Ed.). (1999). *Perspectives on activity theory*. Cambridge University Press.

Engestrom, Y. (2001). Expansive learning at work: Toward an activity theoretical reconceptualization. *Journal of Education and Work, 14*(1), 133–156.

Honey, M., Pearson, G., & Schweingruber, H. (Eds.). (2014). *STEM integration in K-12 education: Status, prospects, and an agenda for research*. The National Academies Press.

Mansour, N., & EL-Deghaidy, H. (2021). Promotion of STEM education in schools through partnerships. In N. Mansour & H. EL-Deghaidy (Eds.), *STEM in Science Education and S in STEM: From pedagogies to practice* (pp. 67–100). Brill Publishers.

Merriam, S. (1988). *Case study research in education: A qualitative approach* (Jossey-Bass Education Series) (1st ed.). Jossey-Bass.

Ministry of Education, MoE&TE. (2021). https://moe.gov.eg/en/what-s-on/news/opening-of-admission-to-stem-schools-1/

Moore, T. J., Johnston, A. C., & Glancy, A. W. (2020). STEM integration: A synthesis of conceptual frameworks and definitions. In *Handbook of research on STEM education* (pp. 3–16). Routledge.

Nadelson, L. S., Callahan, J., Pyke, R., Hay, A., Dance, M., & Pfiester, J. (2013). Teacher STEM perception and preparation: Inquiry-based STEM professional development for elementary teachers. *The Journal of Educational Research, 106*(2), 157–168.

National Academies of Sciences, Engineering, and Medicine. (2016). *Developing a national STEM workforce strategy: A workshop summary*. The National Academies Press. https://doi.org/10.17226/21900

Nguyen, H., Sivapalan, S., & Hiep, P. (2021). The Transformation from STEM to STREAM education at engineering and technology institutions of higher education. *SHS Web of Conferences, 124*. https://doi.org/10.1051/shsconf/202112407003 ICMeSH 2020.

Nowikowski, S. H. (2017). Successful with STEM? A qualitative case study of preservice teacher perceptions. *The Qualitative Report, 22*(9), 2312.

Rissmann-Joyce, S., & El Nagdi, M. (2013). A case study-Egypt's first STEM schools: Lessons learned. *Proceeding of the Global Summit on Education*

(GSE2013). https://goo.gl/FVSkT8; https://doi.org/10.1007/s10798-014-92-90-z; https://doi.org/10.1007/978-3-319-93836-3

Robinson, M., Anning, A., & Frost, N. (2005). When is a teacher not a teacher?: Knowledge creation and the professional identity of teachers within multi-agency teams. *Studies in Continuing Education, 27*(2), 175–191.

Roehrig, G. H., Dare, E. A., Ellis, J. A. (2021). Beyond the basics: a detailed conceptual framework of integrated STEM. *Discip Interdscip Sci Educ Res 3*, 11. https://doi.org/10.1186/s43031-021-00041-y

Roehrig, G. H., Moore, T. J., Wang, H. H., & Park, M. S. (2012). Is adding the E enough? Investigating the impact of K-12 engineering standards on the implementation of STEM integration. *School Science and Mathematics, 112*(1), 31–44.

Sutherland, L., Howard, S., & Markauskaite, L. (2010). Professional identity creation: Examining the development of beginning preservice teachers' understanding of their work as teachers. *Teaching and Teacher Education, 26*(3), 455–465.

USAID. (2011). Support for STEM Secondary Education. https://www.usaid.gov/sites/default/files/documents/1-OEH-EdB-STEM.pdf

USAID. (2017). Basic Education initiative. https://www.usaid.gov/sites/default/files/documents/USAIDEgypt_Education-Basic_Fact_Sheet_2020_EN.pdf

Wenger, E. (1998). *Communities of practice*. Cambridge University Press.

Wilson, S. M. (2011, April). Effective STEM teacher preparation, induction, and professional development. In *NRC Workshop on Highly Successful STEM Schools or Programs*. Retrieved May 2011, from http://www7.Nationalacademies.org/bose/Successful_STEM_Schools_Homepage.html

CHAPTER 7

Preparation of Teachers for STEM Education in Hong Kong

Yu Chen, Chi Ho Yeung, Tian Luo, Qianwen He, and Winnie Wing-Mui So

Introduction

Driven by concerns over potential future shortfalls in qualified STEM professionals, many Asia pacific regions have made significant investments in STEM educational initiatives. The situation is similar in Hong Kong, which has invested resources in terms of increased funding support and policy

Y. Chen
University of Macau, Macau SAR, China
e-mail: llyuchen@um.edu.mo

C. H. Yeung • Q. He • W. W.-M. So (✉)
Hong Kong SAR, China
e-mail: chyeung@eduhk.hk; s1122615@s.eduhk.hk; wiso@eduhk.hk

T. Luo
Capital Normal University, Beijing, China
e-mail: luotian@cnu.edu.cn

S. M. Al-Balushi et al. (eds.), *Reforming Science Teacher Education Programs in the STEM Era*, Palgrave Studies on Leadership and Learning in Teacher Education,
https://doi.org/10.1007/978-3-031-27334-6_7

attention in STEM education to nurture a versatile pool of STEM talents to enhance regional competitiveness (Legislative Council Secretariat, 2020). Teachers are essential for quality STEM education; however, they inevitably encounter problems and obstacles when implementing new initiatives, as they lack experience, confidence, and training. To support teachers for STEM education, the HKSAR government, universities, and other stakeholders have contributed significant resources and funding to provide professional development programmes, workshops, projects, and research to prepare teachers to provide students with relevant school-based STEM learning opportunities.

The purpose of this chapter is to provide an overview of the experiences of Hong Kong in the preparation of teachers for STEM education. This chapter comprises three main components. Firstly, there is a review of STEM education and teacher education policies with the aim of providing justifications for the necessity of teacher preparation for STEM education. Secondly, relevant teacher education programmes are introduced to show efforts of the government and local universities in teacher preparation for STEM education. Thirdly, there is a discussion of research on teacher preparation for STEM education in Hong Kong.

STEM Education Initiatives in Hong Kong

Over the past several years in Hong Kong, there has been continuous effort from the HKSAR government to promote 'school-based' STEM education to meet "the changing needs in our society and the rapid economic, scientific, and technological developments in the 21st century" (Education Bureau, 2016, p. 1).

The promotion of STEM education in Hong Kong can be traced back to the '2015 policy address' that marshalled the HKSAR Education Bureau (EDB) to "renew and enrich the curricula and learning activities of Science, Technology, and Mathematics, and enhance the training of teachers" (The government of HKSAR, 2015, p. 46). In the '2016 policy address', the EDB was recommended to further "promote STEM education and encourage students to pursue the study of these subjects"

(The government of HKSAR, 2016, p. 25). In response, the EDB has paid attention to the renewal of STEM-related curricula for primary and secondary schools. The EDB first issued a critical report in 2016, namely 'Promotion of STEM Education—Unleashing Potential in Innovation', which set out directions for promoting STEM education in primary and secondary schools in a holistic and coherent manner. The report emphasised updating the school curricula of the key learning areas (KLAs) of Science Education (SE), Technology Education (TE), Mathematics Education (ME), and General Studies (GS). Subsequently, the EDB successively released the updated SE, TE, ME, and GS curricula through integrating teaching and learning elements to promote STEM education at the school level from 2015 to 2017 (Curriculum Development Council (CDC), 2017a, 2017b, 2017c). The major renewed emphases related to STEM education of the KLAs are as follows:

For Science education (SE) Curriculum Guide (Primary 1–Secondary 6): Through appropriate connection and integration of the six strands which include topics such as life and living, energy and change, etc., effective promotion of STEM education and infusion of generic skills, values and attitudes, Language across the Curriculum (LaC) and Information Technology in Education (ITE) in curriculum planning, learning and teaching, and assessment, it is hoped that students could develop scientific literacy, recognize the relations among science, technology, engineering and mathematics, integrate and apply knowledge and skills within and across KLAs, and develop positive values and attitudes. (CDC, 2017a, p. 18).

For Technology education (TE) Curriculum Guide (Primary 1–Secondary 6): Great emphasis is placed on integration and application of knowledge and skills when connecting learning in the TE KLA and other KLAs/subject disciplines. This is particularly important in STEM education, which is promoted through three KLAs including TE (CDC, 2017b, p. 18).

For Mathematics Education (ME) Curriculum Guide (Primary 1–Secondary 6): In STEM education, mathematics serves as a discipline that equips students with knowledge and skills on algebra, geometry, data handling and logical reasoning that facilitate students to integrate and apply knowledge and skills across disciplines in solving real-life problems with practical solutions and innovative designs (CDC, 2017c, p. 43).

For General Studies (GS) Curriculum Guide (Primary 1–Primary 6): Schools may enhance curriculum planning to increase science and technology related core learning elements and select mathematical concepts and skills that are suited to students' abilities to enrich learning and teaching activities regarding the application of science and technology in solving daily life problems (CDC, 2017d, p. 6).

In the '2018 policy address', the suggestion that the EDB would "continue to enhance supports for schools in providing students with more learning, exchange, and competition opportunities, and to unleash their potentials in science and technology" (The government of HKSAR, 2018, p. 35) was recapitulated. Additionally, the 2018 policy address highlighted diversifying 'life-wide learning' through organising more out-of-classroom experiential learning activities in STEM education to benefit students' whole-person development. This led to a shift in the focus of the EDB towards greater emphasis on supporting and facilitating the implementation of STEM education beyond school. For instance, the EDB[1] provided a range of resources for teachers to arrange visits to the Science Club, the Computer Club, and the Mathematics Club, and to organize STEM-related events/activities such as an annual STEM Day/Week and STEM-related competitions both within and outside schools.

In 2020, an important report entitled 'Optimise the curriculum for the future: Foster whole-person development and diverse talents' (EDB, 2020) was released by the Task Force on Review of School Curriculum. The Task Force was set up in late 2017 to holistically review the primary and secondary education curricula. In this report, six directional recommendations were made, including the recommendation to further "strengthen STEM education in primary and secondary schools so as to develop students' capacity to apply knowledge and skills acquired in different STEM-related subjects in an integrated and creative manner to solve daily problems" (EDB, 2020, p. 33). This report also proposed specific aspects that the EDB should emphasise in order to enhance STEM education, such as (1) clearly defining STEM education; (2) providing a learning framework or curriculum guides on STEM education; and (3) overseeing the long-term development of STEM education (EDB, 2020). It can be foreseen that sustained efforts will be made by the HKSAR

[1] https://www.edb.gov.hk/attachment/en/curriculum-development/major-level-of-edu/life-wide-learning/know-more/LWL_SE_E.pdf

government to advance STEM education and promote students' pursuit of STEM learning or careers in the future.

Despite the HKSAR government's considerable investment in promoting STEM education, schools and teachers inevitably encounter problems and obstacles when conducting STEM education. On one hand, the implementation of these policies is school-based. That is, each school has the flexibility to adopt different emphases/plans and incorporate different learning elements for the implementation of STEM education (Legislative Council Secretariat, 2020). In fact, the school-based policy is not new to Hong Kong, and school-based management with principals and middle leaders as the key agents has been evidenced to be particularly effective for implementing borrowed reforms in local schools (Szeto, 2020). However, one problem with such a 'school-based' policy is that schools have to make efforts regarding the design and implementation of teaching and learning resources for school-based STEM education by themselves. This creates great difficulties for them as most schools lack relevant experience of carrying out STEM education. On the other hand, STEM is not an independent subject in the current school curriculum. Rather, it is implemented either during the curriculum time of STEM-related subjects such as science or mathematics, or, in various forms of extra-curricular activities like STEM programmes, STEM classes, and STEM days or weeks.

The STEM Teacher Preparation Policies in Hong Kong

Teacher education in the past were mostly discipline-based, following the subject disciplines in the school curriculum, and the interdisciplinary STEM education is new to teacher preparation to nurture qualified teachers with necessary knowledge and skills. As mentioned above, in the Hong Kong context, STEM education is mainly being promoted in SE, TE, ME, and GS. In contrast, engineering education plays a relatively peripheral role (Kutnick et al., 2018). Students' exposure to actual engineering topics in school is limited, and few teachers have backgrounds in engineering (Kutnick et al., 2018). The following section introduces the STEM teacher preparation policies by the government to warrant a competent teaching force for STEM education.

Given the critical role of teachers in promoting STEM education, the EDB has been placing emphasis on the preparation of teachers since 2016.

The '2017 policy address' further highlighted the importance of arranging "a series of intensive training programmes for the leadership tier and middle managers of all primary and secondary schools to enhance their capacity in planning and implementing school-based activities related to STEM" (The government of HKSAR, 2017, p. 26). To enhance the professional development of schools and teachers, the EDB (2016) recommended the following actions to strengthen professional capacity, knowledge transfer, and cross-fertilisation among schools and teachers: (1) organising symposia for curriculum leaders for all schools; (2) organising professional development programmes for middle managers and core teachers to enrich them with the cutting-edge knowledge in STEM-related fields; (3) increasing teachers' exposure to cutting-edge development in the science and technology fields through enhanced collaborations with STEM-related professional bodies; and (4) building communities of practice to enhance knowledge exchange among schools.

It is recognised that teacher preparation for STEM education in Hong Kong should firstly be aimed at developing the professional capability of middle leaders in schools (e.g., curriculum leaders, middle managers, or core teachers). In the literature, middle leaders who have formally designated leadership responsibilities, typically in subject areas, or coordinating cross-curricular specialisms, have shown vast potential to contribute to subject administration and school-based improvement (Bryant, 2019). They may play a prominent instructional leadership role in implementing school-based management or curricular reforms, as they may help connect the top-down expectations by the principals or the HKSAR government and the bottom-up teachers' practices in the classroom, eventually contributing to whole-school participation in the initiatives (Szeto, 2020).

It is also worth noting that the EDB (2016) emphasised updating teachers' STEM subject knowledge and skills to help them address the challenges to articulate the interdisciplinary nature in STEM education. One reason behind this is that education in Hong Kong has long been mainly based on individual subjects, and connections between subjects were seldom explored before STEM education. While the EDB has made efforts to support the professional development of teachers for STEM education, research has indicated that Hong Kong teachers lacked readiness to implement STEM-related learning activities (Geng et al., 2019; Yip & Chan, 2019). For instance, Geng et al. (2019) found that almost half of Hong Kong teachers showed inadequate self-efficacy in teaching STEM. Moreover, Yip and Chan (2019) pointed out that even experienced teachers needed help from professional consultants through building networks and partnerships within a broader STEM community. Lin et al. (2021) also noticed that designing integrative STEM curricula is a significant challenge for teachers, and lacking experience of designing such curricula might result in their low efficacy for designing STEM e-learning. Ali (2021) further argued that the lack of implementation approaches for teachers to organise STEM activities may lead to 'superficial' integration of disciplines, resulting in students' inadequate STEM understanding. These studies indicate that implementing STEM education remains challenging for frontline teachers.

To address this, the Task Force on review of school curriculum (EDB, 2020) further highlighted the need for extensive professional development, and recommended specific strategies for improving teachers' abilities to implement STEM education, including: (1) providing school-based examples of STEM education to illustrate effective implementation strategies and learning and teaching practices; (2) enhancing STEM-related professional development programmes to equip frontline teachers with the necessary knowledge and skills; (3) advising all schools to appoint a STEM coordinator at both the primary and secondary levels; and (4) arranging specific training programmes and workshops for curriculum leaders to enhance their capacity of organising cross-disciplinary STEM learning activities (p. v).

The Task Force is aware that there is a need to place more emphasis on enhancing frontline teachers' STEM pedagogical capabilities, stating that "the next phase of training courses should target frontline teachers. Emphasis should be put on enhancing teachers' teaching strategies and technological/pedagogical content knowledge of specific STEM topics or learning activities" (EDB, 2020, p. 34). Furthermore, the Task Force emphasises developing professional collaborations between teachers and STEM professionals to better prepare teachers for STEM education. This is consistent with previous research (e.g., Grier & Johnston, 2012; Knowles et al., 2018; So et al., 2020) which indicated that teacher training can be more productive if STEM experts are involved.

Though a lot of effort has been put forward to promote STEM education, most of the policies are for in-service teachers. The effort in nurturing new and qualified teachers in STEM education mainly rested on the government funded pre-service teacher education programmes, with the Education University being the leading provider of teacher education programmes, and contribution from education faculties in other universities.

Teacher Preparation for STEM Education

In this section, practices and innovations of teacher preparation programmes at primary and secondary education including STEM education are introduced and discussed.

In Hong Kong primary school, science and technology are taught as integrated parts of the subject General Studies (GS), which aims to enable school students to "use generic skills to enquire issues related to science, technology and society".[2] As it is already an interdisciplinary subject, it is a good venue for STEM education. Besides, the subject Primary Mathematics is also a major player in STEM education.

For secondary school subjects contributing to STEM education, besides Mathematics, two subjects Information and Communication Technology (ICT) and an Integrated Science (IS) are implemented in the junior secondary school curriculum. Senior secondary school students take Mathematics as one of the four core subjects and individual science subjects (e.g., Physics, Chemistry, and Biology) or combined subjects which include two to three of them as elective in the three years of study of the Diploma of Secondary Education (DSE).

Pre-service Teacher Preparation

Pre-service teacher programmes are discipline-focused in order to cater to the local school curriculum. To become a registered teacher in Hong Kong, a person can obtain either a Bachelor of Education (BEd), or a recognised undergraduate degree in a subject discipline and then a Postgraduate Diploma or Certificate in Education (PGDE).[3] To meet the need for subject teachers, innovations are made to parts of these programmes with an emphasis on interdisciplinary nature of STEM education, rather than developing a whole new programme. For the BEd programmes sampled here, they are 5-year programmes with two of them at primary level: BEd (Primary) General Studies and BEd (Primary) Mathematics; three programmes at secondary level: BEd (Secondary) Information and Communication Technology and BEd (Honours) (Secondary) Science programmes, as well as a programme with double degree of BEd and Bachelor of Science (BSc). Besides, there is a minor

[2] General Studies Curriculum Guide for Primary Schools, EDB, 2017.

[3] https://admissions.hku.hk/tpg/programme/postgraduate-diploma-education

programme "Creativity and STEM/STEAM" for pre-service teachers who would like to enrich themselves with more STEM.

Bachelor of Education (Honours) (Primary) General Studies Programme

Among the 156 credits, this programme[4] requires students completing 42 credits major courses related to discipline knowledge of GS including some science and technology related courses such as "Science in the Contemporary World" and "Living in the information age", some courses with social science orientation such as "Perspectives on Citizenship" and "Globalization: Trends and Development", and interdisciplinary courses such as "Science, Technology and Society" and "Interdisciplinary Concepts and Thinking". This wide range of subject knowledge can equip pre-service teachers with the capacity to apply multidisciplinary knowledge to understand and explain daily issues, which is one of the essences of STEM education.

Owing to the development of STEM education in Hong Kong and the responsibility of GS teachers in STEM education, the BEd in GS programme has been revamped to infuse more STEM educational elements in its courses. While there is not a specific course wholly devoted to STEM education in its curriculum at the moment, the rationale behind is that a large part of the GS curriculum is relevant to STEM education and most courses have included STEM educational elements, such that pre-service teachers will be able to incorporate STEM education in different context, which is one of the important characteristics of STEM teacher preparation for primary schools in Hong Kong.

Bachelor of Education (Honours) (Primary) Mathematics Programme

It is stated that on completion of the programme, students are expected to be able to use information technologies and appropriate software to enhance learning and teaching of mathematics; and demonstrate proficiency in coordinating STEM education in primary schools.

Bachelor of Education (Honours) (Secondary) Information and Communication Technology Programme

It is stated that on completion of the programme, students are expected to be able to demonstrate an understanding of basic concepts in major areas

[4] https://www.eduhk.hk/acadprog/infoday/public/static/pdfimg/FLASS/(Website/Materials)/FLASS-11_BEd(P)-GS_PPT.pdf

of ICT that supports the applications of information processing, programming, database and Artificial Intelligence for problem solving, which is a major component of STEM education.

Bachelor of Education (Honours) (Secondary) Science Programme
This programme[5] aims to prepare secondary science teachers, with an expectation that pre-service teachers will possess a solid command of science subject knowledge of physics, chemistry and/or biology and skills together with a firm and thorough grasp of the interrelationship between theory and practice. The wide range of subject knowledge already equips pre-service teachers with the capacity to apply knowledge of physics, chemistry and/or biology to understand and explain daily issues, which is also one of the essences of STEM education. One innovative aspect of the BEd Science programme is that pre-service teachers are required to study a "major-interdisciplinary" course, which involves the use of interdisciplinary tools including mathematical modelling and computing tools for scientific investigation. The course is taught by three professors with respective backgrounds in science, mathematics, and information technology, to achieve the goal of interdisciplinary teaching and learning. Through the course, pre-service teachers understand the interplay among scientific investigation, mathematical modelling, and computational thinking, which lays down the basis for these major STEM-related fundamental concepts for their future teaching career.

Bachelor of Education and Bachelor of Science
The double degree of BEd and BSc programme focuses on preparing secondary science teachers with one unique feature that it integrates the two degrees (a first degree majoring in science, and a teacher training qualification in science teaching).[6] That is, pre-service teachers receive deep training in a specialised subject and at the same time gain pedagogical knowledge and skills related to science and STEM education. Upon graduation, graduates obtain qualifications equivalent to a BSc plus a certification in Education.

In the above programmes, STEM elements are infused in some existing courses so as to support pre-service teachers to develop sufficient

[5] https://www.apply.eduhk.hk/ug/programmes/bedsci
[6] https://www.scifac.hku.hk/prospective/ug/6119-bed-and-bsc

knowledge and skills to design and implement STEM activities. For instance, a course focuses on the pedagogy for STEM education was introduced in the BEd Science programme to improve teachers' knowledge base in the science discipline from a more interdisciplinary perspective. Yip (2020) reported how the pre-service teacher course was reformed for interdisciplinary STEM teaching by following two principles of having experience of effective STEM education programmes similar to those at schools; and enhancing pre-service teachers' cognitive and metacognitive development for interdisciplinary STEM education. The result revealed that the course with an emphasis on experiential learning and cognitive and metacognitive development helped pre-service teachers develop better understanding of STEM education.

Postgraduate Diploma in Education (PGDE) at Primary / Secondary Levels

The Postgraduate Diploma in Education (PGDE) was primarily designed for non-registered teachers or university graduates seeking registered teacher (RT) status. The PGDE is offered at postgraduate level for those with a bachelor's degree in a field other than teaching (Santos, 2019). The mission is to enable the PGDE participants to develop adequate pedagogical knowledge and skills, and to provide effective learning experiences and strategies for pre-service teachers (Smith & Foley, 2015). The subject studies offered by the PGDE programme are in line with the subjects in the school curriculum, with little variation in intake quota depending on the market needs of individual subjects.

Considering the trends of STEM education, the PGDE programmes have been revamped to infuse more STEM educational elements in their courses. Courses related to STEM education included are both theoretical and practical, aiming at promoting pre-service teachers' professional excellence in implementing activities through introducing content such as the history of STEM education and its curriculum, the interdisciplinary learning approach, principles of STEM pedagogy, frameworks for curriculum integration and teaching, examples of teaching and learning, and assessment.[7] In a programme introduced in the study of Bridges et al. (2018), the PGDE pre-service teachers are provided with opportunities to collaborate with expert partners to design, conduct, and revise workshops for school students who choose STEM in extra-curricular school activities.

[7] https://www.fed.cuhk.edu.hk/pgde/cuhk_primary_course_list_and_descriptions.html

Informal Training Received by Pre-service Teacher

Other than the STEM educational elements for pre-service teachers in the formal curriculum when they are working towards their BEd or PGDE degrees, there are ample complementary opportunities for them to gain experience in STEM education through various form of informal learning, for instance, participating as student helpers in the collaboration between universities and schools on STEM education, helping professors to hold professional development workshops, or supporting local schools on their development of STEM education. Some schools also engaged pre-service teachers to lead STEM classes in the extra-curricular curriculum. Besides, some schools may assign STEM teaching tasks for intern teachers during the practicum period. All these are opportunities for pre-service teachers to acquire additional STEM education experience during their studies before they become a registered teacher.

In-service Teacher Preparation

Since STEM education has been only promoted since 2015 in Hong Kong, it is likely that teachers who graduated before 2015 did not receive training in STEM education during their pre-service teacher education programmes. To address this problem, some local universities set up STEM education Master of Arts (MA) or Master of Education (MEd) programmes to improve teachers' STEM perceptions and practices. The EDB also introduced professional development programmes (PDPs), Quality Education Fund Thematic Networks (QTNs), and tendered teacher professional development (TPD) programmes for equipping teachers with better knowledge of STEM education through deepening the collaborations between local universities and schools.

Research on Teacher Preparation for STEM Education in Hong Kong

Research on Teaching and Learning in Pre-service Teacher Education

To prepare pre-service teachers well in STEM education, there needs to have research investigating and supporting the programme design, as well as teaching and learning practices to provide evidence for further development. The followings are research studies focusing on teaching and learning strategies in pre-service teacher education programmes.

Yip (2020) found that existing initial teacher education usually focuses on teaching discrete subject disciplines, which is in contrast with the interdisciplinary nature of STEM, and pre-service teachers may lack the relevant training in design and engineering. Her study designed an initiative of preparing pre-service teachers for interdisciplinary STEM teaching which incorporated the process of "introducing STEM-related theory—hands-on practices—reflection—bridging theory and practice." During this initiative, lesson activities of STEM classrooms engaged the pre-service teachers as "students"; and then they were prompted to reflect metacognitively on how they could support the "students" as teachers. Results indicated the usefulness of engaging the pre-services teachers both as learners and future teachers in a STEM education course to develop their conceptual understanding of, attitudes towards, and readiness for STEM education. Another study is conducted by Leung and Yip (2021) applied experiential learning course with two phases to develop pre-service teachers' STEM literacy and STEM identity. The first phase engaged pre-service teachers in lectures that discussed STEM context, skills, and literacy, and the second phase involved these pre-service teachers in the sessions of creativity problem solving training online workshops for K-12 students. The results showed that the course effectively nurtured pre-service teachers' STEM literacy and STEM teacher identity.

Research on Teacher Professional Development

Amongst the research focusing on STEM education, more of them researched in-service teachers, identifying teachers' readiness and concerns. In Geng et al.'s (2019) study, only a small percentage of teachers regarded themselves as "well prepared" for STEM education implying the need to empower teachers with articulated professional development, pedagogic support, and curricular resources to implement STEM education in practice. For those teachers in Lin et al.'s study (2021) who are having a high propensity for designing STEM learning activities, their engagement in the STEM lesson design process may enhance their capacities of designing and implementing such activities. This is an encouraging result the well-suited teachers should be able to design a STEM curriculum and have positive perceptions of STEM education.

Besides, there have been intervention research studies to examine the effectiveness of teacher professional development strategies. So et al. (2020) found the STEM professional collaboration is having a positive impact on teachers' conceptions of STEM education and STEM professionals. The finding of Chiu et al. (2021) revealed that a professional development programme consisting of a workshop and actual teaching experience as a way of using self-determination theory-based design thinking is beneficial for STEM teachers to increase perceived competence and intrinsic motivation towards design thinking, and to apply what they learned from the workshops in their classroom teaching. So et al.'s (2021) study on using peer coaching with support from peers and due considerations of the special learning needs of Intellectual Disabled (ID) students provides useful insights for teachers to support ID students in STEM learning.

Conclusion: Future Development for Teacher Preparation in STEM Education

Innovative and competent teachers are essential for quality STEM education. As a result of the HKSAR government's efforts, the preparation of teachers for STEM education has received significant attention and support from stakeholders. As Nowikowski (2017) emphasised the need of research or research to inform teacher educators, the limited research conducted with the new initiative of teacher preparation for STEM education in Hong Kong, particularly with pre-service teachers, reported the design of teaching and learning strategies to prepare pre-service teachers with necessary STEM competency and literacy. These are useful for teacher educators to have better understanding of the background and current situation of novice teachers, which are conducive to the future design of teacher education programmes.

Since the newly introduced initiative of STEM education is very different from the other subjects in the local school curriculum, and the existing pre-service teacher programmes are mainly discipline-focused in order to provide the appropriate teaching force to the local curriculum, the interdisciplinary STEM education has been infused in the existing teacher education programmes, mostly in General Studies at primary level and Science at secondary level in various BEd and PGDE programmes to make it better integrated with the existing local school subjects. We have to learn from research recommendations from other nations, like the study by Schmidt and Fulton (2016) that inquiry-based STEM unit can be implemented in existing programmes, but creating and testing these prototypes requires significant effort to meet the learning needs of pre-service teachers; as well as the study by Nowikowski (2017) calling for more purposeful connection between quality field placements and STEM content as the potential for improving STEM experiences for pre-service teachers. Hence, more research is needed to examine the opportunities and challenges of the design which infused STEM element in pre-service teacher education programme, to inform the future development of STEM education in teacher preparation.

Besides, the reforms of programmes may consider providing pre-service teachers with more opportunities to experience truly interdisciplinary STEM education (Milner-Bolotin, 2018) and the different typologies and models of integration (Cheng & So, 2020), and to develop understanding of the "nature of STEM" (Faikhamta, 2020) and the epistemological nature of STEM connections (McComas & Burgin, 2020). What is more, there is a need for continuous research on the ways in which teacher development programmes can effectively foster teachers' STEM education knowledge and skills. Research-based evidence will be useful to build up a teacher education framework or evaluating framework for teacher educators and therefore to promote the quality of STEM education.

References

Ali, M. (2021). State of STEM Education in Hong Kong: A policy review. *Academia Letters, October*, 0–8. https://doi.org/10.20935/al3680

Bridges, S. M., Andrews, S., Tsui, A., Kwai-kuen, C. C., Wang, D., Kwan, T. Y. L., Lam, J. W. I., Harfitt, G. J., Chan, C., Law, W. W., Cheng, M. M. W., Yeung, P. S., Cheung, W. M., & Wang, R. (2018). Designing for integration in initial teacher education curricula: The Hong Kong postgraduate Diploma in Education. In *Innovation and accountability in teacher education* (pp. 295–312). Springer.

Bryant, D. A. (2019). Conditions that support middle leaders' work in organisational and system leadership: Hong Kong case studies. *School Leadership & Management, 39*(5), 415–433.

Cheng, Y. C., & So, W. M. W. (2020). Managing STEM learning: A typology & four models of integration. *International Journal of Educational Management, 34*(6), 1063–1078.

Chiu, T. K., Chai, C. S., Williams, P. J., & Lin, T. J. (2021). Teacher professional development on self-determination theory–based design thinking in STEM education. *Educational Technology & Society, 24*(4), 153–165.

Curriculum Development Council (CDC). (2017a). Mathematics education: Key learning area curriculum guide (Primary 1—Secondary 6). Government of Hong Kong (HKSARG).

Curriculum Development Council (CDC). (2017b). Science education: Key learning area curriculum guide (Primary 1—Secondary 6). Government of Hong Kong (HKSARG).

Curriculum Development Council (CDC). (2017c). Technology education: Key learning area curriculum guide (Primary 1—Secondary 6). Government of Hong Kong (HKSARG).

Curriculum Development Council (CDC). (2017d). General Studies: Curriculum guide for primary schools (Primary 1—Primary 6). Government of Hong Kong (HKSARG).

Education Bureau. (2016). *Report on promotion of STEM education: Unleashing potential in innovation*. Government of Hong Kong (HKSARG). https://www.edb.gov.hk/attachment/en/curriculum-development/renewal/STEM/Education/Report_Eng.pdf

Education Bureau. (2020). *Optimise the curriculum for the future: Foster whole-person development and diverse talents. Task force on review of school curriculum final report*. Government of Hong Kong (HKSARG). https://www.edb.gov.hk/attachment/en/curriculum-development/renewal/taskforce_cur/TF_CurriculumReview_FinalReport_e.pdf

Faikhamta, C. (2020). Pre-service science teachers' views of the nature of STEM. *Science Education International, 31*(4), 356–366.

Geng, J., Jong, M. S. Y., & Chai, C. S. (2019). Hong Kong teachers' self-efficacy and concerns about STEM education. *Asia-Pacific Education Researcher, 28*(1), 35–45. https://doi.org/10.1007/s40299-018-0414-1

Grier, J. M., & Johnston, C. C. (2012). STEM professionals entering teaching: Navigating multiple identities. *Journal of Science Teacher Education, 23*(1), 19–44.

Knowles, J., Kelley, T., & Holland, J. (2018). Increasing teacher awareness of STEM careers. *Journal of STEM Education, 19*(3), 47–55.

Kutnick, P., Chan, R. Y. Y., Chan, C. K. Y., Good, D., Lee, B. P. Y., & Lai, V. K. W. (2018). Aspiring to become an engineer in Hong Kong: Effects of engineering education and demographic background on secondary students' expectation to become an engineer. *European Journal of Engineering Education, 43*(6), 824–841.

Legislative Council Secretariat. (2020). Nurturing of local talent. Research Brief Issue No. 3. https://www.legco.gov.hk/research-publications/english/1920rb03-nurturing-of-local-talent-20200601-e.pdf

Leung, K. Y. P., & Yip, W. Y. V.. (2021). *Promotion of STEM Literacy and STEM teacher identity in Pre-service Science Teacher Education through Experiential*

Learning [Paper presentation]. The International Science Education Conference (ISEC) 2021, Singapore, 22 June–24 June.

Lin, P. Y., Chai, C. S., & Jong, M. S. Y. (2021). A study of disposition, engagement, efficacy, and vitality of teachers in designing science, technology, engineering, and mathematics education. *Frontiers in Psychology, 12*, 1–12. https://doi.org/10.3389/fpsyg.2021.661631

McComas, W. F., & Burgin, S. R. (2020). A critique of "STEM" education: Revolution-in-the-making, passing fad, or instructional imperative? *Science and Education, 29*(4), 805–829. https://doi.org/10.1007/s11191-020-00138-2

Milner-Bolotin, M. (2018). Evidence-based research in STEM Teacher Education: From theory to practice. *Frontiers in Education, 3*(November), 1–9. https://doi.org/10.3389/feduc.2018.00092

Nowikowski, S. H. (2017). Successful with STEM? A qualitative case study of pre-service teacher perceptions. *The Qualitative Report, 22*(9), 2312.

Santos, L. M. D. (2019). Pre-service teachers' professional development through four-step problem-solving model: A seminar method. *International Journal of Education and Practice, 7*(3), 146–157. https://doi.org/10.18488/journal.61.2019.73.146.157

Schmidt, M., & Fulton, L. (2016). Transforming a traditional inquiry-based science unit into a STEM unit for elementary pre-service teachers: A view from the trenches. *Journal of Science Education and Technology, 25*(2), 302–315.

Smith, L., & Foley, J. (2015). Talking together, learning together: The story of English PGCE Student teachers' adventures in classics. *Changing English, 22*(1), 60–71.

So, W. M. W., He, Q., Chen, Y., & Chow, C. F. (2020). School-STEM Professionals' Collaboration: A case study on teachers' conceptions. *Asia-Pacific Journal of Teacher Education, 49*(3), 300–318.

So, W. W. M., He, Q., Cheng, I. N. Y., Lee, T. T. H., & Li, W. C. (2021). Teachers' professional development with peer coaching to support students with intellectual disabilities in STEM learning. *Educational Technology & Society, 24*(4), 86–98.

Szeto, E. (2020). School leadership in the reforms of the Hong Kong education system: insights into school-based development in policy borrowing and indigenising. *School Leadership & Management, 40*(4), 266–287.

The Government of the Hong Kong Special Administrative Region. (2015). *The Executive's 2015 policy address: Uphold the rule of law seize the opportunities make the right choices.* https://www.policyaddress.gov.hk/2015/eng/pdf/PA2015.pdf

The Government of the Hong Kong Special Administrative Region. (2016). *The executive's 2016 policy address: Innovate for the economy improve livelihood foster harmony share prosperity.* https://www.policyaddress.gov.hk/2016/eng/pdf/PA2016.pdf

The Government of the Hong Kong Special Administrative Region. (2017). *The chief executive's 2017 policy address: We connect for hope and happiness.* https://www.policyaddress.gov.hk/2017/eng/pdf/PA2017.pdf

The Government of the Hong Kong Special Administrative Region. (2018). *The chief executive's 2018 policy address: Striving ahead rekindling hope.* https://www.policyaddress.gov.hk/2018/eng/pdf/PA2018.pdf

Yip, V. W. Y., & Chan, K. K. H. (2019). Teachers' conceptions about STEM and their practical knowledge for STEM teaching in Hong Kong. In Y. S. Hsu & Y. F. Yeh (Eds.), *Asia-Pacific STEM teaching practices.* Springer.

Yip, W. Y. V. (2020). Developing undergraduate student teachers' competence in integrative STEM teaching. *Frontiers in Education, 5*, 44.

CHAPTER 8

Status Study on Japanese Pre-Service and In-Service Science Teachers' Preparation in STEM/STEAM Education

Yoshisuke Kumano, Toshihiko Masuda, Yoshiaki Aoki, Takahiro Yamamoto, and Yoshiyuki Gunji

Introduction

Around 2000, many countries started considering the twenty-first century skills or competencies applicable to the coming frameworks for all subjects at all schools. According to analysis by the present researcher, in the United States, the reforms crystallized with the development of the Next Generation Science Standards (NGSS) in 2013 for public schools. The state science standards were influenced by the NGSS, which is a strategy

Y. Kumano (✉) • T. Masuda • Y. Aoki • T. Yamamoto • Y. Gunji
Faculty of Education, STEAM Education Institute, Shizuoka University, Shizuoka, Japan
e-mail: kumano.yoshisuke@shizuoka.ac.jp; aua-toshi-haru@thn.ne.jp; yamamoto.takahiro@shizuoka.ac.jp; gunji.yoshiyuki@shizuoka.ac.jp

S. M. Al-Balushi et al. (eds.), *Reforming Science Teacher Education Programs in the STEM Era*, Palgrave Studies on Leadership and Learning in Teacher Education,
https://doi.org/10.1007/978-3-031-27334-6_8

that aims to exploit STEM/STEAM innovation for the benefit of American society.

This strong STEM/STEAM innovation agenda may influence many countries around the world. In terms of in-service teacher training, the prefectural boards of education (PBOE), which are similar to the state boards of education in the United States, are responsible for, and exert authority over, in-service science teacher education and have developed effective models of the NCOS for all teachers in each prefecture in Japan.

It is important to explain that in January 2016, the Government of Japan, through the Cabinet of Japan, declared "Society 5.0" to be a future target of Japanese society. "Society 5.0" is defined as a "human-centered society that balances economic advancement with the resolution of social problems by a system that highly integrates cyberspace and physical space." Two years later, in 2018, the Ministry of Education (MEXT, 2018) officially indicated that STEM/STEAM educational innovation was needed in Japan. Many official reports followed with detailed considerations for 2019, 2020, and 2021. From that time on, the combination of Society 5.0 and STEM/STEAM education has focused on twenty-first century skills in the Japanese context.

There are approximately 57 Institutes of Technology with five-year programs (from 10 to 15 grade) in all prefectures in Japan. The number of students in all technology schools has been around 10,000 per year for 57 years. Among the graduates from these Institutes of Technology, about 40% have continued their studies at the Faculty of Engineering or through continuing education at the Institute of Technology or Engineering at the Universities. It was found that the respective curricula were developed as Japanese models for STEM/STEAM area learning. Since 2016, many of the 57 Institutes of Technology have been changing their curriculum to align STEAM learning with project-based learning and problem-based learning (PBL).

Another educational system implemented in a formal setting is the Super Science High School (SSH). As of 2022, there are 218 SSH operating in all areas of Japan. The SSH program began in 2002 in Japan. Each SSH school conducts educational practice focusing on research in science, technology, engineering, mathematics, and, especially since 2016, twenty-first century skills.

Other educational systems are conducted in informal settings under the Global Science Campus (GSC) project and the Junior Doctor Project (JDP). The GSC conducts STEM education programs for high school students at universities or research institutions. The JDP conducts STEM education programs for 5th–9th-grade students at universities or research institutions.

One of the characteristics of Japanese STEM educational policy is the decision to promote the general development of twenty-first century skills; however, educational sectors have the freedom to develop their own respective models. Otherwise, the goal is a Japanese STEM/STEAM model for the future that is similar to the NGSS in the United States.

Objective

This chapter describes the narratives of STEM/STEAM-based teacher education programs in Japan and their impacts on Japanese society. Narrative descriptions are used to describe the major changes across the nation and case studies in Shizuoka regarding STEM/STEAM teacher preparedness as the beginning of the first stage of systemic STEAM reform in Japan.

Background

Changes in Education Policy as a Nation

Every seven to ten years, Japan's National Curriculum Standards (*Gakushu Shido Yoryou*) are revised. In July 2017, the NCOS for science in elementary schools was developed for the Japanese public education system. This time, for all subjects, twenty-first century skills or competencies were introduced that involve "proactive, interactive and authentic learning" (so-called active learning) (MEXT, 2021, p. 8).

There were minor changes to the content of the science curricula. However, there were major changes to science lessons, with the introduction of inquiry-based learning, project-based learning, or problem-based learning. About 100 model schools were used for educational trials. In science education, programming and coding instruction and "Monozukuri (making education)" were introduced in the 3rd to 12th grades in Japan. "Making education" means that in order to understand scientific principles, it can be introduced by moving apparatus, for example. In 2018, all the ministries started to mention the importance of "Society 5.0" and the science and technology revolution with artificial intelligence (AI), the Internet of Things (IoT), and Big Data. All current governmental policies are focused on developing original science and technology innovations in Japan to enhance global competitiveness.

The SSHs has been continuously selected from the many nominated high schools. Japan now has more than 218 SSHs specializing in educating highly proficient students who can conduct scientific and technological research. Since 2021, this agenda has been implemented in middle schools. Around 30 governmental universities conduct informal programs in special scientific or technological STEAM education for elementary and middle school students. In addition, more than 45 groups of researchers conduct STEM/STEAM education-related research with the Japanese National Science Foundation (NSF) through the so-called Japan Society for Promotion of Science (JSPS).

Currently, the funding of every STEAM educational area is identified as part of the Science, Technology and Innovation Basic Plan of 2021. Accordingly, the NCOS will be able to add and revise more tactical components in STEAM area subjects; consequently, the teacher training system will be more focused on STEAM area learning. To further this agenda, the Ministry of Education, Culture, Sports, Science and Technology (MEXT) has selected more than 50 schools for model research on STEAM learning at all levels from high schools to elementary schools. Also, school boards at the prefectural government level are increasingly conducting STEAM education in-service teacher training. The present author gives special lectures on STEAM education more than three times every year at the Shizuoka Prefecture Teacher Training Center or other locations.

Methods

The research method of the present study applied descriptive methods to study Japanese pre-service and in-service STEM teacher training from 2016–2022 concerning STEM/STEAM teacher preparedness. Also, some STEM/STEAM education model trials were conducted as part of classes for undergraduate and graduate courses at Shizuoka University. Furthermore, action researches were conducted in both informal and formal education settings. Action research seeks to implement transformative change through the simultaneous processes of taking action and conducting research, which are linked together by critical reflection.

Processes for Selecting Science Teachers in Middle and High Schools

The processes used to select science teachers at middle schools and public schools are very similar at the prefectural or independent city level. As a sample of these selection processes, the case of Shizuoka Prefecture is described below.

Case of Shizuoka Prefecture

In general, all elementary school teachers must be able to teach all of the subjects at an elementary school. Accordingly, the qualifying examinations include scientific knowledge at the middle school level. However, in this short chapter, we mainly describe the situation in middle and high schools. There are two steps in the selection system for middle and high school science teacher selection. The first-level examinations include general common knowledge and special knowledge as a teacher (60 minutes), knowledge of sciences (80 minutes for middle school and 90 minutes for high school), and an interview examination (20 minutes). In 2021, among 12 basic knowledge questions, there was one science question: "One of the planets around the sun does not count as a planet anymore. Choose one of the following items" (Pluto). Question 2 was a question on copyright. Question 3 was about developmental psychology. Questions 4 to 7 focused on various theories of education. Question 5 was about educational law. Question 8 focused on bullying. Question 9 focused on special activities at school. Question 10 focused on academic and career counseling. Finally, question 11 focused on the prevention of crimes and safety. These questions do not have any components of STEM/STEAM education. However, they will change into more questions related to STEM/STEAM education in a near future.

Middle school examinations use high school-level science content, including physics, chemistry, biology, and earth science. For high school science teacher candidates, the level of questions on physics, chemistry, biology, and earth science is usually set at the level of undergraduate general knowledge in those four areas. The last part of the first-level examination is a 20-minute interview with many different types of questions on many subjects.

The second-level examinations include group and individual interview examinations. In the case of Shizuoka Prefecture Middle School, group interviews of five candidates are held with three evaluators for about 30 minutes. Individual interviews for future science teachers generally include a demonstration of science teaching and different topic questions. The patterns of second-level examinations change each year. Therefore, depending on the prefecture, the contexts and content of the interview examinations may slightly vary.

The MEXT promulgated an official order to prefectural boards of education requiring a clear system for the teacher selection process. The board of education in each prefecture and independent city was required to announce changes to their system to be clear and open to outside evaluators. There will be more questions on STEM/STEAM learning and on how to conduct more effective lessons on STEAM learning in 2022.

Impacts of New National Curriculum Standards of Japan and Their Relation to "Society 5.0"

In the case of Japan, many researchers are interested in twenty-first century competencies or skills, such as creativity, high-quality communication skills, system thinking, and intrinsic motivation, which have been discussed in European and North American countries. Around 2000, many countries were comparing and evaluating or assessment items for inclusion among twenty-first century competencies or skills (NSTA, 2011; Windschitl, 2009). Japanese educational researchers in many subjects have also tried to compare such items and develop more effective models for Japanese contexts (Kimura & Tatsuno, 2017; NIEPR, 2013). On March 11, 2011, the East Japan Earthquake struck the northern part of the Japanese island and caused enormous damage and causalities. This and other natural and human-made disasters were the most significant motivators behind the need for educational policy changes as all Japanese citizens realized the importance of innovation in education for a better future. The MEXT reviced the National Curriculum Standards (NCS) in 2017 (MEXT, 2017). It should be noted that the 5th Science and Technology Basic Plan (STBP) was developed in 2016 in accordance with the Science and Technology Basic Law. This plan identified the important concept of "Society 5.0," which was new terminology created by the Japanese government.

One of the efforts connected with the STBP was carried out under the Ministry of Economy, Trade and Industry (METI). Basic planning was discussed, 2018, for one of the projects called by the STBP. As of 2022, three interesting home pages had been introduced for K–12 schools in Japan. The first one is the "STEAM Library," which is an exemplary resolution on STEAM schools, developed through the cooperation of companies, universities, and certain organizations. The second is the "EdTech Library," which is another exemplary resolution on digital transformation projects within schools. The third is "School Business Process Reengineering," which is an exemplary resolution on the management of school administrations. More than 200 schools and more than 80 companies are taking part in such innovative educational STEAM activities as part of METI projects. Each project is supported by funding of around US$60,000–100,000. All of the new STEAM education innovations are identified as new efforts connected with the National Curriculum Standards. Against this backdrop, education faculties at all universities have gradually started integrating the concepts and practices of STEAM education into their course methods, especially regarding how to develop interesting STEAM lesson planning.

Furthermore, it is possible to identify the impact of the Science, Technology, and Innovation Plan of March 2021. The former Suga and present Kishida administration agreed to conduct further innovation and detailed plans for all of the functions of governmental organizations, institutions, and research centers regarding Society 5.0 in the STEAM area, including concerted efforts in the education system in Japan for decades with clear and supportive funding from companies. It can be said that we are living in a historic moment for STEAM innovation in Japan.

Exemplary Pre-service STEAM Teacher Training at Shizuoka University in Shizuoka

It will be highly difficult for Japan to move to project- or problem-based learning (PBL) from the present didactic lecture-style learning at universities. In 2017, the MEXT developed the NCS—the National Curriculum Standards—which call for major shifts toward a PBL system with few changes in subject content for K–12 education. We now find new subjects at the high school level, such as "Inquiry in Science and Mathematics," which is a typical PBL course.

Development of STEM Learning in Undergraduate Method Courses

In light of the above, university methods courses in all subjects should include content concerning PBL. Also, it is of great importance to make undergraduate students aware of twenty-first century skills and STEM/ STEAM literacy for the purposes of establishing Society 5.0. The NCOS identified three basic foci of twenty-first century skills in every subject:

intrinsic motivation, deeper communication skills, and deep learning. From elementary school through high school, all teachers have been undertaking in-service teacher training on the best practices regarding these twenty-first century learning skills. For the NCOS framework in science, the new model was examined with respect to STEAM education at all prefectural teacher-training centers from about 2020 via theoretical and practical training; however, we are still in the initial phases of implementation.

Accordingly, the Method Course of Science has begun including a STEAM learning component among its topics; gradually, many professors have started changing the curriculum to suit the NCOS and Society 5.0 within the Japanese contexts. For example, the contexts are included about more innovations which developed with strong connections among sciences and engineering. Moreover, the national government and local governments have provided one Chromebook per student at all schools in Japan; thus, all science teachers are exploring how to implement major changes in science lessons that Chromebooks make possible.

Methodologies for the Development of STEM/STEAM Teachers in Universities

It is easy to lecture on educational philosophies, such as constructivism; however, undergraduate students don't have enough experiences to put constructivism into practice. The implication is that while knowledge is important for life, it is quite difficult to create innovations detached from real contexts and practices. What types of learning structures are needed for science education methods courses for STEM/STEAM learning? First, e-learning systems, such as Moodle, Blackboard, and Google Classroom, should be fundamental. Second, it is important to let college students identify their own issues or problems in science education (NRC, 2013). Third, they should start their own PBL in their own ways; however, most students do not have educational experience, which means their issues or problems remain shallow and they lack seriousness of meaningful purpose; thus, they might not follow through with their learning. Using the NGSS model helps in finding interesting models for intrinsic motivation, and it identifies the importance of STEM/STEAM area learning with practices. Many learning models in the STEAM Library, which was developed by the METI of Japan, provide us with many interesting learning models for university students. If undergraduate students have rich experiences of PBL in science education, they will have better chances of becoming

STEM/STEAM teachers in the future (Shernoff et al., 2017). It is obvious that changing the learning system for undergraduate education is fundamental to facilitating STEM/STEAM learning and the building of Society 5.0.

As Wieman described in his book, *Improving How Universities Teach Science: Lessons from the Science Education Initiative* (2017), we need to implement major changes in universities in Japan, too. He pointed out that old frameworks could not easily change to a better way of learning because most professors in science-related fields were trained according to the traditional methods of learning. In the context of Japan, strong objections toward PBL might be raised at universities.

The MEXT has established many competitive funding systems in pursuit of Society 5.0. Some of these funding systems for universities in Japan call for the development of new STEAM education faculty and PBL systems. Thus, the MEXT selected approximately 10 universities that began planning innovative STEAM education development starting in 2017 with US$0.5–1.0 million for 5 years. However, STEAM teacher development at most faculties of education might be slow to adopt newer STEM ecosystems in the future.

Development of STEM Action Research in Master's Theses and PhD Dissertations

A search of the relevant literature reveals that research in science education reflects on research questions of science education dissertations in the context of each countries. However, it was found that in the Kumano Laboratory at Shizuoka University, no specific STEM/STEAM research had been conducted before 2011. Table 8.1 below shows the list of master's theses and PhD dissertation titles from 2012 to 2021. It was crucial to develop PhD dissertations because each of the candidates was required to produce edited papers connected to STEM or STEAM action research. These efforts have the vital effect of producing STEM/STEAM learning materials and connections to twenty-first century skills in the context of Japanese science education. As a result, many edited papers were produced (Suwarma & Kumano, 2014; Mutakinati et al., 2018; Sulaeman & Kumano, 2019; Jin-Ichi & Yoshisuke, 2019; Putra & Kumano, 2019; Sakata & Kumano, 2018; Saito et al., 2016; Takebayashi & Kumano, 2020; Takemoto et al., 2020).

Our laboratory adopted the NGSS learning model developed in the United States (Lead States, 2013); however, there are limitations to

Table 8.1 Scholar and Title of STEM/STEAM-Related Thesis at Kumano Laboratory from 2012 to 2021

2012	*Takahashi Shuhei (MD)*	*A Comparative Study of Learning Progressions in Japan and the US: Adaptability in the Domain of Dynamics in Japanese Secondary School Science*
2013	Ilman Anwari (PhD)	The Important Aspects in Improving Metacognitive Skills Through Simulation Cards, Experiments of Assessment, and STEM Implementation in Chemistry and Physics Education
2013	Shimada Tatsuhiko (MD)	Issue-Based Learning for Finding Connections with Society in High School Biology: A Comparison with the New Science Education Initiative (NGSS) in the US
2014	Irma Rahma Suwarma	A Research on STEM Education Theory and Practices in Japan and Indonesia Using Multiple Intelligences Approach
2014	Shido Mayu (MD)	The Research on Theory and Practices about Earthquake Disaster Prevention Education: Education for Foreign People Living in Japan and the Evaluation of STEM Education for School Children
2015	Oda Kotaro (MD)	A Research on STEM Education Using Dagik Earth for Middle and High School Science: Development of Science Instruction Using the Project-Based Learning Program
2016	Okumura Jin-Ichi (PhD)	Action Research on the Lesson Generation of the Subjective and Active Learning among the Students in High School Biology—Based on Studies of the STEM Education in the United States
2016	Saito Tomoki (PhD)	A Research on Creativity in STEM Integrated Learning Environment Based on Task Specific Approach
2017	Lely Mutakinati (PhD)	A Research on Critical Thinking Skill, Attitudes, and Career Interests through Project Based Learning in STEM Education among Japan and Indonesia Middle School Students
2018	Ichikawa Haruka (MD)	A Research on Energy Education Based on "Argument"
2018	Sakata Shoko (PhD)	Implementation of STEM Education to Japanese Science Education—Through the Development and Practices of STEM Education Program to K to 6 Grades Students
2019	Pramudya Dwi Aristya P. (PhD)	The Development and Implementation of Pedagogical Content Knowledge (PCK) in STEM Education for Pre-service Science Teachers in Indonesia
2019	Nurul Fitriyah Sulaeman (PhD)	A Study of STEM Education to Develop Solutions Toward Issues in Renewable Energy in the Context of Japan and Indonesia
2019	Sasaki Hiroto (MD)	The Action Research on "STEM Education" with Generating Intrinsic Learning Motivation, Deep Communication and Deep Learning: The Implementation of Earth Science Unit at Shizuoka Attached Middle School

(*continued*)

Table 8.1 (continued)

2012	*Takahashi Shuhei (MD)*	*A Comparative Study of Learning Progressions in Japan and the US: Adaptability in the Domain of Dynamics in Japanese Secondary School Science*
2020	Kuroda Tomotaka (PhD)	Action Researches of First-Year-Experience of the STEM Human Resource Community in Higher Education: An Approach to Ensure the Capacity Building of Key Competencies in the STEM Human Resource Community
2020	Takebayashi Tomohiro (PhD)	Action Research for the Development of an Earth Sciences STEM/STEAM Education Models Specific to Japanese Geology, Culture, and Industry
2020	Takemoto Iwaki (PhD)	Empirical Research on Platform Construction to Support STEM Education Promotion in Japan
2020	Hakamada Hiroki (MD)	Action Research on the Development of a Japanese STEM Education Model for Elementary School Science: Through Shizuoka STEM Academy and Lesson Practices of 6 Grade Science
2020	Mineta Ippei (MD)	A Research on Data Analysis, Interpretation and Consideration in Science Education and STEM Education
2021	Kosaka Naoko (PhD)	Research on Improving the Quality of Inquiry Activities in High School Biology Classes in Japan—Through an Analysis of the US Science Education Practices Based on the Next Generation Science Standards (NGSS)

conduct the NGSS, such as in 3D learning and learning progressions in each concept of science and engineering. However, we started to develop STEAM learning materials for integrated learning with STEAM. By developing action research, we facilitated learning innovation by implementing the eight recommended practices in each unit of NGSS. Our findings suggest that it is highly difficult for graduate students or science teachers to develop cross-cutting Big Ideas of NGSS in the context of lessons.

Unfortunately, there are few inducements to attend PhD programs in science education in Japan. However, it is imperative to realize that systemic reform in STEM/STEAM innovation requires more special STEM/STEAM area researchers with extensive scientific and engineering experience in STEM/STEAM areas.

Super Science High Schools and Super Global High Schools

Because of the Science and Technology Basic Plan of 2016, with its aim of bringing about Society 5.0, there was a major shift not only in science and technology areas but also in the development of STEAM education. Super Science High Schools (SSHs) originally started in 2002, and this program has continued with remarkable growth results to date. There are more than 217 SSHs all over Japan. SSHs are STEM-oriented high schools where many types of PBL are conducted. In addition, we have SGHs whose focus is teaching the United Nations Sustainable Development Goals (SDGs) with PBL. The major goals of SGHs are addressing global issues or problems by means of PBL. SGHs need to develop communications with other universities or high schools in the world to discover and facilitate solutions. As of January 2022, more than 110 SGHs existed in all of Japan. The funding for SSHs and SGHs is around US$0.1–0.2 million per year. In March 2021, the MEXT developed the Science, Technology, and Innovation Basic Plan of 2021 to help bring about Society 5.0. In the course of this planning, at the Central Education Council Committee, SSHs were identified as STEAM education role models at the high school level in the context of Japanese society.

Shizuoka STEM Academy and Its Expansion

STEM/STEAM educational innovation requires systemic reform in the target country. In Japan, it was deemed necessary to develop a system to encourage 5th–9th-grade students who wish to develop their own research to communicate with university researchers conducting actual research. Before 2012, there were many STEM/STEAM-oriented projects, such as the Science Festivals for Young Children, the Young Astronauts Program, Science Camps, and so on. However, most of them were short-term events, and it was difficult to find ways to allow students to continue their inquiry for a longer period. In 2012, the MEXT started the Fostering Next Generation Scientists Program, which encouraged 5th–9th-grade students to conduct science-and technology-oriented research, guided by real scientists at universities or research institutions. The implementation of these programs revealed that there were quite a few researchers who realized the importance of STEM/STEAM education, especially from the perspective of systemic reform for local communities. Also, from September to December 2012, the authors had the fortunate opportunity as visiting researchers to visit the University of Iowa and conduct various local visits to discover the realities of STEM educational innovation in the states of Iowa, Minnesota, and Washington, as well as in Washington, D.C. It was indeed fortunate to have had fruitful discussions with Professor Robert E. Yager at the Science Education Center at the University of Iowa,

Professor Gillian Roehrig at the STEM Education Center of the University of Minnesota, Professor Jeffery Welds, Director of the Iowa Governor's STEM Advisory Council, Dr. David L. Evans, the NSTA Executive Director, and NSF STEM specialists at that time. This three-month research period in the United States in 2012, supported by the Fulbright Researchers' Program, provided the first present author with such extraordinary insights as a researcher of science education. After returning to Japan, our STEM education team and my students at Shizuoka University worked diligently to develop STEM programs and STEM learning materials supported by Japan Society for the Promotion of Science (JSPS) grants and Japan Science and Technology Agency (JST) grants. In this context, one of the most efficient teams in Japan, the Kumano Laboratory team, conducted the Shizuoka STEM Junior Project at Shizuoka University beginning in 2014. Eight institutions implemented the Fostering Next Generation Scientists Program.

In 2016, with the implementation of the Science and Technology Basic Plan, JST declared a new five-year project called Junior Doctors Fostering as part of the Fostering Next Generation Scientists Program. At the time of writing, there are 29 institutions conducting STEM/STEAM learning for about 40 students in all areas of Japan, with funding of about US$0.1 million for each institution per year.

Shizuoka STEM Academy has received funding for 2018–2023. This program is offered to students in the 5th–9th grades in an informal education setting. Figure 8.1 shows a summary of Shizuoka STEM Academy, which includes three levels, namely, Stage 1.0, Stage1.5, and Stage 2.0. In Stage 1.0, students have about seven STEM learning each year at four locations in Shizuoka Prefecture. These are STEM learning activities, with interesting STEM learning materials provided in the morning. Students are encouraged to conduct individual or group-oriented research. Mentors, present science teachers, retired science teachers, and retired university science and technology researchers have helped develop students' STEM thinking in their own research. However, mentors never directly instruct them on what to do. This has been quite an important point at Shizuoka Academy. Mentors are coaches who help students to conduct their own research; however, they never teach direct solutions. In Stage 1.5, students have about seven STEM area lectures with small-scale STEM/STEAM activities in the morning. They also have face-to-face communication with mentors regarding their research. All of the students in Stage 1.5 are selected from among former Stage 1.0 students. Thus, the

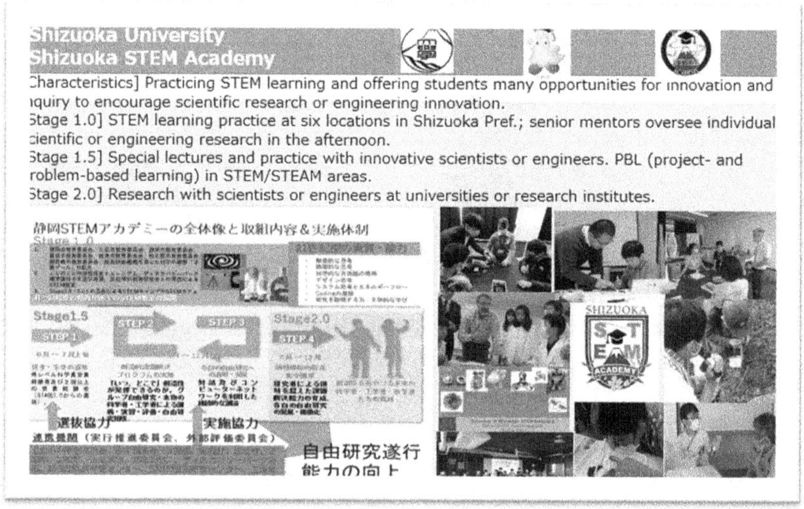

Fig. 8.1 Images of Shizuoka STEM Academy

depth of thinking is more sophisticated compared to Stage 1.0. In Stage 2.0, students have special meetings and discussions to identify appropriate STEM area researchers in certain institutions. If the students and the researchers are a good match, then the 2.0 students visit the researcher's laboratory to study, obtain advice, or conduct research at the university level.

Shizuoka STEM Academy has received assistance from more than 15 current and retired science teachers and more than 30 undergraduate students majoring in science or technology education. In this way, Shizuoka STEM Academy is simultaneously conducting pre-service science teacher education through its yearlong activities.

Discussion and Future Implementation

In March 2021, the Government of Japan announced its Science, Technology, and Innovation Plan for 2021–2026 for the earnest development of Society 5.0. This plan includes systemic reform for the development of STEAM education with PBL and twenty-first century skills. The acceleration of STEAM education, with the help and communication of all governmental institutions, industries, non-profit organizations, and universities, will help to realize Society 5.0.

One of the factors in favor of Japan being able to realize Society 5.0 is that strong human resources exist in the industrial area, where group-oriented innovations have produced a renowned quality control system; however, they possess mainly technical expertise. Many of these technical experts will be replaced by AI or robotics. It will be interesting to provide twenty-first century skills to K–12 students who will become STEAM area experts in the service of Society 5.0. We need to educate science, mathematics, and technology teachers and future teachers in STEM areas to be STEM/STEAM teachers. This means that we need to institute major changes in pre-service and in-service STEM teacher education at all levels of the STEM education system in Japan if we hope to make progress toward Society 5.0.

Conclusion

To develop new curriculum standards for courses of study in Japan, national teams from the Center Council of Education investigated twenty-first century skills or competencies based on observation of other countries before 2013 (MEXT, 2014). It took approximately seven to ten years to develop national curriculum standards for courses of study in all subjects; these were finalized and revealed to the public in 2017. One year prior, the Government of Japan planned Society 5.0 for the nation. The planning started with small steps; however, the declaration strongly communicated that all policy and education systems should start making progress toward Society 5.0.

Now, many universities in Japan are implementing new faculties with a PBL focus with MEXT support. Accordingly, many faculties of education are starting to develop important ideas for STEM/STEAM learning. Many learning models for STEAM education are being developed, and all teachers are being given the opportunity to learn through the governmental STEAM Library. All these functions of STEAM teacher development will contribute to systemic reform toward the goal of Society 5.0.

This will be a historic turning point for the future of the country of Japan, and all Japanese citizens foresee an interesting future with a human-centered society and a high quality of life. Pre-service and in-service teacher training programs at universities and teacher training centers are the key institutions where there will be think tanks producing a variety of STEM/STEAM learning materials and many exemplary learning models for STEM/STEAM teachers and students. The reality of Society 5.0

requires people who know how to develop new solutions, alternative ways of finding new knowledge, innovation methodologies using new technologies, communication skills for the development of new projects, and so on. For the successful realization of Society 5.0, we need to develop a paradigm shift in learning and systemic reform in education. In the case of Japan, a national STEAM education center and prefectural STEAM education centers, funded by the government, will be essential. In this way, the government will be able to elicit the many systemic STEAM education strategies it needs for the realization of Society 5.0.

References

Cabinet Office & METI. (2018). *The 5th science & technology basic plan.* https://www8.cao.go.jp/cstp/kihonkeikaku/index5.html

Jin-Ichi, O., & Yoshisuke, K. (2019). Action research on the differences in influence of classroom experiments and developing technologies on female and male students in high school biology classes from each gender perspective. *Bulletin of the Faculty of Education, Shizuoka University, Educational Research Series, 51*, 143–158.

Kimura, D., & Tatsuno, M. (2017). *Advancing 21st century competencies in Japan.* Center for Global Education.

Lead States. (2013). *Next generation science standards: For states, by states.* The National Academies Press.

MEXT. (2014). *Summary of the panel on educational objectives, contents and evaluation (based on the quality and competencies to be developed) [ikusei subeki shishitsu/ nouryoku wo fumaeta kyouiku mokuhyou/naiyou to hyouka no arikata ni kansuru kentoukai].* Panel on Educational Objectives, Contents and Evaluation, MEXT. https://www.mext.go.jp/component/b_menu/shingi/toushin/__icsFiles/afieldfile/2014/07/22/1346335_02.pdf

MEXT. (2017). *The course of study.* National Curriculum Standards.

MEXT. (2018). *STEAM education.* Committee on Educational Curriculum, National Education Council. https://www.mext.go.jp/b_menu/shingi/chukyo/chukyo3/004/siryo/1420968.htm

MEXT. (2021, March). Overview of the Ministry of Education, Culture, Sports, Science and Technology-Japan. https://www.mext.go.jp/en/content/20210325-mxt_kouhou02-200000029_1.pdf

Mutakinati, L., Anwari, I., & Yoshisuke, K. (2018). Analysis of students' critical thinking skill of middle school through STEM education project-based learning. *Jurnal Pendidikan IPA. Indonesia, 7*(1), 54–65. https://doi.org/10.15294/jpii.v7i1.10495

National Institute for Educational Policy Research. (2013). *Basic principles of educational curriculum organization for nurturing skills or competences adopting social changes.* Report 5 on the Fundamental Research on Educational Curriculum Organization.

NSTA. (2011). *Quality science education and 21st-century skills.* NSTA position statement.

Putra, P. D. A., & Kumano, Y. (2019). Energy learning progression and STEM conceptualization among pre-service science teachers in Japan and Indonesia. *The New Educational Review, 53*, 153–162. https://doi.org/10.15804/tner.2018.53.3.13

Saito, T., Anwari, I., Mutakinati, L., & Kumano, Y. (2016). A look at relationships (Part I): Supporting theories of STEM integrated learning environment in a classroom—A historical approach. *K-12 STEM Education, 2*(2), 51–61.

Sakata, S., & Kumano, Y. (2018). Attempting STEM education in informal Japanese educational facilities through the theme of "sand". *K-12 STEM. Education, 4*(4), 401–411. https://www.learntechlib.org/p/209558/

Shernoff, D. J., Sinha, S., Bressler, D. M., & Ginsburg, L. (2017). Assessing teacher education and professional development needs for the implementation of integrated approaches to STEM education. *Journal of STEM Education, 4*(13), 1–16.

Sulaeman, N. F., & Kumano, Y. (2019). Development of students' perception instrument of new and renewable energy (PINRE). *The New Educational Review*. https://doi.org/10.15804/tner.19.56.2.05

Suwarma, I. R., & Kumano, Y. (2014). Comparison of multiple intelligence undergraduate students' profile in Japan and Indonesia: An undergraduate mathematics and science students' differences in logical mathematical intelligence area. *Global Education Review, 2*(4), 47–57.

Takebayashi, T., & Kumano, Y. (2020). Exemplary STEM education focusing on the geology and culture of Niijima Islands in Japan with cross-cutting concepts. *Southeast Asian Journal of STEM Education, 1*(1), 76–92.

Takemoto, I., Ogawa, H., Horita, T., & Kumano, Y. (2020). Characteristics of the relationship between teachers, researchers and engineers in web-based elementary school STEM class design meetings: Through network analysis using utterance data. *Journal of Science Education in Japan, 44*(4), 338–352.

Wieman, C. E. (2017). *Improving how universities teach science, lessons from the science education initiative.* Harvard University Press.

Windschitl, M. (2009). *Cultivating 21st century skills in science learners: How systems of teacher preparation and professional development will have to evolve.* National Academies of Science Workshop on 21st Century Skills.

CHAPTER 9

Perspectives on Reforming Science Teacher Education Programs Toward Integrated STEM in Malaysia

Muhammad Abd Hadi Bunyamin and Nor Farahwahidah Abdul Rahman

Introduction

According to Koehler et al. (2016), the Science, Technology, Engineering, and Mathematics (STEM) movement started in the early 1990s in the United States (US) by the National Research Council (NRC). The first term used was SMET but was changed to STEM to provide a more substantial meaning to the new term. Now, the US and the global community have adopted the idea of integrated STEM. Many countries, including developing nations (e.g., Malaysia, Thailand, etc.), have started to take up

M. A. H. Bunyamin (✉) • N. F. A. Rahman
Faculty of Social Sciences and Humanities, School of Education, Universiti Teknologi Malaysia (UTM), Skudai, Malaysia
e-mail: mabhadi@utm.my; nfwahidah@utm.my

S. M. Al-Balushi et al. (eds.), *Reforming Science Teacher Education Programs in the STEM Era*, Palgrave Studies on Leadership and Learning in Teacher Education,
https://doi.org/10.1007/978-3-031-27334-6_9

the integrated STEM idea in the education systems (Ministry of Education, 2018; Pimthong & Williams, 2018).

This chapter aims to share the efforts of a teacher education program (TEP) to include the notion of integrated STEM education for pre-service science teachers based on the inputs provided by in-service and pre-service teachers. This study strives to connect pre-service teacher education programs with in-service teachers' perspectives on integrated STEM education to translate the theory of connectivism used in this study.

Theoretical Framework

The researchers adopted the theory of connectivism (Siemens, 2005) in three different ways in this study. First, the notion of integrated STEM education strives for connections between STEM disciplines than the separation of each discipline (Stohlmann et al., 2011). Siemens (2005) mentioned one principle of connectivism, which is the ability of learners to connect different disciplines (e.g., STEM) as the primary skill. Pre-service science teachers are learners of integrated STEM because the notion is relatively very new to many of them. Furthermore, typical pre-service teacher education programs do not prepare them with essential integrated STEM pedagogical and curricula knowledge and skills (Erdogan & Ciftci, 2017; Pimthong & Williams, 2018; Radloff & Guzey, 2017; Ryu et al., 2019). Hence, reforms of curricula and teaching and learning are central in pre-service teacher education programs to prepare them to teach integrated STEM.

However, reforming the pre-service science teacher education programs need to connect with the needs, situations, and context of the schools, because pre-service teachers will eventually teach in real settings after completing their TEP. The perspectives of in-service teachers are valuable because they can inform the strategies, benefits, and challenges in conducting integrated STEM education in schools from a more practical point of view. Thus, the research methodology was oriented toward collecting and analyzing diverse views on STEM education stated by the in-service science teachers. Knowing and learning diverse opinions (e.g., perspectives on STEM) (Siemens, 2005) is applicable in this study. Besides, the inclusion of one government official is relevant for this study to connect pre-service teachers with the ministry's current plans for integrated STEM education. Connecting both parties is especially relevant in Malaysia which practices a highly centralized education system that gives the

Ministry of Education huge power to determine the educational direction of the nation.

Further, the action to reform curricula of pre-service teacher education programs needs to connect with pre-service teachers, especially when they are the first generation of teachers that will experience integrated STEM education. Connecting with them will ensure the curricula reforms could inform the pre-service teachers on the notion of integrated STEM education.

In this study, the authors adopted the perspective of integrated STEM as teaching and learning that combine two or three disciplines of STEM, such as science and technology (Bybee, 2013). The illustration is seen in Fig. 9.1 for the integration of two STEM disciplines: science and technology.

Many STEM perspectives are available (Bybee, 2013) and they should be explored in order to connect possible diverse opinions on STEM education stated by different researchers. Some key questions were explored. How do the research participants conceptualize integrated STEM education? How do they see the benefits of preparing pre-service teachers with integrated STEM education, particularly curricula and teaching? What are the possible challenges in implementing integrated STEM education in real classroom settings? The answers to the questions could equip pre-service teachers with crucial preparations before teaching integrated STEM in schools.

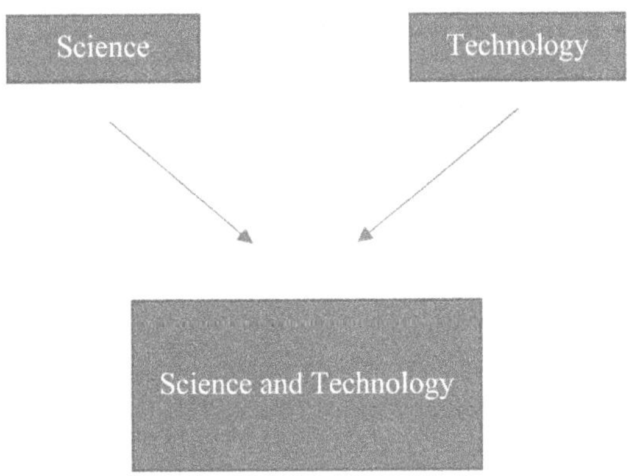

Fig. 9.1 Illustration of the STEM perspective used in the study. (Adapted from Bybee, 2013)

Methodology

National Context

Science teacher education in Malaysia is closely connected with the reforms of the national science curriculum (Mahmud et al., 2018) since the education system is highly centralized and standardized nationwide. In 2018, the Ministry of Education (2018) launched the new curricula of science (physics, chemistry) which were required to be used by all schools in Malaysia by 2020. The ministry fully determines what science contents are covered in the national science curricula. Science teachers are required to teach using the national science curricula because the questions in the national examination of science (physics, chemistry) are constructed based on the scope of the national curricula. The national physics and chemistry exams must be taken by science students at the end of their high school education. The new science curricula emphasize the use of integrated STEM education approaches such as project-based learning and contextual learning (Ministry of Education, 2018, p. 22). In terms of teaching and learning science, teachers are given the freedom to practice relevant teaching approaches. However, the ministry highly recommends science teachers teach using the approaches stated in the national curricula (e.g., project-based learning and contextual learning).

Teacher Education Program Context

The educational setting of the country also paves the design of pre-service science teacher education programs (PS-STEP). The programs should prepare future science teachers to teach according to the national curricula requirement and recommendations. As the national science curricula have promoted the notion of integrated STEM education approaches, teacher educators of the PS-STEP should educate pre-service teachers with such new approaches to teaching and learning science.

In 2017, a group of teacher educators in one public research university in Malaysia, Universiti Teknologi Malaysia (UTM) was tasked to form new curricula for PS-STEP. The main motivation was to start a new type of PS-STEP that emphasized elements of information and communication technology (ICT) because the university focuses on the technological elements in education and research. The university has a philosophy that strives for excellence in science, technology, and engineering for the nation and the globe (Universiti Teknologi Malaysia, 2021). Consequently, the PS-STEP in the university should comply with the university's philosophy. In October 2020, a new, first cohort of students of the PS-STEP in the university started their programs. The curricula of the PS-STEP focus on preparing future science teachers with a STEM approach, largely on the use of ICT in teaching and learning science (physics, chemistry). The use of ICT seems to fit with the theory of connectivism where ICT becomes the tool for connecting learners (pre-service teachers) and the STEM disciplines (Bybee, 2013).

This study was conducted in the setting of university-based teacher education programs. Specifically, it was carried out on two teacher education programs in the UTM School of Education, in Johor Bahru, Johor, Malaysia (the main campus). The two teacher education programs are physics and chemistry education (science education). The programs are offered for four-year of studies (typically eight semesters). They include learning various educational courses such as methods of teaching physics and chemistry, the curriculum of science and mathematics, pure physics and chemistry courses, general educational courses (pedagogy, psychology of education, etc.), general university courses (civilization, ethnic relations, etc.), and elective courses. However, ICT courses are given emphasis to fulfill the demands of the faculty and the university. Besides, the pre-service science teachers in the university are not required to take the Integrated STEM Education course because it is just an elective course, not a core course required to take. Elective means the pre-service teachers may or may not choose the course as their subject to learn in a particular semester.

Integrated STEM Education Course

A new course is to be offered for pre-service science teachers in the university called Integrated STEM Education, starting in October 2022, in the third year of the pre-service teachers' studies for a full semester (14 weeks of lecture). It is planned to be an elective course. Offering the course as an elective could indicate the pre-service science teachers' initial acceptance of that new course. Since it is a new course, the contents (and approach of teaching) are open to any relevant input. Some inputs could be found in the literature on integrated STEM education, such as using engineering design to integrate science and mathematics (e.g., Ng et al., 2020). Yet, to make the course more relevant to the recent needs in schools, inputs from in-service teachers and relevant parties are also crucial. This study is to gather those valuable inputs to know the suitable content that can be included in the new course.

Research Paradigm and Approach

The research paradigm adopted in this study is an interpretive paradigm. Subjectivism becomes the core of this study because it seeks multiple perspectives on integrated STEM from multiple individuals who have different backgrounds and roles in STEM education. The researchers carefully documented the national and pre-service teacher education program contexts that shape the research findings (Taylor, 2014).

The key research approach of this study is qualitative research (Taylor, 2014). Qualitative research is appropriate because it describes the meaning given by research participants on the (multiple) perspectives of integrated STEM education and on how they could inform pre-service science teacher education programs (PS-STEP).

Research Participant

A total number of 25 participants were involved in the study. Three of them were: (1) a government official and (2) two in-service science teachers. Another 22 participants were pre-service physics and chemistry teachers in the PS-STEP.

The government official (Dr. Aishah, pseudonym) is a person who coordinates the STEM initiatives of the nation at the ministerial level. Dr. Aishah was a mathematics teacher and has a PhD in mathematics education from a university in Malaysia. As a government official, she coordinates STEM initiatives for schools. She regularly acts as the person who provides training for in-service teachers regarding integrated STEM education. She was selected as the research participant primarily because she could provide input on the national direction of integrated STEM education and she was a highly experienced mathematics teacher. However, her views did not necessarily represent the ministry's official statement.

The two in-service teachers, Mrs. Alia and Mr. Chua (pseudonym) have academic qualifications in biology education (Mrs. Alia) and physics education (Mr. Chua). They both are science teachers recognized by the Ministry of Education as "excellent teachers" due to their outstanding teaching services. They have taught in schools for more than 15 years and are highly experienced teachers. The main reason for their selection as research participants was their status as excellent teachers who could be exemplary teachers for pre-service teachers.

A total number of 22 pre-service physics and chemistry teachers in the PS-STEP were involved in this study, too. Their involvement was more as the participants in an engagement session that the researchers conducted with them on January 29, 2022. They were exposed to the perspectives and approaches of integrated STEM education by the researchers based on the data provided by the three research participants.

Methods of Data Collection and Analysis

The steps of collecting and analyzing data were as follows. First, all three (3) participants (the government official and the two in-service science teachers) were contacted to inform them about including them in the study. The purpose of the study was told to them. They were invited to participate in this study to which all of them agreed.

Second, interviews with the two teachers were conducted in mid-January 2022. The Google Meet online platform was used for the interview. The sessions were conducted in around 40 minutes and were recorded. The interview questions focused on the participants' perspectives on integrated STEM education definition, challenges and opportunities of practicing integrated STEM approaches, and their views on bringing integrated STEM education to pre-service teachers.

Unfortunately, the government official could not be interviewed due to her tight schedule of work. Instead, she provided written answers to the interview questions as a replacement. Her written answers represented her views and perspectives on integrated STEM education, largely for pre-service science teacher education programs.

Third, data were analyzed to search for the meaning of integrated STEM across the three participants. The common perspective regarding integrated STEM education definition was focused. Besides, common challenges and opportunities for practicing integrated STEM approaches were also found. Their common perspectives on integrated STEM education for the PS-STEP were also discovered. The primary analysis strategy was theming the data (Creswell, 2013) and adopting a holistic style of coding rather than a detailed style.

A cross-case analysis of the data collected was performed. The information gained from the three participants was compared and connected to determine the similarities across each of them. Similar points of view were emphasized because they indicated the strengths of the findings across the research participants. The data from each participant were valued because each of them had the credibility to speak about STEM education.

Then, the data gained from the three research participants were used as the inputs for an engagement session with a number of 22 pre-service science teachers. The session informed the pre-service teachers about integrated STEM education (the needs, benefits, and challenges). The session was to connect inputs from the research participants with the pre-service science teachers. The researchers were the speakers of the session. The session was conducted for almost 40 minutes. The pre-service teachers provided feedback for the engagement session and their feedback was recorded in the materials of the engagement session.

Later, the materials used during the session, including the pre-service teachers' feedback, were shared with the pre-service teachers after the engagement session ended. This action ensured they received important information from the session and would not miss any crucial points.

Findings

Perspectives of STEM Education

The participants showed little variation regarding perspectives on STEM. Many of them thought that integrated STEM is the integration of at least two STEM subjects. The first participant, Dr. Aishah, had the following STEM perspective.

> Integrated STEM is the interconnection between four disciplines of STEM (Science, Technology, Engineering, and Mathematics). In terms of teaching and learning, integrated STEM may combine two or more STEM subjects into the experience of learning (at schools). Besides, integrated STEM education can link scientific inquiry, by formulating questions answered through investigation to inform students, before they engage in the engineering design process to solve problems.

The second participant, Mr. Chua, had a similar perspective of STEM to the first participant, Dr. Aishah. The third participant, Mrs. Alia, had the following perspective on STEM.

> Integrated STEM is an integration of at least two subjects of STEM. We do the integration because we want to prepare students for the current workforce needs. Now, the fourth Industrial Revolution era emphasizes technology and production. I am confident that if students are exposed to integrated STEM, we can prepare students with the needs of the current workforce.

From the data, the participants generally had the perspective that integrated STEM is the integration/connection of two STEM subjects or more. None of them mentioned that STEM is a separation of STEM disciplines. To this extent, the baseline perspective of STEM would be the integration/connection of two STEM disciplines (e.g., science and engineering).

The Most Suitable Subject(s) for Connecting STEM Disciplines

Dr. Aishah thought that no clear subject could be the connector for integrated STEM education. However, she mentioned that:

> Engineering is not the connector itself, but it can be a good choice of connector since engineering itself is not offered as a special subject to all students. Teaching through the engineering design process is one approach to integrating the subjects using a project-based approach that requires students to apply content knowledge to solve problems.

Besides, Dr. Aishah did not think that science, mathematics, and technology could be the connector for integrated STEM because science itself is a robust discipline and will overrule integrated STEM. In contrast, mathematics is a tool to stimulate mathematical thinking and concept. For technology, Dr. Aishah stated that not all STEM activities require technology.

Another participant, Mr. Chua, thought that engineering could be the connector for science, mathematics, and technology because he deemed that engineering can bridge science and mathematics concepts to produce technology. He mentioned that:

> Engineering is a process that connects science, mathematics, and technology. Without engineering, applications of science and mathematics cannot take place. For example, we produce an airplane. We need engineering to produce the airplane. The application of science and mathematics is necessary to produce the airplane."

On the other hand, Mrs. Alia had a different point of view. She believed that physics was the primary connector for integrated STEM. Even though she is a biology and science teacher and did not teach physics, she needed to know physics concepts and applications when doing integrated STEM projects with her students. For instance, doing robotics projects with her students truly motivated her to learn physics. She said that many physics concepts were applied when doing STEM projects with her students, especially when the students were involved in competitions at the national level, such as robotic competitions.

Overall, two possible connectors for integrated STEM were found: engineering and/or physics. As mentioned by two participants (Dr. Aishah and Mr. Chua), engineering is thought the suitable connector because it can be the process that links science and mathematics concepts to produce the outcome, which is technology. Mrs. Alia, on the contrary, thought of physics as the connector for integrated STEM. However, engineering appears to be a stronger connector because it can integrate science and mathematics to produce technologies.

Benefits and Challenges of Integrated STEM Education for Pre-service Science Teachers

This study surveyed the benefits and challenges of exposing integrated STEM education to pre-service science teachers.

Benefits

For Dr. Aishah, she thought that integrated STEM curricula for pre-service teachers could ultimately help school students to get relevant skills and knowledge for future careers. It can be done by preparing pre-service teachers with integrated STEM curricula and emphasizing the importance of integrated STEM. According to Dr. Aishah, the current era is the fourth industrial revolution, which requires different ways of educating pre-service teachers. They need to be well equipped with the necessary knowledge and skills of integrated STEM to teach school students after graduating from the pre-service teacher education programs. A similar thought was found in the case of Mrs. Alia. Additionally, Mrs. Alia thought that exposing pre-service teachers to integrated STEM is a "bonus" because she, as an in-service teacher, needs to learn to teach with integrated STEM approaches by herself. Mrs. Alia had no exposure to integrated STEM during her teacher education program.

Mr. Chua had a similar perspective to Mrs. Alia in admitting that many in-service teachers had no exposure to integrated STEM when they were pre-service teachers. No mention of integrated STEM had taken place during the past era. With the release and use of new national science curricula in 2018, the action to prepare pre-service teachers with integrated STEM is appropriate because the new curricula emphasize the idea of integrated STEM. A new, transformative mindset regarding integrated STEM could be shaped among pre-service teachers to teach using the integrated approaches when they become in-service teachers. By exposing them to integrated STEM, they can transform the landscape of science education to a new level when they teach at schools after completing teacher education programs.

All participants supported the idea of exposing pre-service science teachers to integrated STEM. The critical point is to prepare them with integrated STEM and to implement the approaches when they become in-service teachers. The current pre-service teachers are the new generation of teachers who could be able to implement integrated STEM approaches if sufficient exposure is made to them.

Challenges

Exposing pre-service teachers to integrated STEM is not without challenges. The participants suggested several challenges that need proper solutions. For Dr. Aishah, many in-service teachers have no expertise in many STEM subjects. If pre-service teachers are exposed to integrated STEM, they need to know other STEM subjects besides their subject specialization (e.g., chemistry or general science). Connections between STEM subjects must be made. She added that implementing integrated STEM in actual teaching settings in schools is challenging due to teachers' time constraints. Pre-service teachers would need to be exposed to integrated STEM curricula and teaching that would be workable for them and the school students. Additionally, Dr. Aishah mentioned that insufficient materials for integrated STEM were available in schools. Pre-service teachers would need to develop teaching materials by themselves using integrated STEM approaches. Knowledge and skills in developing educational materials are necessary for pre-service teachers.

For Mrs. Alia, as an in-service teacher, she had faced challenges in implementing integrated STEM teaching. She mentioned the old science curricula that placed little value on integrated STEM. However, with the use of the new science curricula since 2018, she thought that the implementation challenges had been reduced because the new curricula support and encourage integrated STEM approaches. The new curricula recommend that science teachers implement project-based learning or teaching approaches that could integrate STEM subjects.

For Mr. Chua, he was concerned that the current pre-service teachers were taught using the old science curricula when they were secondary school students. Besides, when they were school students, the current pre-service teachers were taught using traditional teaching approaches, especially exam-oriented teaching practice. Their experience might influence their ways of thinking about STEM education. Exposing them to integrated STEM, which is different from the traditional educational approaches, might confuse pre-service teachers. Reorienting their minds with new transformational educational approaches, especially integrated STEM, is critical to ensure they would accept integrated STEM and adopt the approaches in actual teaching and learning.

Overall, all the challenges mentioned are to take into account to ensure pre-service teachers are well prepared with integrated STEM approaches before completing their studies in the teacher education programs. Those inputs are valuable to inform the relevant content for the course of Integrated STEM Education.

Engagement with Physics and Chemistry Pre-service Teachers

An engagement session with the pre-service science teachers was carried out with the aim to connect the research findings from the three persons with the pre-service teachers. The session was conducted using an online platform, Google Meet. A number of 22 pre-service teachers participated in the online engagement session. The information shared with them is based on the questions stated as follows.

1. Why is integrated STEM education needed?
2. What is the common perspective of integrated STEM?
3. What are the benefits of learning (as pre-service teachers) to teach using integrated STEM approaches?
4. What are the challenges of making integrated STEM approaches?

Additionally, the researchers informed the pre-service teachers about a new course offering, Integrated STEM education, in the next semester (in October 2022) as an elective course.

During the engagement session, the pre-service teachers provided valuable feedback to the researchers. Many of them expressed their interest by stating that the new course offered looked interesting and would like to enroll in the course. Yet, the students expressed some concerns. One of them asked about the credit hour by asking:

> "If we take the new course, the total credit hours of our academic program will be higher than usual. Is the course compulsory to take?" The researchers replied that the new course will not provide extra credit hours to the students because the current academic plan already allocated two credit hours for an elective course. Since the new course is elective, it is not compulsory for the students to enroll because they can select other elective courses offered in a semester.

Another student expressed her concern regarding the problem of group tasks. Based on her experience, she did not get good cooperation among team members in the courses she enrolled in previously. She said that:

> Based on my experience, many team members did not really do their work and ended up only a student completed the group task. Can we select our group members?

The researchers replied by saying that the instructor of the new course will take into account the issue of group tasks as mentioned by the student. The students may be given an opportunity to select their group members, but this particular issue will be discussed with the students who enroll in the course in October 2022.

Overall, the pre-service teachers expressed their interests and concerns regarding the new course offering. Their concerns will be taken into account before the course is offered in the future, such as the freedom to choose group members for the group assignments/projects. However, they did not ask questions about concepts or needs for integrated STEM, probably because integrated STEM is new to them and they most likely learned the notion for the first time in this session.

Discussion, Limitation, and Conclusion

Contributions to the Literature

This study managed to enrich the literature in terms of directly connecting inputs or data from the in-service science teachers and the government official to pre-service science teachers. Typical studies in the literature did not include various parties as their research participants. Usually, one party's perspective was investigated, such as pre-service teachers (e.g., Pimthong & Williams, 2018; Radloff & Guzey, 2017) or in-service teachers only (Roehrig et al., 2012; Hackman et al., 2021). Rarely two or more parties were involved in a single study on integrated STEM education.

The key contribution of this study to the literature is mainly the methodology adopted. Collecting and connecting data from and with various parties will allow a holistic understanding of strategies and steps to empower pre-service teachers with integrated STEM approaches. The typical studies did not adopt this kind of research methodology. Perhaps, from now onward, scholars and researchers will imitate this type of research methodology, which is directly connecting research on in-service science teachers with pre-service teachers.

Contribution to the STEM Teacher Education Practice

Many research participants believed that engineering is a suitable connector for science and mathematics concepts. Their views align with the literature by Bybee (2013) and Ng et al. (2020). The implication is that pre-service teachers will need to be exposed to engineering, particularly engineering design approaches. Many scholars have also mentioned the importance of engineering design approaches as an integral component of integrated STEM education (Bryan et al., 2016; Moore et al., 2016). Thus, teaching pre-service teachers about engineering design approaches might allow them to design and conduct integrated STEM projects systematically.

For the new course of Integrated STEM education, the data gained from this study is valuable to inform the formulation of the core components of the course. As the course is very new and was never offered to students before, it needs to include data from the research participants to enrich the course with relevant and significant content for pre-service science teachers' learning. The suggested points are:

1. Teach the pre-service science teachers about engineering design approaches to expose them to the key pedagogy of integrated STEM. Teaching engineering design will train the students to integrate science with other STEM disciplines, such as mathematics. This suggestion mainly came from the views of the in-service teachers and the government official.
2. When assigning group tasks, the instructor should consider giving students the freedom to choose team members. Discussion with students should be made before asking them to start doing group projects. This suggestion mainly came from pre-service teachers' points of view during the engagement session with them.

As the course of Integrated STEM education is very new for the academic program at the university, the structure and content of the course will be designed according to the inputs gained from the study conducted.

Conclusion

The general understanding around the globe is that integrated STEM education is not well placed in teacher education programs. Offering a new course, titled Integrated STEM Education, in particular, will ensure pre-service science teachers are exposed to the new approach to teaching and learning science. Connectivism is one particular theory that helps frame this whole study. Connecting pre-service teachers with data provided by external parties is central because pre-service science teachers will be able to understand the actual scenario of integrated STEM in real settings in schools from the views of in-service teachers. This effort will ensure the sustainability of the integrated STEM education agenda.

References

Bryan, L., Moore, T., Johnson, C., & Roehrig, G. (2016). Integrated STEM education. In C. Johnson, E. Peters-Burton, & T. Moore (Eds.), *STEM road map: A framework for integrated STEM education* (pp. 23–37). Routledge.

Bybee, R. W. (2013). *The case for STEM education: Challenges and opportunities*. NSTA Press.

Creswell, J. (2013). *Qualitative inquiry and research design: Choosing among five approaches* (3rd ed.). Sage.

Erdogan, I., & Ciftci, A. (2017). Investigating the views of pre-service science teachers on STEM education practices. *International Journal of Environmental and Science Education, 12*(5), 1055–1065.

Hackman, S. T., Zhang, D., & He, J. (2021). Secondary school science teachers' attitudes towards STEM education in Liberia. *International Journal of Science Education, 43*(2), 223–246.

Koehler, C., Binns, I., & Bloom, M. (2016). The emergence of STEM. In C. Johnson, E. Peters-Burton, & T. Moore (Eds.), *STEM road map: A framework for integrated STEM education* (pp. 13–22). Routledge.

Mahmud, S. N. D., Nasri, N. M., Samsudin, M. A., & Halim, L. (2018). Science teacher education in Malaysia: Challenges and way forward. *Asia-Pacific Science Education, 4*(1), 1–12.

Ministry of Education. (2018). *Physics: Standard curriculum of secondary schools*. Ministry of Education of Malaysia.

Moore, T., Johnson, C., Peters-Burton, E., & Guzey, S. (2016). The need for a STEM road map. In C. Johnson, E. Peters-Burton, & T. Moore (Eds.), *STEM road map: A framework for integrated STEM education* (pp. 3–12). Routledge.

Ng, H. G., Bunyamin, M. A. H., & Khamis, N. (2020). Perspectives of STEM education from physics teachers' points of view: A quantitative study. *Universal Journal of Educational Research, 8*(11C), 72–82.

Pimthong, P., & Williams, J. (2018). Pre-service teachers' understanding of STEM education. *Kasetsart Journal of Social Sciences, 40*, 1–7.

Radloff, J., & Guzey, S. (2017). Investigating changes in pre-service teachers' conceptions of STEM education following video analysis and reflection. *School Science and Mathematics, 117*(3–4), 158–167.

Roehrig, G. H., Moore, T. J., Wang, H. H., & Park, M. S. (2012). Is adding the E enough? Investigating the impact of K-12 engineering standards on the implementation of STEM integration. *School Science and Mathematics, 112*(1), 31–44.

Ryu, M., Mentzer, N., & Knobloch, N. (2019). Pre-service teachers' experiences of STEM integration: Challenges and implications for integrated STEM teacher preparation. *International Journal of Technology and Design Education, 29*(3), 493–512.

Siemens, G. (2005, January 1). *Connectivism: A learning theory for the digital age*. International Journal of Instructional Technology and Distance Learning. http://www.itdl.org/Journal/Jan_05/article01.htm

Stohlmann, M., Moore, T. J., McClelland, J., & Roehrig, G. H. (2011). Impressions of a middle grades STEM integration program: Educators share lessons learned from the implementation of a middle grades STEM curriculum model. *Middle School Journal, 43*(1), 32–40.

Taylor, P. C. (2014). Contemporary qualitative research: Toward an integral research perspective. In N. G. Lederman & S. K. Abell (Eds.), *Handbook of research on science education volume II* (pp. 38–54). Routledge.

Universiti Teknologi Malaysia. (2021). Vision & Mission. https://www.utm.my/about/vision-mission/

CHAPTER 10

Science Teacher Preparation in Oman: Strengths and Shortcomings Related to STEM Education

Mohamed A. Shahat and Mohammed Al Amri

Introduction

Historical Overview of the Science Teacher Preparation in Oman

Science education has been targeted as an important specialization for student teachers. Male and Female Secondary Teacher Institutes (MFSTI) were established in 1977–1978 (Al-Salmi, 2001), and they originally accepted students who had completed middle school (grade 9). The study

M. A. Shahat (✉)
College of Education, Sultan Qaboos University, Muscat, Oman

Faculty of Education, Aswan University, Aswan, Egypt
e-mail: m.shahat@squ.edu.om

M. Al Amri
College of Education, Sultan Qaboos University, Muscat, Oman
e-mail: mhalamri@squ.edu.om

S. M. Al-Balushi et al. (eds.), *Reforming Science Teacher Education Programs in the STEM Era*, Palgrave Studies on Leadership and Learning in Teacher Education,
https://doi.org/10.1007/978-3-031-27334-6_10

period was three years, after which, students received a certificate in primary school teaching. The study system was based on a system of general studies in teacher education in many different subjects (Al-Amri, 2005, 2015).

These institutes were later upgraded, and in the academic year 1984–1985 they became Intermediate Teacher Training Colleges (ITTC), whose students were secondary school graduates (completed grade 12) aiming to become primary school teachers. The length of the course was two years with four semesters, and at the end of their study, students received a diploma in primary school teaching (Al-Amri, 2005). Teachers trained how to teach all school subjects; science specialists studied science as a major and other teacher education candidates studied science as a minor. Under the ITTC system, science education was established as an area for specialization in primary school education. According to Al-Salmi (1994), there were nine Intermediate Teacher Training Colleges (ITTC) beginning in 1984, four for females and five for males.

Just as with other disciplines, the science teacher preparation program at ITTC was designed to prepare trainee teachers to teach all of the school curricula in the first three primary grades (1–3) and to specialize in one area, such as science education or another specialist subject, in the upper three primary grades (4–6) (Al-Salmi, 2001).

The ITTCs used the Competency-Based Teacher Education (CBTE) approach and prepared primary science teachers through college-based teaching and school-based training. Science student-teachers had to attend a range of classes tailored to prepare them for classroom teaching. ITTC graduates were expected to complete 75 credit hours in total for their whole degree. According to the Ministry of Education (1985), learning modules were distributed across four semesters. The study program at ITTC was divided into five domains of study: (1) General Culture Requirements, (2) Practical Studies and Activities, (3) Professional Education, (4) Primary Education Specialization, and (5) Academic specialization (Al-Amri, 2005, 2015).

In the science academic specialization, student teachers studied 21 credit hours of courses: Introduction to Chemistry 3, Cells, Biology of Living Organisms, Electromagnetism and Modern Electrons, General Chemistry, Mechanics and Wave Phenomena, Astronomy, and Geology. Each specialist course counted towards three credit hours (Ministry of Education, 1992).

Al-Salmi (2001) mentioned three shortcomings of the ITTC programs for training primary science teachers:

1. The standard of students accepted into these programs in the first (primary) and second (intermediate) stages was inappropriate for the teaching profession.
2. The length of the programs was insufficient for training student teachers to an acceptable level.
3. The subjects taught in the program were unsuitable for training primary school teachers. (p.91)

As a result of these shortcomings, in 1995, the ITTCs were further upgraded and became Colleges of Education which granted university degrees in education. In the same year, the responsibility for their operation was transferred to the Ministry of Higher Education (Ministry of Information, 2000). Science teacher programs were available in these colleges throughout the country, including the one at SQU.

The science teacher education program first began at the bachelor's level upon the establishment of SQU in 1986. The first batch of teachers from all specializations accepted into the college of education consisted of 250 students in total, who graduated on October 30, 1990. The first cohort of the science teacher program was 30 students (8 males and 22 females). According to Ambusaidi and Al-Shuaili (2009), the college of education was one of the first colleges in the university. It started by offering six specializations, including science education. The college's stated goals were to "(1) prepare teachers to work in public schools, mainly in upper primary, preparatory and post-basic schools (i.e., the second cycle of basic education [Grades 5–10] and post-basic schools [Grades 11 and 12]), (2) serve the local community by organizing lectures, workshops, seminars, and other related cultural and educational activities, and (3) conduct research related to educational issues to improve quality of teaching, learning, and assessment" (p. 215).

In 2016, the science teacher education program at SQU was recognized by the National Science Teachers Association (NSTA) and accredited by the National Council for Accreditation of Teacher Education (NCATE), which is now known as the Council for the Accreditation of Educator Preparation (CAEP). This accreditation has meant that the science teacher program in Oman has adopted an international quality standard based on new trends in the discipline; this has resulted in improvement in the quality of teaching and learning of science in Omani schools according to the recent Trends in International Mathematics and Science Study (TIMSS) international assessment results in 2019 (Mullis et al., 2020).

Structure of the Science Teacher Education Program at SQU

Purpose of the Program

The science teacher program at SQU follows the College of Education's conceptual framework, which focuses on five main themes. They are knowledge and specialization experience, diversified teaching and developmental experience, values, research culture, and technological skills. The bachelor's program in science teacher education aims to produce science teachers who have sufficient scientific knowledge to teach effectively. These teachers are qualified to teach general sciences in basic education schools (grades 1–8) and biology, physics, and chemistry in post-basic education schools (grades 9–12). Science teacher preparation programs in Oman have their own characteristics depending on whether they are offered in public or private universities (Ohle-Peters et al., 2022).

Requirements for Faculty

Faculty members at the College of Education are required to have the necessary qualifications to train Oman's future teachers. Teaching effectiveness is measured according to Omani Authority for Academic Accreditation (OAAA) standards and the quality of education is monitored by the Omani Ministry of Education.

Admission Requirements

Students can enroll in a teacher preparation program if they completed a general high school diploma (Al-Malki, 2017). The teacher training program has precise mechanisms to ensure the correct placement of students; these include a specialized test and an interview to evaluate a student teacher's cognitive competency and orientation towards teaching. This process allows promising high school graduates with general diplomas to have access to this teacher training program. Usually, graduates joining the program have excellent academic records (i.e., 90%+). A central admission office selects candidates to join the programs. Successful candidates typically have a very good high school record (grade B+) in their science subjects (biology, chemistry, and physics) and mathematics. Admission is granted after a personal interview to verify the motivation of applicants for entering the teaching profession and to determine their ability to meet the program's requirements for graduation. Students must also pass an intensive English language program before starting the credit courses. The science teachers' program at SQU is designed to be completed in 4 years (8 semesters) (Al Barwani & Bailey, 2016).

The courses that student teachers have already completed are considered in determining the distribution of required credit hours on the three main components (educational, specialized, and cultural) of the program. This distribution must fit into the following percentages for the three parts: 50–60% for the specialized science component, 25–30% for the educational component, and the cultural component must make up 5–10% of the total credit hours for the program. If the courses are divided into three parts among various departments, there must be precise coordination mechanisms (Public and Private universities in Oman, 2021). Over the whole course at least 350 hours of training are provided either continuously over one semester or distributed over more than one semester (Al Barwani & Bailey, 2016). An academic study plan consists of 125 credit hours, consisting of 6 hours of University Requirements (UR), 89 credit hours of Major Requirements (MR), 24 hours of departmental requirements, and six credit hours of university electives. To continue with the program's study plan and choose a major, a candidate must obtain a minimum GPA of 2.00 (C grade) in three of the following four first-year courses: mathematics, physics, chemistry, and biology.

Furthermore, the candidate must obtain at minimum of a C grade in the compulsory English language course. The part of the program that is offered by the College of Science at SQU provides the candidates with specialized scientific knowledge and a deep understanding of the inquiry-based nature of science. In addition, professional preparation at the College of Education enables students to gain practical experience as teachers. As far as the academic component of the teacher training program is concerned, different faculties coordinate to teach students the Cambridge science curricula, which are currently implemented in Omani schools. Hence, these courses cover science, mathematics, technology, psychology, and educational theory and leadership in an integrated way.

There is also a parallel program called the Teacher Qualification Diploma (TQD). The TQD program aims to train university graduates to become teachers over two semesters after receiving their BSc from arts, science, and technical colleges. This diploma program focuses on classes covering pedagogical knowledge, and field training in public schools (Ohle-Peters et al., 2022).

Design of Science Teacher Education Programs to Change to STEM-based Instruction

Cycle One (Grade 1–4) teacher education is only for female teachers, as all Cycle One teachers are female. These programs strongly emphasize pedagogy and only around 30% of the curriculum is devoted to the instructors' specializations (e.g., mathematics, Science, English, or the humanities). Cycle Two teacher programs (grade 5–10) place more emphasis on subject matter (Council of Education Oman, 2017). During the teacher training program at SQU, the student teacher undergoes field training at a real school during which they put into practice the teaching skills and theory they learned about in lectures (Shahat et al., 2022a).

Starting in 2019, cohorts have had some courses related to practical teaching such as Science Teaching Methods 1 and Science Teaching Methods 2. Candidates are expected to train at a school for four weeks (4 hours a week) in the former, whereas they attend eight weeks (4 hours a week) in the latter. In total, they will obtain 48 hours of pre-service classroom experience. In addition, each major has its own specialized content course, which requires six field experience hours (one visit per week for two weeks) (College of Education at SQU, 2021).

The study plan also consists of three courses (educational psychology, counseling psychology, and psychological measurement and evaluation), which, combined, total 20 hours. Additionally, service courses from the foundation of education and the department of psychology offer courses that include classroom teaching experiences for candidates. Since 2018, the evaluation of candidates' teaching practice has improved through the use of portfolios. The assessment is now based on the candidate's portfolios which are designed to help them reflect on their achievement and accumulated experience from the beginning of their enrolment in the teacher preparation program. This portfolio is assessed at the end of the teaching practicum. As for the formative assessment process during the practicum, the supervisor and cooperating teacher are required to evaluate candidates based on a classroom evaluation form and provide them feedback on their teaching performance (College of Education at SQU, 2021).

In the recently approved degree plan from 2019 onwards, a professional practice course has been added to all major degrees to support candidates' field experience. This course is offered to candidates in semester 9 and aims to prepare the candidate for the reality of their professional life in its various dimensions by providing practical experiences based on the college's conceptual framework. Candidates spend a full day (6 hours) in a school each week for the whole semester (15 weeks). In total, they will undertake 90 hours of professional practice courses (Al-Busaidi, 2019).

Content Knowledge and Pedagogical Knowledge

The 27 major based science courses are taught by the physics, chemistry, and biology departments at the College of Science. These courses are based on unit plans, which are descriptions and content analysis of a single unit of study from one science book in the Oman curriculum. Students must study and analyze a unit of their choice (taken from Grades 5–10) and present the results as a written project and oral presentation; this assessment has proven effective at measuring candidates' knowledge, skills, and dispositions. The Teaching Practice Observation form reports on a student teacher's performance, highlighting areas of strength and areas for improvement. The scoring rubric means that both student and supervisor can easily see where a student is performing in relation to the expected standards. All of the above-mentioned assessments meet the Science Teacher Education Standards by NSTA, which focus on science content, unit plans, student teaching evaluations, and professional development.

Recent data collected by the College of Education in 2020 and 2021 have revealed that science teacher education candidates are relatively successful in their major courses (e.g., general biology, physics, chemistry, calculus) with an overall mean of 2.76 out of 4 in 2020 and 2.61 out of 4 in 2021. Candidates are also performing well in planning active inquiry lessons; and using various teaching methods, assessments, and inquiry approaches. Their mean scores in these subjects were 3.13 out of 4 in 2020 and 3.20 out of 4 in 2021. Additionally, candidates performed very well in teaching students in schools, meeting most science teacher education standards (College of Education at SQU, 2021).

Teaching placement data analyses indicate that the ability of candidates to impact student learning in schools is very high. According to Shahat et al. (2022b), the SQU education program promotes STEM education by integrating STEM disciplines and having students examine the construction of a physical product that solves a human problem. Student teachers learn and apply the following steps involved in engineering design: (1) identifying a problem; (2) researching possible solutions; (3) picking the best solution; (4) building a prototype; (5) testing the prototype; and (6) repeating any steps needed to improve the design. An engineering design approach is not yet standard practice in many science classrooms in Oman; this may be partly due to science teachers lacking guidance or training in designing investigations in ways that facilitate hands-on student inquiry and critical learning (Shahat et al., 2022b). However, the engineering design approach is in line with the methods of teaching science in Omani schools that has been requested by the Ministry of education (Shahat et al., 2022b).

Effect on Student Learning

The authors of this chapter conducted a government-funded project at SQU to explore the differences in science teachers' self-efficacy beliefs in teaching science using an engineering design approach at SQU. The project revealed significant differences between students' personal self-efficacy beliefs in the two programs (BSc and Diploma) in favor of the BSc students, with a medium effect size on the whole scale $F(1,71) = 7.33$, $\rho < 0.05$, $\eta^2 = 0.09$. The results confirmed the continued high quality of the bachelor's program in the use of the engineering design approach to integrate the four STEM subjects (Shahat et al., 2022b). The authors also note that the knowledge, skills and experience acquired during their preparation program contributed to these high self-efficacy beliefs. One of the central courses in both the BSc and TQD programs is a science methods course, which exposes the teachers to the idea of teaching science through an engineering design approach. This science methods course discusses the different steps of the engineering design process (e.g., identifying the problem, planning solutions, finding the best solutions, production, and testing, communicating results, and improving solutions) when covering other science teaching methods and related topics such as inquiry-based learning, problem solving, STEM education, project-based learning, the science learning cycle, and Next Generation Science Standards (NGSS).

Students are also given the opportunity to plan and deliver a science lesson in the micro-teaching section of the science methods course. Each student must plan and teach a science lesson for 15–20 minutes to their peers and then reflect on how to improve their performance. We argue that this direct exposure to planning and teaching a lesson through an engineering design approach enhanced the participants' self-efficacy beliefs and led to them considering their science teaching highly successful. The high levels of efficacy suggest that a high quality BSc program is in place at SQU, and this is confirmed by reports from NSTA (Shahat et al., 2022b). An examination of the content of the teaching methods courses at SQU also lends support to the notion of a quality program. Teacher trainers devote weeks to reading and discussing different topics related to STEM education and engineering design, and the related science and engineering practices in NGSS. Through the micro-teaching session, student teachers also have practice integrating the engineering design model and STEM education into the Omani national science curriculum. This integration practice is an important characteristic of STEM education and an engineering design approach to science teaching. Other data has confirmed the need to revise the science teacher preparation program's content and pedagogical content knowledge to be more focused on STEM education (Ambusaidi et al., 2022). There is a need for a new description of the content knowledge courses of the teacher preparation program that assures the integrity and consistency of (1) the STEM content taught to candidates, (2) their experiences in pre-service placements, and (3) the teaching methods courses (College of Education at SQU, 2021).

Clinical Experience

To ensure the science teacher program is more STEM education focused, school placements have been increased. The new program has extensive early school placements and an expanded student teaching experience. Student teaching is now five days a week (6 hours a day) for 15 weeks of the semester to allow for effective STEM integration. Students are given the opportunity to plan and teach science lessons during the supervised time at schools using inquiry-based learning, problem solving, STEM education, project-based learning, science learning cycle, and Next Generation Science Standards (NGSS). SQU is also currently designing a STEM postgraduate program for teachers and practitioners in science, mathematics, and technology education.

STEM OMAN Program in Omani Schools

According to the Ministry of Education (2021), the STEM Oman program was implemented in three main stages:

Stage 1 in 2017–2018
The program targeted 420 students from secondary school (Grade 10), 14 science teachers and supervisors, four schools from the Muscat Governorate, and two schools from the Governorates of Al Batinah South

and Al Dākhilīyah (Oman Observer, 2018). It included selecting six schools in governorates close to the Ministry's general office to facilitate the follow-up process and feedback. The program was given to the selected schools and implemented in one lesson per week during the second semester of the academic year for 13 weeks (Ministry of Education, 2021).

Stage 2 in 2018–2019

The trial STEM program was expanded to include a further 12 boys-only and girls-only schools for a total of 18 schools. The program teachers provided workshops and presentations for the participating teachers at the National Week for STEM sciences activities from 10 to14 March, 2019.

Stage 3 in 2019–2020

The process of expanding the implementation of the STEM OMAN program continued during the 2019/2020 academic year to include a further 12 separate boys and girls schools. They were selected from various educational directorates and added to the previous schools. A total of 30 schools participated from all governorates in Oman, and teachers in these schools participated in a STEM in Omani schools' science training program. Omani science teachers who were expert in STEM provided workshops and presentations as part of the STEM OMAN program in the Oman Science Festival 2019, which was held at the Oman Convention and Exhibition Centre from 4–8 November, 2019. They also presented a paper on the STEM program during a symposium at the same festival.

Training Programs Implemented by STEM OMAN

According to the Ministry of Education (2021), training programs (professional development workshops) have been provided by the Ministry of Education to prepare science teachers for the STEM OMAN program. These programs can be summarized as follows:

The Initial Training Program of the STEM OMAN Program

The Ministry of Education offered this training to provide participants with skills and experiences to enable them to start implementing the STEM OMAN program during the second semester of the 2017–2018 academic year. From 19–23 November, 2017, in conjunction with the British Rolls Royce Foundation, 12 male and female teachers from the schools assigned to implement the STEM OMAN program were invited to join. Also participating in the training were six experts, education supervisors, specialists from the Department of Innovation and Scientific Olympiad in the Ministry, and other members of the Innovation and Scientific Olympiad departments in the General Directorates (Ministry of Education, 2021).

Professional Overseas Training Program on STEM OMAN
The second STEM education training occurred at the STEM Centre at York University in the UK between April 30 and May 4, 2018. This external training program provided trainees with theoretical and practical STEM education skills, knowledge, and experiences. Fourteen male and female science teachers from various educational directorates were invited. The goal was to train them in more hands-on and technical matters relating to the implementation of the STEM OMAN program in Omani schools. The teachers who participated will be asked to train other teachers as experts in the STEM OMAN program, in line with the plan to expand the application of the program to the rest of the Omani schools (Ministry of Education, 2021).

The Second Stage STEM OMAN Training Program at the National Level
This training program was supervised by the British expert Mark Langley from the STEM Centre at York University in the UK (Ministry of Education, 2021). The program was implemented under the supervision of the Innovation Department and the Ministry of Education. It was carried out by national trainers who were qualified after attending the STEM OMAN external program for the training of trainers at York University, UK. The training period lasted five days, from 26–30 August 2018, at the Specialist Institute for the Professional Training of Teachers in Muscat. It targeted 22 science teachers (male and female) from the educational directorates applying to join the program, and the goal was to provide them with the skills and experiences to allow them to start implementing the STEM OMAN program in the twelve new schools. The program included 13 (grade 10) teaching lessons for subjects such as movement, power, and weights.

The Third Stage STEM OMAN Training Program at the National Level
This training workshop organized by the Ministry of Education targeted 20 male and female science teachers. It took place from 18 to 22 August

2019 at the Specialist Institute for Professional Training of Teachers in Muscat. Its aim was to provide science teachers with the skills and experiences to implement the STEM OMAN program in the twelve new schools in the third stage (Ministry of Education, 2021).

According to the Oman Observer (2019a), several papers on STEM education were presented by international scholars at the 2019 Oman Science Festival (Oman Observer, 2019a). The STEM OMAN training program was run as part of the festival and it outlined the overarching role of STEM in promoting teaching and learning science education. In 2021, the National Science Week STEM took place between 21 and 25 March 2021 as an online event due to the COVID-19 pandemic. The central theme for this national week was 'Our Sustainable Environment', and it ran for five consecutive days with morning and evening sessions every day (March 22, 2021a; Oman Observer, March 27, 2021b). Examples of topics covered in the National Science Week STEM are summarized in the following Table 10.1.

The Positives and Shortcomings of Science Teacher Education (STE) Regarding STEM Education

Positives

Specialized international organizations such as CAEP set and monitor the standards for the preparation of science teachers. In addition, all enrolled students in the science teacher program in Oman are qualified in STEM disciplines with high grades in their general diplomas. Furthermore, science teacher preparation programs teach many specialized courses that correspond to STEM related subjects, such as science, mathematics, technology, engineering, educational psychology, educational technology, active teaching methods, and qualitative methods in educational research; in these major and academic courses students are given assignments based mainly on scientific inquiry and engineering design projects.

Another positive aspect of SQU courses is that students apply what they have learned—both in terms of content and pedagogical knowledge—in courses, professional practice, and field training. For example, one of the compulsory courses in the BSc and TQD programs is a science methods course, which exposes teachers to the idea of teaching science through an engineering design approach. Furthermore, this science methods course discusses different engineering design processes when covering other

Table 10.1 Examples of topics covered in the National Science Week STEM (Oman Observer, March 22, 2021a; Oman Observer, March 27, 2021b)

First Day	*Second Day*	*Last day*
• Smart Shopping • Farming without Soil • Renewable Energy is the Best Choice for Environmental Sustainability • Plastic Waste Disposal • Methods for using Lab Equipment to Detect Food Safety • Falaj Alassarni Drought Turned into Tourist Environment • Green School initiative • Smart City Design • Food Security System • AI for Environmental Protection • Marine Pollution Control • Precision Instruments in Oil and Gas Fields and their impact on preserving the environment • The Green House • GLOBE Program's Environmental Impact	• Alternative Energy • Palm Waste Recycling • Weather Changes • Implementation of the Aquaculture System. • The Scientific Café • Malpractice towards the Environment. • Using Moths to Conserve the Environment. • Satellite Environmental Application. • Biodiversity	• Ras Al Jinz Turtle Reserve: An integrated ecosystem. • Air pollution • How do I make products from environmental waste? • Environmental photography skills. • Environmental compensation project for OQ8 Company • Simple ways to recycle waste to use it in our home, school, and community • Sustainability for waste resources. • How to transfer knowledge of the sustainable environment to the market • Peaceful unclear techniques in the fields of environment and agriculture • Eco 3D Environment • How do we reduce our carbon footprint? • Use of augmented reality technology to promote and teach environmental sustainability • Our sustainable environment and solar energy

science teaching methods and related topics such as inquiry-based learning, problem-solving, STEM education, project-based learning, science learning cycle, and Next Generation Science Standards (NGSS). Students are also allowed to plan and deliver a science lesson in the micro-teaching section of the science methods course whereby each student has to design and teach a science lesson for 15–20 minutes to their peers and then reflect on how to improve their performance. There is also a pre-service training course at schools for both BSc and TQD programs. In this course, students are required to plan and teach several science lessons at school over 15 weeks. Students implement different engineering design processes to teach various science topics in these lessons. The students also conduct actual research as an integrated part of field training in their BSc; and a separate course for the TQD students focuses on studying an educational phenomenon and then providing opinions and solutions regarding it while considering the steps of scientific research (Ambusaidi et al., 2022). Student teachers also practice the engineering design model and STEM education in the Omani national science curriculum in their teaching methods and field training courses. This integration of practice is essential to a STEM education and engineering design-based curriculum. The following is an example of integration in unit design that the student-teacher at SQU uses:

- Title of the Unit: Living Organisms in the Environment (Science Curriculum for Sixth Grade)
- Integration fields: Science, Mathematics, Art, Engineering
- Unit Concepts: Nutrition—Food Chains—Ecosystem—Adaptation—Acid Rain.

During and after the execution plan of the lesson, the student is required to:

- Recognize the range of different food chains. (Science)
- Compare a group of food chains. (Science)
- Calculate the number of food groups surrounding the environment near it. (Science & Mathematics)
- Design images of food chains. (Science & Technology)
- Design your own food chain. (Science & engineering)

All of this aligns with the aims of the science teaching classes and field training courses, which devote significant time to teaching topics related to STEM.

Shortcomings

There is a gap between school requirements and the content taught in STEM programs. For example, the MOE and World Bank (2012) noted the importance of teacher education programs to ensure their courses prepare prospective teachers to teach the national school curriculum. However, the SQU teacher training program lacks cohesion between scientific and educational disciplines. Specialized subject courses are studied in isolation from each other and they are not unified with pedagogy courses. There seems to be little integration across STEM subjects and evaluation processes (such as the NSTA), which are very much based on individual subjects. The preparation program should consider courses such as communication, technology, and curriculum design, the engineering design process in math and science education, transdisciplinary learning approaches, and the implementation of STEM in the classroom. Also, more consideration must be made regarding integrating STEM subjects through reflection on student teaching, field-based experiences, and, more specifically, teaching during microteaching (College of Education at SQU, 2021). There is a need to reduce the number of specialized courses and offer a more integrated range of subjects. There is also a need to focus more on the practical than the theoretical aspects of science teaching. Providing more activities that incorporate problem solving and engineering design are therefore essential, and these could be improved by producing prototype lessons, allowing students to solve realistic problems, and providing creative ideas.

Some national research studies (e.g., Ambusaidi et al., 2015; Elayyan & Al-Shizawi, 2019) investigated teachers' perceptions of integrating STEM in Oman Schools. Their research findings showed positive perceptions of the science teachers towards integrating STEM in teaching science to help students acquire important skills and competencies. Other studies showed that most teachers believed they were hampered by the poor quality of their school internet and the insufficient time allocated to implement the STEM activities (Alkharusi, 2020). The MOE needs to set standards consistent with the needs of schools regarding STEM education; however, STEM education in Omani schools is not considered by the MOE as a formal part of education but as an enriching activity that is only provided to grade 10 students. As a result, there are no preparation programs or schools explicitly prepared for STEM education and there are no teachers officially trained to teach according to STEM—only science and mathematics separately (Shahat et al., 2022b). A more recent study, by Ealyyan and Al-Mazzroi (2020), revealed three types of obstacles, from a teachers' point of view, limiting the implementation of the STEM approach in science education—they were content related, the learning environment, and teachers. Teachers thought that the curriculum content was not presented as fully integrated subjects, that the learning environment makes implementing the activities very challenging, and that teachers were not entirely prepared regarding STEM education requirements. The study concluded that this type of education has material, training, and logistical requirements that Oman should seek to remedy.

Possibilities for Implementing STEM Education in Oman

Science teachers in Oman need to improve their skills in producing and changing teaching materials to meet the needs and interests of their students and support the teaching and learning of crucial twenty-first century skills. In order to implement STEM education, Omani teachers should understand that they must go beyond textbooks to provide relevant and challenging materials for their students to allow them to acquire twenty-first century competencies and abilities (Council of Education Oman, 2017). Developing a model for teaching and assessing STEM for use in Oman is needed. This STEM education model should create lesson plans on various integrated subjects at different school stages and examine their effect on student learning outcomes. Constructing a new framework that provides a novel prototype for STEM education in order to develop and assess effective and *cost*-effective teaching that can be applied in Oman is required. This prototype would help guide both teachers and teacher educators in Oman on the important task of planning and constructing active learning situations using different STEM content for classroom implementation. We also need to emphasize the importance of teacher's professional knowledge in the teaching of STEM in Oman. Therefore, it is important to pay close attention to STEM teacher preparation—in terms of content knowledge and pedagogical content knowledge—by establishing national standards for STEM teacher preparation. A modern and efficient teacher development system is the precondition for a successful school system that produces competent students that can contribute to society and the economy of the country and region. We need to help teachers and teacher educators improve instructional quality, including student learning outcomes, for which there are increasingly higher expectations internationally and in Oman. To adapt teacher training successfully, it is necessary to reform to the current science curricula content and the learning environment. There is a need, for example, to have schools focused on STEM education. The adapted teacher preparation program should consider courses such as communication, technology, and curriculum design, the engineering design process in math and science education, transdisciplinary learning approaches, and the implementation of STEM in the classroom. This STEM program would be expected to support students' engagement, motivation, perseverance, and integration into the community. Insisting on a nation-wide rollout of STEM education in schools in cooperation with the promising STEM Oman program will provide education practitioners in the Sultanate with a STEM-based toolkit, which will develop science teachers' competence in teaching STEM disciplines. Additionally, it may help promote the sustainable development of Omani society by getting students interested in STEM and STEM based research, and motivating them to take up STEM careers.

References

Al Barwani, T., & Bailey, J. (2016). Local challenges, global solutions: Oman's experience with accreditation: The Case of Sultan Qaboos University. In N. Michelli, R. Dada, D. Eldridge, R. Tamim, & K. Karp (Eds.), *Teacher quality and teacher education quality* (pp. 151–166). Routledge.

Al-Amri, M. (2005). *An evaluation of the art teacher preparation programme within art studio courses at Sultan Qaboos University* [Unpublished Ph.D. thesis]. The University of Manchester. Manchester, UK.

Al-Amri, M. (2015, April 2–5). Preparing teachers of art at Sultan Qaboos University in Oman. In *The Sixth Asian Conference on arts & humanities* (pp.667–683). The Osaka International Convention Center.

Al-Busaidi, S. (2019). Exploring college of education students' aversion to teaching. *Pertanika Journal of Social Sciences & Humanities, 27*(1), 149–163.

Alkharusi, A. (2020). *Perceptions of teachers and students participating in the STEM OMAN program* [Unpublished Master Thesis]. Sultan Qaboos University. Muscat, Sultanate of Oman.

Al-Malki, M. (2017). *Assessing classroom performance of pre-service English language teachers in Oman.* https://doi.org/10.25904/1912/1551

Al-Salmi, M. N. (2001). *Training programmes for Islamic education teachers in the Sultanate of Oman: Descriptive and evaluation* [Unpublished PhD Thesis], University of Edinburgh.

Al-Salmi, T. (1994). *Teacher education in Oman: Selection and training of primary school teachers* [PhD thesis]. University of Birmingham, Birmingham, UK. https://doi.org/10.1016/0738-0593(95)00008-q

Ambusaidi, A., Al-Harthi, A, & Al-Shuhaimi, A. (2015, May 5–7). Science teachers' beliefs in the Sultanate of Oman towards science and technology and engineering and mathematics (STEM) and their relationship to some variables. In *The 1st Excellent Conference in teaching & learning in science and mathematics.* King Saud University, .

Ambusaidi, A., & Al-Shuaili, A. (2009). Science education development in the Sultanate of Oman. In S. BonJaoude & Z. Dagher (Eds.), *The world of science education* (pp. 205–219). Sense Publishers.

Ambusaidi, A., Shahat, M. A., & Al Musawi, A. (2022). Science education in Oman: Taking Oman to better future. In R. Huang, B. Xin, A. Tlili, F. Yang, X. Zhang, L. Zhu, & M. Jemni (Eds.), *Lecture Notes in Educational Technology. Science education in countries along the belt & road: Future insights and new requirements* (pp. 113–127). Springer. https://doi.org/10.1007/978-981-16-6955-2_8

College of Education. (2021). *The internal quality of instruction* [Unpublished report]. Author.

Council of Education-Oman. (2017). *Philosophy of education in Oman.* Ministry of Education.

Elayyan, S., & Al-Mazroi, Y. (2020). Obstacles that limit the implementation of STEM approach in science education from teachers' point view. *Journal of Educational and Psychological Sciences., 4*(2), 57–74. https://doi.org/10.26389/AJSRP.S061119

Elayyan, S., & Al-Shizawi, F. (2019). Teachers' perceptions of integrating STEM in Omani schools. *International Journal of Education, 8*(1), 16–21. https://doi.org/10.34293/education.v8i1.1136

Ministry of Education. (1985). *The basic organization of the intermediate colleges for males' and females' teachers.* Printing press Ruwi.

Ministry of Education. (1992). *Official student's transcript.* Intermediate Teacher Training Colleges. Muscat, Sultanate of Oman.

Ministry of Education-Oman. (2021). STEM Oman. Ministry of Education.

Ministry of Information. (2000). *Oman 2000.* Oman Establishment for Press, News, Publication and Advertising.

Mullis, I. V., Martin, M. O., Foy, P., Kelly, D. L., & Fishbein, B. (2020). *TIMSS 2019 international results in mathematics and science.* Boston College.

Ohle-Peters, A., Shahat, M. A., & Ambusaidi, A. (2022). Text-picture-material in science education: A comparison of Omani and German teachers' attitudes, motivational orientations and self-regulatory skills. *Educational Studies.* Advance online publication. https://doi.org/10.1080/03055698.2022.2117542

Oman Observer. (2018, February 21). *First phase of STEM Oman' launched in six public schools.* https://www.omanobserver.om/article/61954/Local/first-phase-of-stem-oman-launched-in-six-public-schools

Oman Observer. (2019a, November 5). *Ministry of Education launches new educational platform.* https://www.omanobserver.om/article/21617/Main/ministry-of-education-launches-new-educational-platform

Oman Observer. (2021a, March 22). *National science week STEM begins with online events.* https://www.omanobserver.om/article/1784/Local/national-science-week-stem-begins-with-online-events

Oman Observer. (2021b, March 27). *Science Week observed with focus on environment.* https://www.omanobserver.om/article/1558/Local/science-week-observed-with-focus-on-environment

Public and Private universities in Oman. (2021). *National reference document for teacher preparation programmes in Oman: A project to improve and raise the efficiency of teacher preparation in public and private universities in Oman (Preliminary draft).* Ministry of Education.

Shahat, M. A., Al-Balushi, S. M., & Al-Amri, M. (2022b). Investigating pre-service science teachers' self-efficacy beliefs for teaching science through engineering design processes. *Interdisciplinary Journal of Environmental and Science Education, 18*(4), e2291. https://doi.org/10.21601/ijese/12121

Shahat, M. A., Ohle-Peters, A., & Ambusaidi, A. (2022a). Teaching with Texts and pictures in science classes: Teachers' attitudes and motivational orientations at different school levels. *Journal of Science Teacher Education, 33*(1), 107–123. https://doi.org/10.1080/1046560X.2021.1909231

CHAPTER 11

STEM Education in the Spanish Context: Key Features and Issues

Teresa Lupión-Cobos, Digna Couso Lagarón, Marta Romero Ariza, and Jordi Domènech-Casal

Introduction

STEM Education in the Spanish Context

The use of the acronym STEM or STEAM in the Spanish educational context is a recent phenomenon. The STEMmania which Sanders (2009) referred to in his early works on STEM education in the US context

T. Lupión-Cobos (✉)
Faculty of Education Sciences, University of Málaga, Málaga, Spain
e-mail: teluco@uma.es

D. C. Lagarón • J. Domènech-Casal
Universitat Autònoma de Barcelona, Barcelona, Spain
e-mail: digna.couso@uab.cat; jdomen44@xtec.cat

M. R. Ariza
Department of Didactics of Sciences, University of Jaen, Andalucía, Spain
e-mail: mromero@ujaen.es

S. M. Al-Balushi et al. (eds.), *Reforming Science Teacher Education Programs in the STEM Era*, Palgrave Studies on Leadership and Learning in Teacher Education,
https://doi.org/10.1007/978-3-031-27334-6_11

arrived here more than 10 years later. However, being a global trend, STEM education in Spain has not arrived timidly: it has been fueled, like everywhere else, not mainly by educational or pedagogical inputs, but mostly by political, social, and economic forces. Today STEM or STEAM as a promise of innovation and preparation for the future is becoming familiar not only to both pre and in-service teachers and educators but also to students and parents through a diversity of programs, initiatives, and resources both in- and out-of-school (Couso, 2017).

Despite the diversity of programs and approaches available, we can summarize the way STEM education has arrived at Spanish schools as following two strategies. On the one hand, there have been several initiatives generally organized out of the educational system, including those developed by scientific research centers such as CSIC (e.g., Science in the Neighborhood or 11th of February); by private companies and foundations in the tech sector (such as YOMO festival of GMSA or GENIOS from Google Foundation); by administrations and also initiatives associated with research and transfer projects initiated at the University level. Despite all these initiatives relying on different meanings of STEM, having different formats, and pursuing different objectives of STEM education, they have in common the aim to involve enthusiastic teachers at very different levels of commitment and learning potential. On the other hand, and despite "Increasing STEAM vocations, especially in girls" being mentioned as one of the 10 challenges that the Spanish educational system must face to "Modernize the educational system" since the past Organic Law 2/2006 LOE, there has not been a nation-wide effort or strategy toward STEM education (Estévez-Mauriz & Baelo, 2021), neither regarding this vocational objective nor regarding a STEM literacy approach. This is not surprising, as the Spanish educational system is not centralized, with most official educational programs implemented in the country at the regional level.[1] Therefore, most official STEM educational programs have been launched at different autonomous communities, and they have had a limited impact in both pre-service and in-service training.

[1] See Eurydice portal for a complete description: https://eacea.ec.europa.eu/national-policies/eurydice/content/spain_en

Several plans for STEM education have been launched in the recent years all over Spain, starting in 2017 with the STEMCat plan[2] of Catalonia. Some other regions elaborated similar plans, including the proposal STEAMEuskadi,[3] the Plan of STEM Madrid,[4] or the "Plan for Science, Technology and Innovation"[5] in Asturias. Other regions were not involved in the process of defining a common strategy with clear goals but organized directly different initiatives of teacher training, such as DigiTalent[6] in Galicia or the ESERO STEM project in Andalusia.[7] Each of these initiatives signals the existence of myriad interventions, rather than a common strategy, along the different regions of Spain.

Regarding initial teacher education, the situation is similar according to the analysis of existing subjects in pre-service teacher education programs for primary school in the 39 public universities offering these studies in Spain of Castro-Rodríguez and Montoro (2021). This research reveals that despite important characteristics of STEM education (such as problem-solving, contextualization in real situations and interdisciplinary) are already included in most of these subjects, explicit references to STEM education are truly scarce and the presence of Engineering as a specific subject is non-existent. In fact, there are very few national or regional initiatives explicitly devoted to STEM in initial teacher education, with only one university (Universitat de Lleida) offering a specific STEM specialization in the primary school teacher grade and few other universities offering STEM optional subjects (e-g Design of STEM projects at UAB). This contrasts with the existence of lots of post-graduate and master level programs addressed to in-service, usually beginning teachers specifically on STEM education, signaling how the official university programs are arriving late to the STEM education wave. In the following sections, we offer some paradigmatic case studies of introduction of STEM education in teacher education programs in Spain specifying in which ways they are connected with initial teacher education.

[2] https://participa.gencat.cat/uploads/decidim/attachment/file/2784/Annex4_Pla_STEAM.pdf

[3] https://steam.eus/es/i-estrategia-de-educacion-steam-euskadi/

[4] http://educacionstem.educa.madrid.org/

[5] https://asturias4steam.eu

[6] https://amtega.xunta.gal/digitalent

[7] https://www.juntadeandalucia.es/educacion/portals/web/ced/innovacion-educativa/investigacion/proyectos/proyecto-steam/investigacion-aeroespacial

Three Case Studies of STEM Education Programs

The IndagaSTEAM Escuela Case

One STEM education case in the Spanish context is offered by a university teaching and research group (**UTRG**) at the University of Malaga called the science education and competences research group. The project is called the "IndagaSTEAM Escuela" project, a cooperation between schools and universities. This project is conducted by making interventions at schools in order to help the in-service science teachers (**INSTs**) develop key competences in their students that support them to be successful learners and promote their critical thinking.

School projects with inquiry and contextualization strategies have been established as useful training scenarios to apply STEM education goals (Morrell et al., 2020; Lupión-Cobos et al., 2022). With this orientation, the project has been developed for three years from a vision of STEM education as a framework to bridge knowledge and understanding across the interrelated strands of the discipline-specific content of the areas involved (Science, Technology, Engineering, Mathematics, Arts, and understanding) taught in a context (as a human endeavor). The STEAM rationale used promotes students' ability to make informed decisions, develop evidence-based arguments about local, national, and global issues, and put in action their key competencies in a collaborative way of working.

This project is developed in two instructional settings in order to promote the professional development of the participating science teachers:

- University classrooms, with specific modules taught by pre-service science teachers (**PSSTs**), through the curriculum of the subjects of the bachelor's degree (Early Childhood and Primary Education) and master's degree in teaching (Secondary Education).
- State schools, by INSTs who voluntarily participate from regional public schools of Andalusia (Fig. 11.1).

STEM education is promoted in schools through (El Nagdi et al., 2018): (a) content and teaching strategies of the teaching areas; (b) using

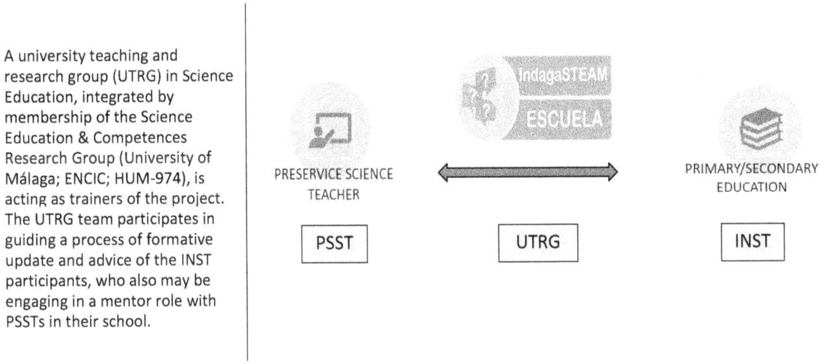

Fig. 11.1 The IndagaSTEAM Escuela project

teaching strategies; (c) managing classroom activities; and (d) assessing student learning.

Regarding ***science pre-service teachers***, a teaching, learning, and assessment program using banded content (Science as a human endeavor and Science inquiry skill strands) and year-by-year content (Science understanding strand) is addressed through training modules in compulsory subjects of the Degree/Master Study Plan.

The program has been implemented so far with some 240 pre-service teachers, including a brief immersion program in the teaching of science by inquiry and contextualization. Aspects related to the nature of science and the interdisciplinary treatment of STEM education are addressed with special emphasis on its curricular treatment, with didactic strategies on practices, as well as promoting positive attitudes toward S&T and the values of gender integration.

The learning of the pre-service teachers is built through four stages performed by specific workshops (16 hours): 1. *Focus on initial knowledge*. It is dedicated to introducing the theoretical-practical relationship of the inquiry approach through a multidisciplinary and integrating STEAM vision of the scientific-technological processes involved in the problems or situations analyzed; 2. *Training for the design*. The pre-service teachers built by students' Lesson plans, the conceptual frameworks and the concepts and procedures of the STEM subjects involved in selected didactic proposals; 3. *Inquiry/Stem Skills*. The pre-service teachers develops practical work through the inquiry cycle, acting in the role of students; 4. *Applying professional learning*. The role of teacher is acting by the pre-service teachers; analyzing a didactic proposal of their own design, strategies for implementation and evaluation of students where they carry out a didactic transposition for any cycle of Primary or Secondary education.

The program has been positive in its contribution to scientific-technological literacy. However, the development of proposals for didactic transpositions for the Primary Education classroom, evidencing the difficulties, among other aspects, on the design of activities and the true meaning of inquiry in the classroom. Likewise, we find that a more extensive training in scientific knowledge and skills is required to integrate these epistemic practices.

Regarding ***In-Service Primary and Secondary school teachers***, the interventions at schools have been carried out during three editions and followed as a case study adapted to their characteristics and needs. About seven teachers from Primary Education and three teachers from Secondary Education have participated in these cases with teacher educators from UTRG and seven university researchers in science education.

The implementation of STEM projects focused on teaching practices in terms of the STEM community, STEM integration, and STEM assessment, depending on the school type. Specifically, the engineering discipline worked on engineering design processes and activities using robots and the use of Legos, but trainers found that teachers who were not initially familiar with the engineering design processes had improvement in their perceptions of such processes. The content descriptions are accompanied by content elaborations providing illustrations and/or examples that teachers may choose to use in the classroom or as inspiration for their own activities. More information is available on the website https://indagasteamescuela.uma.es/.

Taking into account the level of teachers' professional development and the needs of the students, the interventions in the schools are structured in seven phases, with the following main objectives: *Introduction & Diagnosis* (Focus Initial knowledge); *Training for the intervention* (Learning & Observations in STEAM Workshops/Seminars); *First intervention* (Observations of manage classroom activities and Self reflection I, counseling and monitoring returns); *Middle Evaluation* (Focus Group Discuss & Reflection on practice); *Training for the design* (Learning of STEAM Proposals); *Second intervention* (Observations of manage classroom activities and Self reflection II, counseling and monitoring returns) and *Global Evaluation* (critical reflections by Focus Group Discuss & Skills Global Assessment).

Materials for students and teachers are available in the public repository of the University of Malaga, as well as contributions to educational research in congresses and scientific publications (Lupión Cobos, 2021).

Results achieved regarding students show that they have been able to identify questions, look for information, develop hypotheses, and take measurements which have allowed them to record data and establish relationships between variables, make scientific explanations, and argue based on evidence. Furthermore, they manufactured small prototypes of engineering and got involved in social and artistic aspects by establishing knowledge connections between different areas.

Regarding teachers, they have deepened numeracy across the curriculum, built content knowledge, and improved the selection and sequence of content for learning, designing their own STEM projects in order to promote in their students the development of critical thinking, contributing to the formation of participatory and reflective citizen actions with positive attitudes toward S&T and gender perspective. Moreover, we have received positive teacher evaluations of the contribution of STEM education and the use of new strategies, both about the design of teaching proposals and the dynamics and management of the classroom.

The Case of STEAMCat

The STEAMCat program[8] has been promoted at the regional level by the Department of Education of Catalonia as an educational response to the ambitious and multisectoral Pla STEMCat. We selected this program to be analyzed in this chapter due to the emphasis it has placed on self-reporting, generating an abundance of local publications and documentation that allows us to examine its genesis, strategies, and characteristics (Albalat et al., 2022). In the following section, we describe the conceptual focus,

[8] https://projectes.xtec.cat/steamcat/

deployment, and teacher training strategies of STEMCat during the 2018–2022 academic years. The STEAMCat program is not a program of teacher training, but includes teacher training as an action axis.

Considering STEM to be a well-recognized polysemic term, the program started by setting a collaboration between CRECIM Research Institute of the Autonomous University of Barcelona and the Department of Education to develop a common STEM vision based on two standpoints:

- a critical standpoint that emphasizes the importance of sustainability, social justice, and equity values in STEM education (Couso, 2017). The PLa STEMCat mandates that STEM education must serve the triple political STEM goals (1. To promote STEM vocations; 2. To correct the gender and socioeconomic biases in STEM professions; 3. To develop STEM literacy for citizenship). The definition of STEM education used in Catalonia explicitly separates itself from highly criticized geostrategic and economy-based proposals (Bogdan & García-Carmona, 2021) and focuses in the second and third goals for STEM education. The final ambition is that of a more emancipated citizenship, scientifically and technologically, rather than of developing more and better STEM professionals.
- a second standpoint that views STEM education neither as a specific teaching method nor as a pedagogical approach but as the diversity of appropriate teaching methodologies, adequate technologies, and suitable pedagogical perspectives used to promote the above-described goals. The focus on perspectives is particularly important, as movements such as the STS one, which had considerable visibility in Spain, influence present STEM education.

This conceptual core was specified by identifying which methodologies (PBL, design thinking, gamification, etc.), technologies (3D printing, programming and robotics, etc.), and perspectives (inquiry, SSI, etc.) should be recruited as *STEM tools* for their possible contribution to the three *STEM goals* (Fig. 11.2).

The STEAMCat teacher training focused on three main axes: (1) Viewing the school as the unit of change. Efforts focused on articulating the training of teachers in a way oriented to the organizational and methodological changes necessary within the school. This was done avoiding the figure of the individual innovator and promoting the generation of

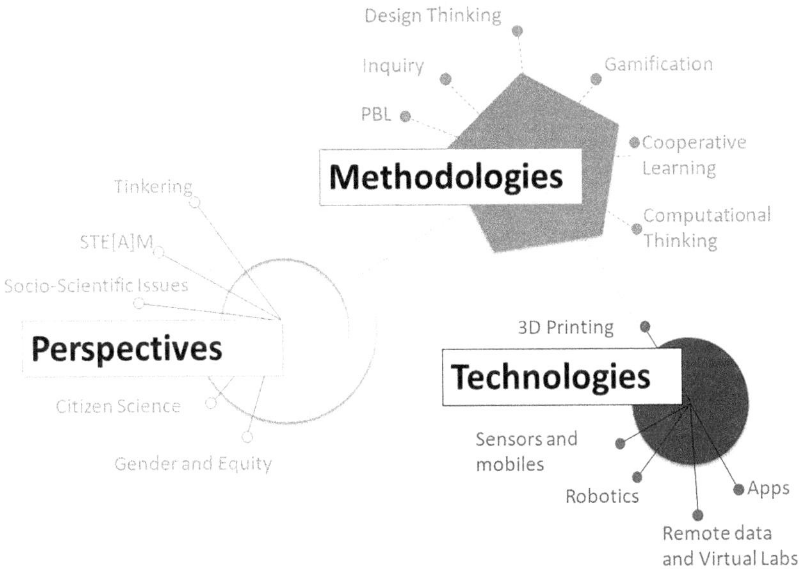

Fig. 11.2 *STEMTools* Map of the STEAMCat program (https://ateneu.xtec.cat/wikiform/wikiexport/materials/stemcat/index)

"reference STEM schools" in the territory; (2) The creation of partnerships with other stakeholders (e.g., scientific and technological research centers); (3) Growing from what is already being done and prove successful. This involves identifying successful practices already present in the territory, in a decentralized way, helping to develop and disseminate them.

To substantiate these axes, several actions were undertaken. Initially, the program used a cascade teacher education model to train the trainers via a centralized course for all official teacher educators in the Catalan territory. This initial action helped to establish a network of trainers who shared a common view. Subsequently, different actions were undertaken during three academic years (2019–2022), including:

1. The deployment of an Educational STEAMCat Innovation Plan that involved more than 150 schools of different K12 educational stages. These schools received tutoring for the drafting of their School STEM Innovation Plan, advice, materials, and specific training for deployment. Each of these schools had a STEAMCat driving

team (4–5 teachers from the school) who also participated in semestral inter-center meetings for exchange and training with other schools in the program.

2. The offer of three specific training lines for in-service teachers, including the following 20 h courses : (1) training on the STEMTools framework, (2) monographic trainings on some of the STEMtools (programming with Apps, Robotics, etc.), and (3) training on specific pedagogical content knowledge of different areas (Science, Mathematics, Technology, and Arts).[9] Altogether, this involved the training of more than 1000 teachers. The development of specific 2 h modules on STEMtools in pre-service teachers following training in Universitat Autònoma de Barcelona and Universitat Pompeu Fabra, including 170 pre-service teachers.
3. The creation of the role of the *STEAMCat Ambassadors*: active teaching staff, expert in one of the STEMTools, based in different parts of the territory, acting as an advisor in its territory and a global benchmark in the STEMTool of their expertise.
4. The articulation of a web platform and an agenda of STEAM conferences and events, organized by the program itself or by others, recruiting efforts from other parallel or previous programs of the same institution or other European institutions (mSchools, *STEM a l'espai*, etc.).

The implementation of the program is currently active, and from the observation of some of the outputs of the program (training activities and assessment, innovation plans designed by the schools, etc.), we have identified the following:

(a) A strong orientation of the teacher as a designer of teaching-learning sequences. In particular, the Project-Based Learning (PBL) methodology is clearly linked to the program. Preliminary studies on teaching-learning designs developed by participants in the training efforts of the STEAMCat program show low interdisciplinarity

[9] This is peculiar of the Spanish context: teachers in primary school often present a disengagement from the STEM field and secondary school teachers accessed (until few years ago) the profession with very little pedagogical and didactic training. This is why it was considered especially necessary the training on specific pedagogical content knowledge.

and occasionally low development of practices of STEM areas (Domènech-Casal et al., 2019).

(b) A wide variety of usages of the different STEMTools. Different schools adopt very different profiles in their School STEM Innovation Plan; some schools prioritize the inclusion of technologies, while others focus on methodologies and perspectives.

(c) The need for specific training on organization and cooperation. Schools did not receive specific training in the design and evaluation of plans, which often results in actions that are not aligned with the goals, inadequate tools for their evaluation, or difficulties in differentiating conjectural actions from structural ones.

(d) The hybridization of STEM training frameworks with other pedagogical and social frameworks. In training activities and innovation plans created by schools, STEM has also been associated with an improvement in formative assessment, attention to diversity, and feminism.

(e) No regulatory support for the deployment of the program in the curriculum. The drafting of a new curriculum in Spain (during the third year of development of the STEAMCat plan) practically does not mention STEM. Its regional specificity in Catalonia even reduces the amount of hours devoted to teaching technology.

(f) A lack of visibility of Professional Careers (in Spain, called FP and Cycles) and the need to improve in the field of student guidance.

The program is ongoing, involving more schools every day. Despite that the identified limitations have not been tackled yet, the participating teacher educators, teachers, and ambassadors continue to engage in deep reflections on STEM education and developing tools such as the online community STEMarium[10] to support this process.

The MaSDiV Case

The other potentially inspiring case aimed at promoting the implementation of STEM education through specific teacher professional development is the one related to the European project MaSDiV in Spain. Here,

[10] https://www.stemarium.cat/

453 secondary school STEM teachers from six different European countries participated in a specialized training program implemented in two waves (2018 and 2019), engaging 54 and 102 Spanish teachers, respectively. The teachers were selected in a national call in collaboration with the Spanish Ministry of Education, following the usual selection process. Therefore, the sample of teachers may be considered representative of the teachers who usually enroll in this kind of program.

The STEM education model underlying this case emerges from criticism to transmissive teaching and the use of irrelevant learning activities and scenarios. It responds to the need to better prepare individuals for an uncertain and rapidly changing world, deeply influenced by S&T, where robotics, automatization, and the easy access to multiple sources of information question educational models with a focus on knowledge acquisition or the solution of routine exercises. There is a need to generate critical, responsible, and responsive citizens who understand the role and nature of S&T and are able to solve complex problems in a creative way, incorporating different perspectives and considering fundamental and civic values. Therefore, the main argument justifying the STEM education model presented herein has to do with (a) current educational demands and (b) the pedagogies conducive to the intended learning outcomes.

In order to define the STEM educational model related to this case, we draw on three referent points: the kind of learning outcomes pursued, the pedagogies orienting the implementation of the model, and the theories backing the model.

In relation to the educational objectives used as referent points, the model advocates not only for a highly qualified work force in the STEM fields ensuring scientific and technological advancement, but also for the education of STEM literate citizens. STEM literacy refers to the knowledge, values, and skills necessary for active participation and informed decision making in today's societies, regardless of personal career or professional choices. In addition, the model emphasizes the integration of democratic and fundamental values and transversal skills, such as creativity, critical thinking (Ariza et al., 2021a), and the ability to tackle complex and wickedly defined problems, where different perspectives and implications should be considered (Ariza et al., 2021b).

A key aspect of this model is the selection of teaching scenarios that support meaningful and transferable learning, contextualized in the solution of authentic problems; this naturally provides opportunities for interdisciplinary learning and the achievement of learning outcomes relevant for different subject matters. From this perspective, interdisciplinarity comes naturally and not artificially, where learners draw on knowledge and techniques from different disciplines while trying to make sense of complex realistic situations that may be successfully tackled by applying key STEM practices (Ariza et al., 2021c). The targeted STEM practices considered are based on those proposed by the National Research Council (NRC, 2012). This approach promotes the development of key competences, bringing a sense of meaning and purpose to the learning taking place and fostering cognitive and emotional engagement in learners.

But the question is what kind of pedagogical approaches can afford this highly demanding set of educational goals for science, technology, mathematics, and engineering learning. The response can be linked to our second referent point, the methods or pedagogical approaches that guide the implementation of the STEM education model and are conducive to the intended learning outcomes. The model supports the use of those pedagogies that foster context-based interdisciplinary STEM learning with a focus on problem-solving and the integration of fundamental values and citizenship education (Maass et al., 2021). This is the case of those pedagogies supporting active, collaborative, and reflective learning through the use of inquiry and socio-scientific scenarios (Ariza et al., 2021b).

In relation to the third referent point, we can see how the previously mentioned pedagogies are aligned with a constructivist view that considers that people build explanatory mental models when making sense of their world around them and their interaction with others. In addition, the STEM education model is consistent with current advances in neuroscience showing the key role of cognitive and emotional triggers and meaningful connections in supporting effective learning.

In Spain, the MasDiV teacher professional development program involved 70 h of teacher training throughout several months, around three main thematic modules aimed at developing specific teaching competences related to the use of (a) inquiry approaches, (b) interdisciplinary context-based education and (c) inclusion and the integration of fundamental values in STEM education. A more detailed description of the program and the modules may be found in Ariza et al. (2021c). Figure 11.2 represents the key elements of the teachers' professional development program that supported the implementation of the MaSDiV STEM educational model. The program built on teachers' previous experiences and beliefs about teaching and learning and provided multiple opportunities to test new teaching materials and approaches, identify links to the school

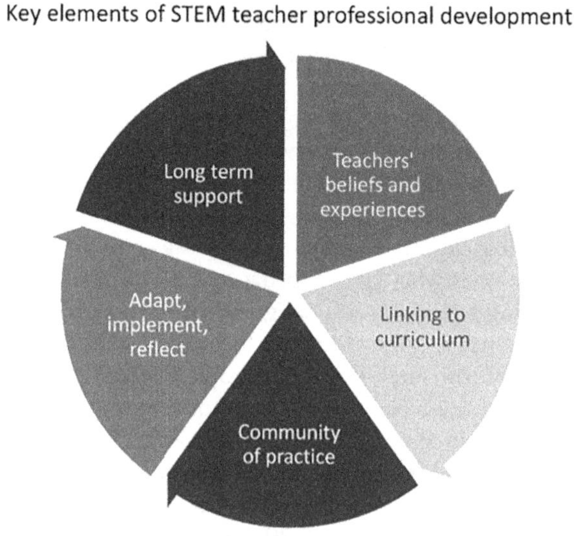

Fig. 11.3 Key elements of STEM teachers' professional development in the MaSDiV project (Spanish case)

curriculum, and adapt materials to their daily practice. They could implement them and share their experience with other colleagues. There was an emphasis on discussion and reflection, providing long-term support and fostering the creation of communities of practice. Figure 11.3 shows the key elements of the STEM teachers' professional development program implemented in the MaSDiV project.

In relation to the research evidence available on the impact of this experience on STEM teaching and learning, results from a pre/post research design showed that the STEM teachers' professional development program was successful in supporting the development of teachers' self-efficacy, learning-related beliefs, and practices of the intended STEM education model, revealing significant differences between the pre and post scores (Ariza et al., 2021c). The qualitative analysis of the teachers' reflections about the program showed that the most appreciated aspects of the experience were transferability to practice, the pedagogical resources offered, the benefits of the model on students' learning, the methodological transformation involved, and the opportunity to exchange ideas and practices with colleagues in a professional learning community (Ariza et al., 2021c). These results have been described and discussed in detail in previous publications reporting on the international sample (Maass et al., 2021) and the experience on a national level in Spain (Ariza et al., 2021c). These outcomes are of great interest since they reveal the utility and feasibility of the STEM education model, and they are potent in promoting transformational teacher professional development in the STEM education field.

Conclusions

The above-described programs are only a taste of the multitude of proposals taking place in the Spanish educational context in recent years, chosen due to their focus on teachers' professional development. Through different means (including cascade train-the-trainers models, ambassador support, university-based professional development courses, or school cooperation, among others) in all these initiatives, teachers faced important challenges.

We found some interesting commonalities in these diverse approaches. When introducing STEM education, all the initiatives invested significant effort in conceptualizing and sharing with teachers their vision of the STEM approach, clarifying both its educational purposes and selected perspectives and methodologies. Interestingly, all reported initiatives are far from the tech-based STEM that is also common in smaller-scale teacher training initiatives in our context. Whatever the educational perspectives favored (STS, PBL, inquiry, etc.), in these case studies, STEM education is strongly based on what we already know from Science, Engineering, or Mathematics education, with the addition of the potentiality and limits of disciplinary integration. As such, STEM provides new opportunities to share high-quality pedagogical content knowledge and nature of STEM with teachers via intensive professional efforts.

In all the described case studies, STEM teachers' professional development has been closely linked to the "teacher as a designer" model, which has set important challenges to teachers. We understand that designing is a high-order professional competence for teachers, and one may wonder if, due to the lack of enough well-designed examples of STEM curricular activities, the focus has been too much on design instead of selecting, adapting, and sequencing existing teaching and learning units. The reality is that in Spain we lack examples of research-based curricular proposals that can support teachers in the double effort of embracing the STEM education framework and implementing it adequately. This is even more challenging regarding pre-service teaching, where there is a very important focus on the design of interventions that fit the school needs, usually in the context of the practicums or school-base internships that pre-service teachers do. In this sense, we identify a contradiction between the wish and in certain context even push to schools for introducing STEM education in their curriculum while there is very few STEM training at pre-service teachers' level. Changing the picture needs for pre-service teachers to experience, both as students and as teachers-to-be, the potential of adequate STEM education units.

Finally, we wish to emphasize that, perhaps due to the systemic nature that entails introducing a new and demanding approach such as STEM education, the initiatives reported involve different levels of collaboration between educational administrations, educational research institutions, and teachers and schools. We think this three-axis model is a *sine qua non* condition for supporting a transformation that implies strong changes in not only the teaching practice but also in the curriculum, school organization, professional development models and teaching materials, among others. The close collaboration with educational research, particularly on didactics of the disciplines or pedagogical content knowledge, shows the need to promote more cohesive and well-founded frameworks and support more systematic evaluation efforts that use research evidence to guide improvement. We realize, however, that in all the models presented, the students and their families' voices are absent, and researchers should determine ways to include them in future STEM education efforts.

Acknowledgments This work was part of the R&D project PID2019-105765GA-I00 "Citizens with critical thinking: a challenge for teachers in science education," funded by the Spanish National R&D Plan, and the Coordination Project "Development of Teaching Competences in PST of Early Childhood, Primary and Secondary Education, with the teaching of scientific practices of inquiry and STEM approaches in science education. Coordination for the improvement of educational practice," funded by the University of Málaga. Second author received the support of the ACELEC research group, ref.2021 SGR 00647. The authors wish to acknowledge all participants in the aforementioned projects.

References

Albalat, A., Mateo, E., Couso, D., & Domènech-Casal, J. (2022). STEMtools: una proposta per a planificar el desplegament STEM a l'escola [STEMtools: A proposal to plan STEM development at school]. *Revista Ciències, 44*, 72–87.

Ariza, M. R., Christodoulou, A., Harskamp, M. V., Knippels, M. C. P., Kyza, E. A., Levinson, R., & Agesilaou, A. (2021b). Socio-scientific inquiry-based learning as a means toward environmental citizenship. *Sustainability, 13*(20), 11509. https://doi.org/10.3390/su132011509

Ariza, M. R., Quesada, A., Abril, A. M., & Cobo-Huesa, C. (2021c). Changing teachers' self-efficacy, beliefs and practices through STEAM teacher professional development. *Journal for the Study of Education and Development, 44*(4), 1–33. https://doi.org/10.1080/02103702.2021.1926164

Ariza, M. R., Quesada, A., & Estepa, A. (2021a). Promoting critical thinking through mathematics and science teacher education: The case of argumentation and graphs interpretation about climate change. *European Journal of Teacher Education*, 1–20. https://doi.org/10.1080/02619768.2021.1961736.

Bogdan, R., & García-Carmona, A. (2021). De STEM nos gusta todo menos STEM. Análisis crítico de una tendencia educativa de moda. [From STEM we like everything except STEM. Critical analysis of a fashionable educational trend]. *Enseñanza de las Ciencias, 39*(1), 65–80. https://doi.org/10.5565/rev/ensciencias.3093

Castro-Rodríguez, E., & Montoro, A. B. (2021). Educación STEM y formación del profesorado de Primaria en España[STEM education and teacher training for Primary Education in Spain]. *Revista de Educación, 393*, 353–378.

Couso, D. (2017). ¿Por qué estamos en STEM? Un intento de definir la alfabetización STEM para todos y con valores [Why are we in STEM? An attempt to define STEM literacy for all and with values]. *Revista Ciències, 34*, 22–30.

Domènech-Casal, J., Lope, S., & Mora, L. (2019). Qué proyectos STEM diseña y qué dificultades expresa el profesorado de secundaria sobre Aprendizaje Basado en Proyectos [What STEM projects do you design and what difficulties do secondary school teachers express about Project-Based Learning?]. *Revista Eureka sobre Enseñanza y Divulgación de las Ciencias, 16*(2), 2203.

El Nagdi, M., Leammukda, F., & Roehrig, G. (2018). Developing identities of STEM teachers at emerging STEM schools. *International Journal of STEM Education, 5*(36). https://doi.org/10.1186/s40594-018-0136-1

Estévez-Mauriz, L., & Baelo, R. (2021). How to evaluate the STEM curriculum in Spain? *Mathematics, 9*, 236. https://doi.org/10.3390/math9030236

Lupión Cobos, T. (2021). Training for the transfer and professional development of science teachers. Challenges and opportunities for treating inquiry and the STEM approach. *Boletín ENCIC, Revista del Grupo de Investigación HUM-974, 5*(2), 60–69.

Lupión Cobos, T., Girón-Gambero, J., & García-Ruiz, C. (2022). Building STEM inquiry-based teaching proposal through collaborations between schools and research centres: Perceptions on students' learning and predictors of vocational careers. *European Journal of Educational Research, 11*(2), 899–915.

Maass, K., Sorge, S., Romero-Ariza, M., Hesse, A., & Straser, O. (2021). Promoting Active Citizenship in Mathematics and Science Teaching. *International Journal of Science and Mathematics Education, 20*(4), 727–746. https://doi.org/10.1007/s10763-021-10182-1

Morrell, P. D., Park Rogers, M. A., Pyle, E. J., Roehrig, G., & Veal, W. R. (2020). Preparing teachers of science for 2020 and beyond: Highlighting changes to the NSTA/ASTE standards for science teacher preparation. *Journal of Science Teacher Education, 31*(1), 1–7.

National Research Council (NRC). (2012). *A framework for K-12 science education: Practices, crosscutting concepts, and core ideas.* National Academies Press.

Sanders, M. (2009). STEM, STEMEducation, STEMmania. *Technological Teach*, 20–27.

CHAPTER 12

An Exploration of Co-Teaching in STEM Teacher Professional Development Programs in Turkey

Defne Yabaş, Sedef Canbazoğlu-Bilici, Tuğba Abanoz, B. Sumeyye Kurutas, and M. Sencer Corlu

Introduction

STEM Education in Turkey

STEM education in K-12 settings has been on the agenda of Turkey for the last decade. STEM activities in formal settings are mostly integrated into the middle school science curriculum, focusing on design-based engineering practices. The importance of STEM education was also included

D. Yabaş (✉)
Bahçeşehir University, İstanbul, Turkey
e-mail: defne.yabas@rc.bau.edu.tr

S. Canbazoğlu-Bilici
Gazi University, Ankara, Turkey
e-mail: sedefcanbazoglu@gazi.edu.tr

S. M. Al-Balushi et al. (eds.), *Reforming Science Teacher Education Programs in the STEM Era*, Palgrave Studies on Leadership and Learning in Teacher Education,
https://doi.org/10.1007/978-3-031-27334-6_12

in formal education policy papers (Ministry of National Education [MoNE], 2016). STEM activities in out-of-school settings are also common. Mainly science teachers are held responsible for the implementation of STEM activities. In the Turkish context, STEM education has a critical role in pre-service science teacher education. However, courses that focus directly on STEM education are not explicitly included in the pre-service science teacher education program. In the current book chapter, we presented a research-based co-teaching model for teachers' professional development (PD) that can also serve as a teaching model for the pre-service science teacher education program.

The Power Dynamics of Co-Teaching

Co-teaching has been associated with either a partnership in the classroom among teachers with different expertise/subject areas or a learning practice of a novice teacher from a more experienced teacher. A typical example of co-teaching with equal partnership was the cooperation between special education and general teachers (Bauwens et al., 1989). A less familiar example was observed in curricular programs with an interdisciplinary focus (Hurd & Weilbacher, 2017). In contrast, examples of co-teaching with unequal partnership occurred between pre-service teachers and their mentor teachers at schools or between teaching assistants and professors at universities (Jardí et al., 2022; Roth et al., 2004). Regardless of the balance of power in the partnership, research showed that partners benefited professionally from co-teaching because it created ample opportunities for the learners (Rytivaara et al., 2019). Co-teaching has been a propitious practice for teaching and learning in the classroom.

T. Abanoz
Ankara University, Ankara, Turkey
e-mail: tabanoz@ankara.edu.tr

B. S. Kurutas
University of Delaware, Newark, DE, USA
e-mail: sumeyyek@udel.edu

M. S. Corlu
Oslo Metropolitan University, Oslo, Norway

Bahçeşehir University, İstanbul, Turkey
e-mail: MSencer.Corlu@oslomet.no

Building an equal partnership for a successful co-teaching practice was described as a complex and dynamic process. Establishing parity in design/implementation roles emerged as critical to the success of co-teaching (Leatherman, 2009). Although the interpersonal differences between partners would be expected to arise in any collaborative effort, Pratt (2014) indicated that challenges in achieving a compatible partnership could be resolved if partners showed an effort to learn from each other's differences and strengths. For partners to learn from one another, it was vital whether they could overcome their individualistic teaching cultures (Jang, 2006).

A relatively unexplored challenge to co-teaching at the teacher education level emerged when partners needed to adapt the self-perception of their recurring roles (i.e., teachers, pre-service teacher educators, or researchers) into PD facilitators (Perry & Boylan, 2018). Thus, the purpose of the current study was to address this specific challenge and explore co-teaching at the teacher education level by investigating how STEM teachers perceived their roles as PD facilitators and their respective partner's roles across a series of PD programs. To achieve this goal, we proposed the following research question:

- How can STEM teachers' perceptions of their roles in co-teaching be described?

Methodology

In this multiple holistic case study (Yin, 2014), collecting and analyzing qualitative data from four PD programs, each focusing on a different subject area of STEM, provided significant variation across the cases (Merriam, 2009).

Research Context

The online PD program was organized by the STEM education center of a private university in Turkey. The center has been the epicenter of one of the largest communities of STEM teachers, teacher educators/researchers, and pre-service teachers in the region since 2015. More than 1000 teachers participating in the center's online or face-to-face STEM PD programs each year is an example of the broader impact of the center (Corlu, 2017).

Recently, center administrators reached out to several "Teacher Educators" (TERs) in the community and invited them to propose an online PD program. The TERs were asked to collaboratively design and implement their proposed program with a practicing teacher. All invited TERs were active researchers with experience in qualitative research. In addition, the center's invitation included some other requirements so that the selected programs could be exemplary practices of co-teaching at the teacher education level: Some of these requirements were:

- All programs needed to include one hour of a synchronous weekly meeting for seven weeks.
- All programs needed to include selection criteria (i.e., letter of application), an attendance requirement, and a final summative project (i.e., lesson plan) for the participating teachers.

Table 12.1 presents a detailed description of the selected programs.

Table 12.1 Description of the PD programs

Program title	*PD program outcomes*
Team 1 (science): Teaching sustainability in science at the early childhood level	• Evaluate the current problems in science and environmental science • Integrate science and technology in *STEM education* lesson planning • Develop effective strategies to ensure family participation
Team 2 (mathematics): Data science and modeling with data loggers (LabStar)	• Identify misconceptions about data literacy and relevant statistical concepts • Integrate mathematical modeling and scientific inquiry in *STEM education* lesson planning • Develop strategies to use just-in-time data collection for solving real-life problems
Team 3 (engineering): Engineering design-based thematic STEM activities	• Justify the use of the nature of engineering and the engineering design process for teaching science • Integrate engineering design-based thematic activities for science in *STEM education* lesson planning • Develop strategies to use different measurement tools in the classroom
Team 4 (technology): From algorithmic thinking to computational thinking	• Analyze how computers work • Integrate programming and computational thinking into mathematics in *STEM education* lesson planning • Develop strategies to motivate students to learn rigorous mathematics

Participants

Partner teachers in the co-teaching teams were recruited based on their STEM teaching experiences and previous participation in TERs' PD programs. Corresponding to the criteria, teachers had 5–15 years of experience and implemented STEM education in their classrooms. T2 also has a STEM management position in her school. Teachers were pre-school (T1), science (T2, T3), and math (T4) teachers. The number of participating teachers in each program ranged from 9 to 27.

Data Collection

Each TER conducted semi-structured interviews with their partner teacher. The research team designed the interview protocol. The interview protocol included questions about STEM teachers' perceptions of their roles: (1) preparation for co-teaching, (2) roles in co-teaching teams, and (3) negotiation of the decisions throughout the design, preparation, implementation, and evaluation phases. The interviews lasted approximately 60 minutes. The interviews were conducted on a popular digital communications platform. Video-recorded interviews were transcribed verbatim.

Data Analysis

First, each TER/researcher conducted a preliminary content analysis of their data independently, resulting in 62 codes. Second, the research team discussed translating some of the similar codes and grouped all resulting codes under six categories by critically evaluating previously conducted research on co-teaching (Perry & Booth, 2021; Rytivaara & Kershner, 2012; Rytivaara et al., 2019): (1) attributed roles, (2) designer, (3) enrichment, (4) collaborator, (5) embodiment, and (6) learner. Each category appeared in at least two of the four interviews. Third, 30% of the interview transcripts were double-coded independently by two raters to ensure trustworthiness. The IRR coefficient was calculated as 90%, which indicated a high IRR (Miles & Huberman, 1994). Some important codes under each category were as follows:

- Attributed Roles: Teacher educator as a mentor, teacher as facilitator/practitioner.

- Designer: Instructional activities /materials/tools, learning objectives, and content.
- Enrichment: Interdisciplinary thinking, integrating theory and practice
- Collaborator: Joint decisions, communication.
- Embodiment: Understanding/empathy about teachers' learning.
- Learner: Teaching competency, peer learning, self-evaluation.

Findings

Each case illustrates the unique experiences and perspectives of the co-teaching team, and all four cases encompassed the six categories. The categories also reflected the roles of each partner teacher in co-teaching teams.

Co-Teaching Team 1 (Science): Teaching Sustainability in Science at The Early Childhood Level

In the preparation session, T1 emphasized that the TER was a mentor in *attributed roles*. In addition, T1 explained her role as a role model, practitioner, and provider of feedback/evaluation and reported the teacher educator's role as a content initiative. In the implementation process, T1 underlined the mentor role of the teacher educator with the following statements: "*Due to your* [TER] *systematic preliminary preparations, I think the system works very well since the insight about where and how I should use the materials comes from you.*"

Regarding the *designer role*, T1 explained her role in determining learning objectives for instructional activities of the course and preparing related materials. In terms of *enrichment*, T1 emphasized the role of enriching the content in the context of presenting theory and practice as a meaningful whole. For this, T1 shared photos and videos of the classroom practices. She explained that she tried to show how the information in the book was put into practice:

> *You* [TER1] *explained the theoretical part; then, I gave an example that we do this practice in the classroom. In coordination with you, we were able to do theory, technique, and practice sequentially in the eight weeks.*

T1 contributions to the weekly meetings during the preparation process to agree on the content were in relation to the *collaborator role*. In these regular meetings, T1 also discussed her observations about the previous lesson and evaluated what she could do to improve the quality:

> *This is the information we see in the book, but we have been communicating with you in a coordinated way about how to put it into practice. Of course, I think we have achieved that. That is why we planned the content, prepared it with you* [TER1], *and the pre-meetings allowed us to convey this during the lesson precisely.*

Regarding the *embodiment,* T1 underlined that she attempted to learn the topics she was not familiar with by researching the content throughout the PD. She contributed to this role with her willingness and enthusiasm for learning throughout the course. She developed empathy for participants' learning; she stated that she was a practitioner, like the participants. Within this role, she empathized with the participants' learning and contributed to the PD content.

Regarding the *enrichment* role, T1 explained her role in facilitating and connecting the participants' learning to the teaching practice through examples. That made the integration of theory and practice possible:

> *As the implementation phase is very important, I can also convey my role as a practitioner support. I can also say that is a bit of a facilitator; maybe I think that being able to take the information and adopt it, maybe my presence there made the participants more comfortable with us.*

T1 reported that she contributed to the preparation of the content by preparing materials and conducting research and emphasized that the guidance of the TER was essential.

Regarding the *learner* role, T1 stated that the PD course had an impact on her own professional development and evaluated this effect by considering three aspects:

1. Concerning individual development, she evaluated the effect of the PD course with the following statements:

> *Being a teacher means doing research and learning to read, in this sense, this education process has made me progress incredibly. I can say that it increased my sense of curiosity even more. I found articles about education, and I read them. While reading an article, I came across another*

article there. I discovered new things. Professionally, this eight-week course, its preparation and the process after completion provided me with the most significant contribution.

2. Concerning the teachers working in the same school, she assessed the impact of the PD course by expressing that she shared what she had learned in the PD course in conversations with the teachers she worked with and conveyed what she had gained.
3. Concerning the children in her class, T1 evaluated the effect of the PD course on the children, stating that her communication with the children changed owing to the knowledge and experience she gained, which affected the synergy of the class.

Moreover, T1 stated that she had the chance to test her teaching during the PD and underlined that what she learned from her research relevant to the PD content was highly effective.

Co-Teaching Team 2 (Mathematics): Data Science and Modeling with Data Loggers (LabStar)

Regarding the *attributed roles*, T2 underlined her role as a practitioner and facilitator. Providing feedback and evaluation came forth within the attributed roles. T2 also emphasized that being a *STEM leader teacher* contributed to her role. This background of T2 helped her in the role of providing feedback and evaluation: *"I give feedback in line with my experience; otherwise, I am a teacher, and they are also teachers."*

Regarding the *designer* role, T2 focused on her role in planning and implementing instructional activities separately. By planning the instructional activities, she explained that she contributed to developing the PD program content based on her subject-matter knowledge. She also contributed to decision-making regarding the scope of the PD program during the preparation period. She brought her knowledge about specific instructional strategies to her designer role within the implementation.

T2 focused on integrating theory and practice dimensions, which contributed to the *enrichment* of the PD program. By integrating theory and practice, T2 asserted that she aimed to reflect the theoretical aspects of *STEM Education* in the daily life of participating teachers from diverse backgrounds and needs. Furthermore, T2 used her background and teaching experience to bring many practical implementations of various disciplines to the PD context. T2 thought that being in a co-teaching team enabled the team to show the interdependence of theory and practice throughout PD:

> *You* [TER2] *have much more academic information, for example, statistical information and its use in science. You could also guide me in this sense. I was also able to give you information about practical in-class applications. It was like a mutual thing; there was always feedback between us.*

Regarding the role of *the collaborator*, T2 emphasized the effectiveness of communication between the co-teaching team. T2 underlined weekly regular meetings and the way the co-teachers negotiated the content and structure of the PD course through continuous communication. The decisions about the PD course were centered around the participant teachers' learning, according to T2. More precisely, the collaboration between co-teachers occurred to enhance the learning experiences of participant teachers: *"This is always a joint decision, and as I said, we forced ourselves* [the co-teaching team] *to meet the needs of the participant teachers."*

T2 built the *embodiment* throughout the PD by her understanding and empathy about how participating teachers' learning occurs. Her professional background enabled this understanding, and she established a relationship with participating teachers accordingly. Therefore, T2 was especially attentive to creating a horizontal relationship rather than a hierarchical one: *"There is a risk in teacher education that there may be a reaction like 'you are teaching me my job'."* With her willingness and enthusiasm, T2 also contributed to the *embodiment* of the course. She believed that her willingness to explore and share new ways of teaching within and beyond her discipline encouraged the participant teachers to engage in the activities through the PD program.

T2 embraced the *learner's role* throughout the PD course. She pointed out that with the co-teaching experience, she engaged in self-evaluation of her teaching. T2 underlined that being open to self-evaluation was crucial to improving herself in adult education. She explained that as a teacher educator, she has the responsibility to learn from participant teachers and be a part of the professional learning community: "*I learned from a participating chemistry teacher that the bubbling sound, which is an indicator of that reaction time, can also be measured by the sound sensor.*" In the learner's role, T2 reflected on her teaching competency in adult education settings. T2 explained how she struggled with the participant teachers to enhance their active participation at the beginning of the PD course: "*But I think it was a little more difficult to be a little more interactive, to be able to attract them* [participant teachers] *to the lesson.*" T2 explained that she improved her content knowledge of other STEM disciplines. T2, as an experienced physics teacher, pointed out that she learned a lot from teachers of other STEM disciplines, which further improved her role as a *STEM leader teacher.*

Co-Teaching Team 3 (Engineering): Engineering Design-Based Thematic STEM Activities

In the preparation stage of the course, T3 emphasized his role as a leader in *attributed roles.* T3 also explained the TER's role as both a leader and mentor. He perceived himself as a leader in determining the content and activities aligned with the STEM experiences. He especially emphasized the mentor role of the TER: "*I had my ideas for preparing the syllabus, and I shared these ideas with the teacher educator in the co-teaching team. Based on the common idea, we decided on the final version with the TER's guidance.*"

T3 emphasized that he trusted the TER's experience during the lessons regarding the attributed roles. He stated that the TER played a mentor role during the course and the preparation phase. T3 explained that while the TER was a role model for himself and the teachers in life lessons, he could also be a role model for teachers. Moreover, he stated that the role of the TER in evaluating teachers' STEM activities and giving feedback was noteworthy.

Considering the *designer*'s role, T3 focused on his role in determining instructional strategies and materials. T3 also emphasized his designer's role in determining the content of engineering design-based STEM activities and providing more examples of these activities. He thought that sharing these examples motivated the participants to perform an engineering design-based activity: "*I mostly gave engineering design-based examples to teachers and focused on the difficulties they might encounter in practice. I think these examples have been beneficial for encouraging and motivating teachers.*"

The teacher's roles in sharing and owning pedagogical content knowledge (PCK) for STEM were underlined regarding the enrichment roles. T3 stated that giving examples of the activities and sharing his experience enriched the course. T3 considered participating teachers' misconceptions about engineering design-based STEM activities in the teaching process, owing to his experiences and postgraduate education. He also stated that he did not take any STEM-focused courses in his pre-service education as a limitation. T3, a STEM teacher leader and Ph.D. candidate emphasized that his confidence in implementation roles was mainly influenced by prior teaching experience.

> *I paid attention to sharing more practice examples with teachers. The difficulties they may encounter in the classroom, the difficulties they will experience in the practice process after preparing the lesson plan.*

T3 emphasized that the content initiative role of the TER was significant in enriching the course. T3 especially stated that his theoretical knowledge on the subject was limited compared to the TER and explained that the TER's theoretical knowledge of the content enriched the process: "*The TER focused more on the theoretical part of the course, and I focused on the practice part. My theoretical knowledge of the content was much more limited than the knowledge of the teacher educator.*"

In terms of the *collaborator* role, T3 stated that as a teacher, making decisions and cooperating with the TER had a role that enhanced the teacher and the course. T3 explained that he had previously given individual online PD to the teachers and emphasized the importance of teacher-TER cooperation compared to this course. He also pointed out that the courses conducted only by the TER would not be sufficient and that the cooperation between the teacher and the TER is more effective than the other individual courses.

T3 also stated that the attributed roles of the teacher and TER were related to the *collaborator*'s roles. For instance, he explained that they made decisions together under the TER's mentorship by collaborating. Moreover, T3 emphasized that empathy in teachers' learning (embodiment role) strengthened teacher-TER cooperation. Regarding this collaboration, he argued that considering the content and teaching the course from the participating teachers' perspective made the course more productive.

In terms of *embodiment roles*, T3 focused on his role in feeling empathy with teachers and confidence. In addition, in line with his experiences, he perceived himself as a problem solver and could empathize with the participating teachers' problems during the practice process. For example, T3 emphasized that he considered himself highly competent in preparing an engineering design-based lesson plan.

> *I know how to write and not write an engineering design-based lesson plan. I know how to write a lesson plan. I know the elements in a lesson plan that the student will receive well and what should not be included.*

The *learner* role of T3 was also evident. Regarding the learner role, T3 expressed himself as one of the participating teachers who developed content knowledge and teaching competency and as a learner by self-evaluation. For instance, T3 explained that the TER's theoretical knowledge of science subjects and engineering design-based activities during teaching contributed to developing his science content knowledge and competencies, such as teamwork, communication, and discussion. He also explained that providing feedback on the lesson plans prepared by the participating teachers enabled learning from the participating teachers. As a result of what he learned and of self-evaluation, he concluded that these experiences played an important role in PD.

Co-Teaching Team 4 (Technology): From Algorithmic Thinking to Computational Thinking

Two years before their co-teaching experience for this study, TER4 participated in a PD course designed and implemented by T4. The course helped TER4 learn how some programming languages could be used in teaching mathematics. Thus, their *attributed roles* in the current study were likely influenced by this past encounter.

When helping other teachers during the PD program, T4 explained his role as someone who helped them cope with the change. He advocated that teachers were not given the autonomy, tools, or enough time to adapt to the changes in the curriculum. They were simply not ready for abrupt changes in the high-stakes testing systems or the fast-changing needs of the new generation of learners. He added that the teachers themselves were not immune to change as they gained experience over the years: *"I could see where they lacked and where they were effective in the classroom. Not perfectly, though.* [Because teacher professional development] *is a continuous process, an iterative process".*

According to T4, TER4's role in the partnership was to help T4 see the bigger picture of teacher needs because T4's experiences were bounded by the teachers he knew. T4 seemed appreciative of TER4 bringing what research suggested into the co-teaching partnership.

In the *designer* role, T4 expressed his content with their agreement to follow a backward design, starting from what they want to teach and what participating teachers want to learn at the end of the PD program. It was easy to spot his words implying that the PD program created a community of learners, including T4, TER4, and the participating teachers.

> *I adore this concept. It all starts with the outcome. Picturing the end was everything to us; it was what we hoped to achieve, what we wanted to learn together from coding, and how I would integrate it into mathematics. Both* [mathematics and computers] *have no boundaries. They are intertwined like the double helix of DNA, and yet, at times, they are very different. It is critical that we know* [the outcome]*; otherwise, they drag you under.*

Considering the *enrichment roles*, T4 complained that teaching technology or mathematics with technology could not be bound by a document. T4 emphasized that "*curriculum lags the teachers; it is way behind the students. It is behind life.*" However, T4 and TER4 agreed that the standard pre-service teacher education curriculum in Turkey was far away from preparing future teachers for the changing needs of today's students at schools. Thus, T4 found himself helping teachers fill the gaps in their pre-service education:

> *I was surprised that technology teachers were not taught how to design an algorithm* [at the pre-service level]. *They knew some coding but no algorithms. We needed to show them that algorithms were not about the sequencing of events; it is how we can make a computer do it...Mathematics teachers knew how to find the greatest common divisor by drawing a line next to the numbers, but why would we need Euclid's algorithm? No mathematicians need it...but computers do.* [My role in this PD program] *was to show that how you make a computer solve a problem differs from how you solve it in real-life or how it is solved in mathematics or physics. We wanted* [the participants of the PD program] *to see this difference.*

As part of the *collaborator* role, T4 emphasized the importance of parity in all roles assumed by the partners for the success of the PD program.

> *As a matter of fact,* [referring to TER4], *your academic knowledge was evident during our meetings with the teachers. However, your contribution to the PD program materialized because of your self-perceived role as a teacher first*

> *and a colleague with whom I partnered. We could work in tandem; not one* [theory] *after the other* [practice] *and not one over the other.*

Regarding the *embodiment* roles, T4 emphasized that making teachers ask questions about life and being curious about their subject matter was what mattered the most to the PD program:

> *How does a computer add numbers? How does it use 0s and 1's; let us do it with logic operators whether it is in the curriculum or not. I learned rings and fields; I was all over the place and in the nth space, but I did not know what good polynomials were. Teachers try to make abstract structures more real to the students; instead, teachers should help students make the real-life more abstract, which is not applying mathematics, that is, doing mathematics, and that starts by asking questions about life.*

Discussion and Conclusion

Partner teachers in co-teaching teams evaluated their roles in six categories: attributed roles, collaborator, learner, embodiment, designer, and enrichment. Regarding the attributed roles, teachers underlined a mentor-facilitator role balance between teachers and TERs. Following this role attribution, participant teachers could facilitate theory and practice integration throughout the PD courses within their enrichment role. One possible explanation for these findings is that the teaching experience of the participant teachers helped them integrate in-class examples and lived stories into the theoretical perspective of PD courses. Participant teachers were aware of the curriculum's needs, leading them to decide more precisely on the specific instructional activities and materials. This aspect also contributed to the designer role of participant teachers. Another reason participant teachers embraced a designer role could be related to the mentor role of the TERs. The decisions on the theoretical perspectives were attributed to the TERs, whereas participant teachers mainly designed specific instructional activities (Leatherman, 2009).

Regarding the embodiment role, participant teachers mainly emphasized that they could empathize with the PD audience. One possible explanation could be that teachers were confident about how teachers learn. They anticipated possible challenges during the PD course and contributed to the solution. In their collaborator role, participating teachers underlined how they negotiated the decisions about the course through continuous communication between co-teachers. This likely demonstrates that teachers believed in both partners' active contributions to the PD course (Jang, 2006; Jardí et al., 2022). The learner role of the participant teachers was also evident during the interviews. It appears that participant teachers have found opportunities to evaluate themselves and set goals for improvement.

The findings indicated that co-planning and co-assessing occurred along with the co-teaching process. The members of each team shared a balanced responsibility based on their varied roles. The results revealed evidence of equal partnership regarding the co-teaching process (Hurd & Weilbacher, 2017). Relevant research also pointed out that teaching teams share a balanced responsibility in planning, teaching, and assessing processes (Conderman, 2011).

In conclusion, the proposed co-teaching model is also promising for pre-service science teacher education. Establishing co-teaching teams in science teacher education can facilitate theory and practice integration in university-school partnerships. The co-teaching model can be a guide to strengthening university-school partnerships. The first implication was that teachers and TERs should share a mutual understanding in the field. This can be because the co-teaching teams were established individually instead of in a top-down approach. It was believed that with careful selection and planning, both parties embraced the instructional roles and collaborated effectively throughout the course. The top-down approach, on the contrary, causes both parties to feel mostly overwhelmed and not engage in the course content. Moreover, practicing teachers do not get any recognition for the coursework.

The roles underlined in the research findings can guide effectively establishing co-teaching teams within university-school partnerships where both parties can benefit. Future research on pre-service teacher education can contribute to solving the complex and dynamic nature of teacher and teacher educator partnerships in universities.

Acknowledgments The authors acknowledge the feedback received from the following individuals in writing this book chapter: Sevinç Ağgül, Hakan Ataş, Senem Bademci, and Uğur Sarıçam.

References

Bauwens, J., Hourcade, J. J., & Friend, M. (1989). Cooperative teaching: A model for general and special education integration. *RASE. Remedial & Special Education, 10*(2), 17–22. https://doi.org/10.1177/074193258901000205

Conderman, G. (2011). Middle school co-teaching: Effective practices and student reflections. *Middle School Journal, 42*(4), 24–31.

Corlu, M. S. (2017). STEM: Bütünleşik öğretmenlik çerçevesi [STEM integrated teaching framework]. In M. S. Corlu & E. Çallı (Eds.), *STEM Kuram ve Uygulamaları [STEM theory and practice]* (pp. 1–10). Pusula. https://doi.org/10.19128/turje.332731

Hurd, E., & Weilbacher, G. (2017). "You want me to do what?" the benefits of co-teaching in the middle level. *Middle Grades Review, 3*(1), article 4.

Jang, S. J. (2006). Research on the effects of team teaching upon two secondary school teachers. *Educational Research, 48*(2), 177–194. https://doi.org/10.1080/00131880600732272

Jardí, A., Webster, R., Petrenas, C., & Puigdellívol, I. (2022). Building successful partnerships between teaching assistants and teachers: Which interpersonal factors matter? *Teaching and Teacher Education, 109*, 103523. https://doi.org/10.1016/j.tate.2021.103523

Leatherman, J. (2009). Teachers' voices concerning collaborative teams within an inclusive elementary school. *Teaching Education, 20*(2), 189–202. https://doi.org/10.1080/10476210902718104

Merriam, S. B. (2009). *Qualitative research: A guide to design and implementation.* John Wiley and Sons.

Miles, M. B., & Huberman, A. M. (1994). *Qualitative data analysis* (An expanded sourcebook ed.).

Ministry of National Education. (2016). STEM Education Report.

Perry, E., & Booth, J. (2021). The practices of professional development facilitators. *Professional Development in Education*, 1–13. https://doi.org/10.1080/19415257.2021.1973073

Perry, E., & Boylan, M. (2018). Developing the developers: Supporting and researching the learning of professional development facilitators. *Professional Development in Education, 44*(2), 254–271. https://doi.org/10.1080/19415257.2017.1287767

Pratt, S. (2014). Achieving symbiosis: Working through challenges found in co-teaching to achieve effective co-teaching relationships. *Teaching and Teacher Education, 41*, 1–12. https://doi.org/10.1016/j.tate.2014.02.006

Roth, W. M., Tobin, K., Carambo, C., & Dalland, C. (2004). Coteaching: Creating resources for learning and learning to teach chemistry in urban high schools. *Journal of Research in Science Teaching, 41*(9), 882–904. https://doi.org/10.1002/tea.20030

Rytivaara, A., & Kershner, R. (2012). Co-teaching as a context for teachers' professional learning and joint knowledge construction. *Teaching and Teacher Education, 28*(7), 999–1008. https://doi.org/10.1016/j.tate.2012.05.006

Rytivaara, A., Pulkkinen, J., & de Bruin, C. L. (2019). Committing, engaging and negotiating: Teachers' stories about creating shared spaces for co-teaching. *Teaching and Teacher Education, 83*, 225–235. https://doi.org/10.1016/j.tate.2019.04.013

Yin, R. K. (2014). *Case study research design and methods* (5th ed.).

CHAPTER 13

Entanglement of the United States and Turkish Science and Mathematics Educators Through the Lens of *Becomings*: Conceptualizing STEM Education Using a Bakhtinian Dialogic Approach

Sophia Jeong, Kathryn M. Bateman, Sevil Akaygun, Fatma Aslan-Tutak, Mutlu Şen-Akbulut, and Reyhan Ada Safak

S. Jeong (✉) • R. A. Safak
The Ohio State University, Columbus, OH, USA
e-mail: jeong.387@osu.edu; safak.2@buckeyemail.osu.edu

K. M. Bateman
The Pennsylvania State University, State College, PA, USA
e-mail: kbateman@psu.edu

S. Akaygun • F. Aslan-Tutak • M. Şen-Akbulut
Boğaziçi University, Istanbul, Turkey
e-mail: sevil.akaygun@boun.edu.tr; fatma.tutak@boun.edu.tr; mutlu.sen@boun.edu.tr

S. M. Al-Balushi et al. (eds.), *Reforming Science Teacher Education Programs in the STEM Era*, Palgrave Studies on Leadership and Learning in Teacher Education,
https://doi.org/10.1007/978-3-031-27334-6_13

Theoretical Framework

We utilize a Bakhtinian dialogic approach (Bakhtin, 1982) to examine our experiences and *becomings* (Barad, 2007) in research and teaching of STEM education, and science and mathematics teacher preparations. In this approach, dialogic is "an ongoing interplay of articulation that both builds on what has come before and contributes to what has and has yet to come" (Sherman et al., 2021, p. 284). We engage in Bakhtinian dialogic research practices to juxtapose science and mathematics teacher preparations at two research-intensive, public universities in Midwestern and East Coast regions in the U.S. and the northwestern region of Turkey. This interplay of articulation allows for vexations, which each of the authors face in developing preservice teachers for STEM education, to emerge. The dialogic is both a method and means of analysis where by dialogues and written artifacts are analyzed to (1) juxtapose STEM teacher preparation programs in Turkey and U.S. with a critical lens, (2) highlight vexations that need to be addressed and further problematized, and (3) examine our place and becomings as STEM teacher educators in an assemblage of the global educational contexts.

Drawing on Barad's (2007) work on the notion of *becomings*, we are part of an assemblage that is organized, re-organized, and composed of heterogeneous actors that are entangled. Our findings of the dialogic interactions illustrate how these heterogeneous actors work in entangled, messy, non-linear ways, and demonstrate our place or becomings in the assemblage. We examine how our becomings may overlay with one another in not only generating productive tensions but also answering salient research questions: (1) what are the frameworks of STEM education in each country and how does each country's framing impact how we prepare preservice teachers for STEM education? (2) What can we learn from what is happening in the U.S. and Turkey to create locations of possibilities (Brandt, 2008) to address what we may be lacking and conceptualize teacher preparation programs for STEM education in ways that have yet to be thought.

Background and Literature

STEM Education

The history and inception of STEM education is beyond the scope of this chapter. However, achieving STEM literacy appears to be a common yet an amorphous global goal (Blackley & Howell, 2015; Rocard et.al., 2007; Aksela, et al., 2020). The discussion of improving STEM education has been amplified at all levels of education in Turkey and the U.S. (see Radloff & Guzey, 2016 for US context; and Baran et al., 2016 in Turkey). What follows the narratives on improving STEM education is the need for educating effective STEM teachers (Akaygun & Aslan-Tutak, 2020; Radloff & Guzey, 2016), though little is known about how preservice STEM teachers develop their integrated conceptions of STEM teaching (Radloff & Guzey, 2016). In this chapter, we support an integrated approach to STEM education, rather than a traditional siloed approach (see Moore et al., 2014; Radloff & Guzey, 2016). For instance, Johnson (2013) frames STEM education as an integrated instructional approach by foregrounding STEM thought processes and practices instead of the traditional emphasis over content. In Turkey, developing scientific or mathematical literacy drives the concerns of the national curricula; however, integrated STEM education programs are still needed to develop students' STEM literacy in terms of real-life problem solving (Baran et al., 2016). Our position does not advocate for the abolishment of science, math, technology, and engineering as educational programs, but rather, we value crossing disciplinary boundaries to more closely resemble the integrated practices of professional scientists, mathematicians, computer scientists, and engineers.

Approaches to STEM Education

Carla Johnson (2013) delineates between different STEM education approaches as being STEM enhanced courses, interdisciplinary electives, and truly integrated courses. STEM enhanced and interdisciplinary take the approach of *more is more*, while integrated courses take what exists and bring the disciplines together to highlight the practices as working together. We recognize each of these as constructive moves toward improving STEM education and STEM teacher preparation in our thinking about STEM education in Turkey and the United States.

The trajectory of STEM education needs to change as the practices evolve, technology improves, and new knowledge is acquired. Radloff & Guzey (2016) have found that STEM education is often discussed in the three following ways as: (1) instruction, (2) integrated disciplines, and (3) dependent on the stakeholders' context in which STEM education is operationalized. Likewise, Bybee (2013) suggests that the conception of STEM education should emerge from an educator's context and needs. Zollman (2012) also writes, "STEM literacy should not be viewed as a content area but as a shifting, deictic means (composed of skills, abilities, factual knowledge, procedures, concepts, and metacognitive capacities) to gain further learning" (p. 12). The communities of STEM practitioners and stakeholders shape and change the STEM fields, and conversations around what counts as STEM education must continue to evolve. Thus, we return to the purpose of this chapter: to juxtapose the different approaches to STEM education and STEM teacher preparation in Turkey and U.S. to explore locations of possibility in integrated STEM education.

Our Learnings to Research Question 1

What are the frameworks of STEM education and how does each country's framing impact how we prepare science and mathematics preservice teachers for STEM education?

STEM Education and Policy in Turkish Context

In Turkey, the Turkish Ministry of Education (MoNE)'s strategic plan for the years 2015–2019 includes goals to strengthen the STEM education in Turkey. MoNE's report published in 2016 emphasizes the need for increasing the qualified research-minded manpower who could work in the private sector of STEM-related areas. It also prioritizes an innovative and high-tech transformation in order to empower entrepreneurship capacity and form a qualified employment infrastructure for transforming a knowledge-based economy. (MoNE, 2018).

In 2018, Turkish science curriculum was restructured to expand "Science, Engineering and Entrepreneurship Applications," in middle school science curricula of Grades 4–8 (MoNE, 2018; Kayacan & Ozluleci, 2021) using a particular lesson called "Technology and Design." Since then, Turkey has continued to place emphasis on strengthening the collaboration among secondary schools with higher institutions to support the goals of developing students' scientific digitalization, entrepreneurship skills, as well as improving the vocational and technical education in terms of their curricula and digitalization (MoNE, 2018). Consequently, in 2020, "Design and Skill Workshops (Tasarım Beceri Atölyeleri)," which was intended to provide space for implementing integrated STEM curriculum and applied education (Arslan, 2021), became available for K-12 teachers and students in Turkey. Despite these efforts to establish and improve STEM programs in Turkey, there is still no explicit STEM policy document that provides guidance on how to enact integrated STEM teaching. To this end, Ay and Seferoğlu (2021) argue that efforts from other ministries, industry, business, civil society organizations, and stakeholders should participate in the discourse and not just the voice of MoNE.

STEM Education and Policy in U.S. Context
By contrast to the more centralized approaches to STEM education in Turkey, U.S. generates education policy at national, state, and local levels; yet the actuality of education is a "states right" under the tenth Amendment in the U.S. Constitution. Policies are put in place through the federal Department of Education but are also entangled with the state-level policies as they make their way into local contexts. For example, the legacy of No Child Left Behind (NCLB) authorization from 2001 in the U.S. education policy remains strong. NCLB mandated that states implement standards and assess those standards in K-12 education, first only for reading and mathematics, which has had a lasting impact on science education (Penfield & Lee, 2010). Though science was added to required testing in 2007, implementation combined with historical norms of focus on reading and mathematics has relegated science in the U.S. education to a backseat, particularly in the elementary (K-5) grades (Milner et al., 2012). Technology and engineering are not explicitly included in the policy.

Standards in science and mathematics are developed at the state level with nationally recognized, but not required, standards currently available for states to use. The Common Core State Standards for Mathematics are currently in place in forty of the fifty states (Common Core State Standards Initiative, n.d.). The NGSS Lead States developed the Next Generation Science Standards, which 20 states adopted as state standards while 24 are building their state standards based on the NGSS (NSTA, n.d.). Two states in which the authors engage in STEM teacher education have not adopted the NGSS, fully or partially when the authors were teaching.

STEM educators of this chapter teaching in these U.S. contexts often expect preservice STEM teachers to become familiar with both the NGSS and the appropriate state science standards. The authors learned that teachers would be expected in their schools to evaluate students' progress toward the mastery of the state standards, which might not align with NGSS in terms of goals, expectations, or modes of assessments. For example, a multiple-choice focused test does not allow for measurement of the three-dimensional goals of the NGSS and its performance expectations (Judson, 2013; Sondergeld, et al., 2016). This misalignment creates a dilemma for STEM teacher educators. To prepare preservice STEM teachers to understand the nationally recognized standards and framework is logical, but awareness of the state standards currently in place in the classrooms in which they will teach is also critical.

STEM Teacher Preparation in Turkish Context

We learned through our dialogues that there are similar "governing" bodies (such as accreditation) that influence the curriculum of teacher preparation programs. The Turkish Council of Higher Education (Turkish Higher Educational Council, 2018) drives the recommendations for STEM teacher preparation. These recommendations focus on inclusion of courses such as Philosophy of Education, Sociology of Education, and History of Turkish Education. Most universities in Turkey adopted their suggestions, while some institutions chose not to follow the recommendations. Turkish STEM scholars of this chapter along with their colleagues at their institution developed a report providing a rationale as to why their institution chose to determine their own curriculum instead of following the Council's suggestions. Prompted by this report, the Council decided to allow curricular decisions to institutions.

Course instructors play a significant role in shaping the philosophy, rationale, and content of courses in Turkish STEM teacher programs. STEM educators with different skills and understanding of what STEM education means led to diverse methods and emphases in courses and programs. For example, one of the Turkish scholars of this chapter draws on Blackley & Howell's (2015) conceptual framework of STEM education development that includes five steps: (1) STEM political agenda, (2) STEM enacted as S.T.E.M., (3) STEM interpreted as S.t.e.M., (4) the rise of STEM education, and (5) integrated STEM education. While acknowledging the importance of integrated STEM education as conceptualized in Blackley and Howell's (2015) work, Turkish science and mathematics educators of this chapter emphasize the impact of specialization in the instructors' area of expertise on conceptualizing STEM education, and that interdisciplinary thinking should have a foundation in the disciplinary or content specialization areas. To this end, content courses in Turkish STEM teacher preparations are often taught by scientists and mathematicians while methods or pedagogy courses are taught by science and mathematics educators. In content courses, the focus tends to be about providing intensive theoretical knowledge in STEM disciplinary areas without the consideration of interdisciplinary thinking that STEM teachers need to teach higher level of thinking to K-12 students (Yilmaz et al., 2018). Though STEM education should not be viewed as a singular outcome process, courses in Turkish STEM programs can aim to provide a space for STEM teachers to see exemplars of integrated STEM teaching, curriculum resources and applications.

A sequence of courses in the STEM teacher preparation program at the authors' institutions in Turkey typically begins with a set of content courses and introduction to pedagogy. In the second year, educational courses such as educational psychology are offered. Courses on pedagogical content knowledge are taken by Turkish preservice teachers at the end of second year to learn about writing learning outcomes and lesson planning. In the third year, methods and content courses continue along with courses on educational technology. The Turkish STEM scholars of this chapter indicated that coursework at their institutions emphasize the importance of content. As teacher certification in Turkey tends to silo STEM teachers to content in their certified area, teachers are not often encouraged to integrate their content area with the other STEM disciplinary areas and consequently, integrated STEM teaching is not seen in the classrooms in Turkey (Çınar et al., 2016). However, in order for K-12 students to receive STEM education that uses an interdisciplinary approach, STEM teachers need to develop the ability to relate their content area to the knowledge and skills from other disciplines (Çınar et al., 2016). To this end, "unit zero" was developed (MoNE, 2018) to support the enactment of STEM teaching and learning. Starting from Grade 4 (Age 9–10), this unit zero on "Science, Engineering, and Entrepreneurship Applications" is embedded in the curricula. However, the overall perception of STEM education still seems to be very much an afterthought. Many teachers see STEM education as an addendum instead as an integration of the disciplinary areas in education. STEM scholars of this chapter often saw that K-12 STEM teachers have difficulties integrating technology and engineering (see third step S.t.e.M in Blackley & Howell's model) and asserted that aiming to reach the fifth step from Blackley & Howell's

(2015) model would be a productive goal to teach K-12 STEM teachers' interdisciplinary way of thinking, teaching and learning.

STEM Teacher Preparation in U.S. Context

We previously discussed the differences in standards available or required by the national and state levels. Here, we discuss the different goals present inside of U.S. higher education, specifically, goals of programs, instructors, and their interactions in the K-12 systems. At the program level, the penultimate goal is to prepare highly qualified K-12 STEM teachers, but what that looks like can vary between programs. For example, the U.S. science educators of this chapter experienced diverse teaching contexts in K-12 levels working with both preservice and in-service teachers in various learning formats including in-person, hybrid, and on-line (synchronous and asynchronous). Between many areas of expertise and experiences, we found that the goals of the courses and programs can vary and change. For example, at one of the author's research-intensive (R1) institution, preparing secondary preservice STEM teachers (certifications in biology, chemistry, physics, and earth and space science) focused on science with some engineering design aspects, while at another author's research-intensive institution, engineering by design, as an integrative nature of STEM education in comparable methods courses, was emphasized. Variation at the programmatic level found in our dialogues across our experiences was that mathematics education courses may or may not be separate and may or may not be required of preservice teachers. Variations across programs to include engineering and technology were also significant and the level of integration was often dependent on the course instructor.

We learned that the instructors' goals for the courses play a role in what was emphasized and taught. Though course syllabus was closely followed, instructors can emphasize different components that they value. For example, a science educator in this chapter with an expertise in policy work emphasized educational policies in the U.S. and their role in shaping STEM instruction, while focusing on earth science content. Another science educator with research interests in equitable and inclusive teaching practices shifted the orientation of the courses to highlight diversity, equity, and inclusion issues in STEM education in the U.S., while leveraging bioengineering content knowledge to model integrative approaches to STEM teaching and learning.

Finally, we learned that interaction with the school level influenced the learning of preservice teachers. Called by a variety of names, (i.e., student teaching, intern teaching, field experience) preservice teachers' practical application of teaching skills in the field is an important part of their preparation. In this experience, preservice teachers are assigned a mentor teacher who has their own goals for teaching STEM, which can be in conflict with what the preservice teachers learned in their coursework and methods courses (see Cohen et al., 2013). Prior work by one of the science educators in the U.S. (McDonald et al., 2020) worked to collapse these layers and align the goals between mentor teachers, preservice teachers, and the university instructors by working as a triad. In so doing, mentor teachers participated in a professional learning community with the university instructors to align their views on STEM education. This type of collaborative working relationship can be an effective approach for STEM education, but only if goals are co-created with university instructors, mentor teachers, and preservice teachers and have policies at the university and national level to support STEM education.

Our Learnings to Research Question 2

What can we learn from what is happening in the U.S. and Turkey to create locations of possibilities to address what we may be lacking and conceptualize science teacher preparation programs for STEM education in ways that have yet to be thought?

Locations of Re-Imaginations, Possibilities and Critiques

We discussed locations of possibilities to bolster integrated STEM education in these areas: (1) sociocultural resources, (2) physical and fiscal resources, and (3) policy changes. We discussed these areas in terms of the literature that supports the need for these changes, and re-imagine locations of possibility (Brandt, 2008) in the practical application of our own contexts. In particular, we identified the fostering of communities of practice, re-imaginations to STEM teacher preparation curricula, and increased and modified resources for integrated STEM education.

A community of practice is fostered when individuals engage and participate in collective learning in a shared domain (Wenger, 1998). Research in communities of practice in teacher education have shown to increase self-efficacy (Tseng & Kuo, 2014), improve respectful discourse (Bannister, 2015), and reduce feelings of isolation (Patton & Parker, 2017). We assert that fostering communities of practice for both teachers and teacher educators in STEM education would enhance the implementation of integrated STEM education. In our dialogues, we identified the key players to bring into conversations to re-imagine possibilities and drive change:

- Between universities and local schools, there needs to be co-construction of a shared understanding of what STEM teaching looks like in their local context in order to develop and share resources such as exemplar curricula to support teachers to enact integrated STEM curriculum. STEM teacher education is grounded in the philosophy of apprenticeship (Brown et al., 1989) and they need good models of interdisciplinary teaching and of how to assess students in that context. Through collaborations with mentor teachers, we can learn to navigate the landscape of the day-to-day teaching in the classrooms while creating a community of practice where mentor teachers, university instructors, and preservice teachers co-participate in discourses about integrated curriculum, re-imagine ways to support and consider what STEM education means, and what STEM teaching and learning can look like in their local context.
- Between and within universities, there needs to be a re-imagination of courses to foster preservice teachers' understanding of interdisciplinary approaches to STEM education. We can re-imagine methods and content courses as a space for a collaboration between content experts and STEM educators in order to re-imagine a more integrated learning experiences for preservice teachers.
- Policy makers and institutions must work toward policy changes grounded in cutting-edge research that fosters equity across all educational contexts. Broadly, as STEM educators, we have experienced policies that left lasting impacts on schools in our respective context. Policies matter and therefore, we need to continue to re-imagine policies and standards that create space for STEM teachers to innovate their teaching without feeling defeated by standardized testing mandates.

Our Becomings as STEM Educators and Entanglements with Other Actors

Considering the broader international context, STEM educators of this chapter engaged in dialogues and reflected on the need to prepare future STEM teachers to face wicked problems (Carter, 2011) in STEM education. These challenges are both localized and global where actors are entangled with other actors who are always and already in the milieu or "middle" (Deleuze & Guatarri, 1987) of becoming *Homo sapiens textilis*, the human that knows it is interwoven (Jeong et al., 2021). Facing these challenges, STEM educators need to not only educate future generations of STEM teachers and K-12 students in interdisciplinary, collaborative, and transdisciplinary way of thinking, but they also need to consider what STEM education could become—what actors can we assemble into this conceptualization of STEM education as it is today in order to re-assemble it to work and effect changes in a meaningful way in the future?

Locations of possibilities emerged during four modes of dialogic encounters: (1) Articulation, (2) Reflection, (3) Analysis, and (4) Re-articulation (Jeong & Lewis, In Press, 2022). We articulated our positionalities and reflected on the state of STEM teacher preparation in our respective context in relation to one another. We analyzed and juxtaposed similarities and differences in STEM teacher programs in Turkey and U.S. and re-articulated the conceptualizing of what STEM education could become. In so doing, we acknowledged and were diffracting what we were "seeing," as our positions were entangled and interacting in an assemblage (see Fig. 13.1). In more localized contexts, we were entangled with our teachers, students, and colleagues. In a broader context, we saw a larger discourse that snared us into the entanglement of what STEM should be, could be, and would be. We shared the challenges and

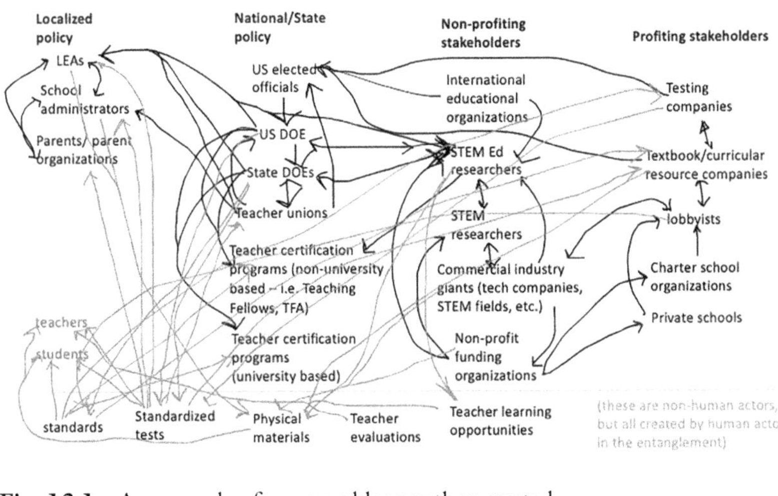

Fig. 13.1 An example of an assemblage author created

approaches to STEM teacher programs and began to sketch out the entanglements we noticed in this process (i.e., what were the actors that could be moved or were immovable and how were these actors pulling on us). We were participants of discourses that had a clear impact on our scholarship, teaching, research, and positionalities.

The influence of U.S. education policy moved beyond the nation's borders and impacted STEM education abroad. In Turkey, STEM educators participated in practices different from the U.S. scholars', as the purpose of STEM education was tied to economic development goals. In Turkey, students' attitude toward STEM was generally positive (see Yamak et al., 2014) because the perception is that STEM-related careers help with social and economic mobility (see Lissitsa & Chachashvili-Bolotin, 2021). We saw similar perceptions in the U.S. where STEM education was often used in the metaphors of creating a "pipeline of STEM workers" for strengthening and maintaining the U.S. position in the global economy (Cannady et al., 2014). As STEM educators, we felt compelled to critique and help teachers navigate their participations in these different discourses that would likely continue to co-exist and have a real impact on their day-to-day teaching.

Drawing on the state of STEM education context in both U.S. and Turkey, we were navigating the lack of STEM educator's representation in policy making at the national level. Since inception in 1979, the Secretary of Education position has only been held by one STEM teacher (Ted Sanders, 1990–1991) and one scientist (Lauro Cavazos, 1988–1990), diminishing the voice of STEM stakeholders. In the Turkish context, the Ministry attempted to do a top-down recommendation on what STEM should be. However, Turkish institutions and faculty members collectively took a stance to push back on the top-down approach. To that end, the conceptualization of STEM education, what it could become, and its potentiality need to be inclusive of multiple stakeholders in STEM education.

Conclusion with a Conceptualization-In-Motion

Our chapter's goal of re-assembling and re-imagining STEM education is not a singular process nor does it produce a singular concept, or an end result. Our becomings, entangled in an assemblage of STEM education in our context, are ever evolving, and so should be the conceptualization of STEM education. We encourage STEM teachers, educators and stakeholders to continue to re-imagine what STEM education could become in their context and its potentiality to do work by leaving material marks or effects on the actors and rendering them to become response-able (see Haraway, 2016) interdisciplinary thinkers and address wicked problems.

To that end, we end with a few recommendations to consider: First, we recommend that STEM educators identify the wicked problems or questions (Carter, 2011) still to be answered in their context and examine possibilities in which STEM education can become a vehicle to do meaningful work in educating K-12 students and teachers. Second, we suggest STEM educators and stakeholders to consider ways to support the classroom teachers to integrate content in their context. Teachers need good examples and a place to start re-imagining their teaching (such as OpenSciEd in the U.S. context or integrated curriculum models in the 2017 updated curricula of Turkey). We not only advocate supporting teachers to be able to effectively use existing curricular resources but also advocate creating a space for them to raise questions that may impact STEM education policies.

References

Akaygun, S., & Aslan-Tutak, F. (2020). Collaboratively learning to teach STEM: A model for learning to integrate STEM education in preservice teacher education. In V. L. Akerson & G. A. Buck (Eds.), *Critical questions in STEM education* (pp. 147–163). Springer.

Aksela, M., Lundell, J., & Ikävalko, T. (Eds.) (2020). *LUMA Finland -Together we are more*. LUMA Centre Finland. https://www.luma.fi/en/download/luma-finland-together-we-are-more/

Arslan, Ö. (2021). A different perspective on design-skill workshops and STEM education: Teachers' opinions. *Journal of STEM Teacher Institutes, 1*(1), 58–65.

Ay, K., & Seferoğlu, S. S. (2021). An investigation on various countries' STEM education policies and implications for Turkey. *Erzincan University Journal of Education Faculty., 23*(1), 82–105.

Bakhtin, M. (1982). *The dialogic imagination: Four essays by M. M. Bakhtin*. University of Texas Press.

Bannister, N. A. (2015). Reframing practice: Teacher learning through interactions in a collaborative group. *Journal of the learning sciences, 24*(3), 347–372.

Barad, K. (2007). *Meeting the universe halfway: Quantum physics and the entanglement of matter and meaning*. Duke University Press.

Baran, E., Canbazoglu Bilici, S., Mesutoglu, C., & Ocak, C. (2016). Moving STEM beyond schools: Students' perceptions about an out-of-school STEM education program. *International Journal of Education in Mathematics, Science and Technology, 4*(1), 9–19.

Blackley, S., & Howell, J. (2015). A STEM narrative: 15 years in the making. *Australian Journal of Teacher Education, 40*(7), 102–112.

Brandt, C. B. (2008). Discursive geographies in science: Space, identity, and scientific discourse among indigenous women in higher education. *Cultural Studies of Science Education, 3*(3), 703–730.

Brown, J. S., Collins, A., & Duguid, P. (1989). Situated cognition and the culture of learning. *Educational Researcher, 18*(1), 32–42.

Bybee, R. W. (2013). *The case for STEM education: Challenges and opportunities.* National Science Teachers Association Press.

Cannady, M. A., Greenwald, E., & Harris, K. N. (2014). Problematizing the STEM pipeline metaphor: Is the STEM pipeline metaphor serving our students and the STEM workforce? *Science Education, 98*(3), 443–460.

Carter, L. (2011). Gathering in threads in the insensible global world: The wicked problem of globalisation and science education. *Cultural Studies of Science Education, 6*(1), 1–12.

Çınar, S., Pırasa, N., Uzun, N., & Erenler, S. (2016). The effect of STEM education on pre-service science teachers' perception of interdisciplinary education. *Journal of Turkish. Science Education, 13*(special), 118–142.

Cohen, E., Hoz, R., & Kaplan, H. (2013). The practicum in preservice teacher education: a review of empirical studies. *Teaching Education, 24*(4), 345–380.

Common Core State Standards Initiative. (n.d.). Standards in your State. Standards in Your State | Common Core State Standards Initiative. Retrieved February 26, 2022, from http://www.corestandards.org/standards-in-your-state/

Deleuze, G., & Guattari, F. (1987). *A Thousand Plateaus: Capitalism and Schizophrenia*. London: Continuum.

Haraway, D. J. (2016). *Staying with the trouble: Making kin in the Chthulucene.* Duke University Press.

Jeong, S. & Lewis, S. (In Press, 2022). Leveraging technology to foster high school students' online presence and engagement as *becomings*: An integrated STEM lesson on trebuchet and parabolas. In F. Allaire & J. Killham (Eds.), *Teaching and learning online: Science for secondary grade levels.* Information Age Publishing.

Jeong, S., Sherman, B., & Tippins, D. J. (2021). The Anthropocene as we know it: Posthumanism, science education and scientific literacy as a path to sustainability. *Cultural Studies of Science Education, 16*(3), 805–820.

Jeong, S., Tippins, D. J., Haverkos, K., Kutner, M., Kayumova, S., & Britton, S. (2019). STEM education and the theft of futures of our youth: Some questions and challenges for educators. In *Converting STEM into STEAM programs* (pp. 285–305). Springer.

Johnson, C. C. (2013). Conceptualizing integrated STEM education. *School Science and Mathematics, 113*(8), 367–368.

Judson, E. (2013). The relationship between time allocated for science in elementary schools and state accountability policies. *Science Education, 97*, 621–636.

Kayacan, K., & Ozluleci, M. (2021). An analysis of the seventh-grade science textbook in terms of science, engineering and entrepreneurship applications. *Journal of Qualitative Research in Education, 27*, 319–345.

Lissitsa, S., & Chachashvili-Bolotin, S. (2021). Occupational reproduction and mobility in STEM–parental narratives of their child's occupational choice. *Educational Studies.* Advance online publication.

McDonald, S., Bateman, K., & McCausland, J. (2020). Ch. 10: Practice-embedded methods courses for preservice teachers. In D. Stroupe, K. Hammerness, & S. McDonald (Eds.), *Preparing science teachers through practice-based teacher education.* Harvard Education Press.

Milner, A. R., Sondergeld, T. A., Demir, A., Johnson, C. C., & Czerniak, C. M. (2012). Elementary teachers' beliefs about teaching science and classroom practice: An examination of pre/post NCLB testing in science. *Journal of Science Teacher Education, 23*(2), 111–132.

Ministry of National Education, MoNE. (2018). Science lesson curricula, elementary and middle school grades 3, 4, 5, 6, 7, and 8. (Fen bilimleri dersi öğretim programı.ilkokul ve ortaokul 3., 4., 5., 6., 7. ve 8. Sınıflar) Turkish Republic Ministry of Education (T.C. Milli Eğitim Bakanlığı). http://mufredat.meb.gov.tr/ProgramDetay.aspx?PID=325

Moore, T. J., Stohlmann, M. S., Wang, H. H., Tank, K. M., & Roehrig, G. H. (2014). Implementation and integration of engineering in K-12 STEM education. In J. Strobel, S. Purzer, & M. Cardella (Eds.), *Engineering in precollege settings: Research into practice* (pp. 35–60). Sense Publishers.

National Science Teacher Association. (n.d.). About the next generation science standards. NGSS@NSTA. Retrieved February 26, 2022, from https://ngss.nsta.org/about.aspx

Patton, K., & Parker, M. (2017). Teacher education communities of practice: More than a culture of collaboration. *Teaching and Teacher Education, 67*, 351–360.

Penfield, R. D., & Lee, O. (2010). Test-based accountability: Potential benefits and pitfalls of science assessment with student diversity. *Journal of Research in Science Teaching, 47*(1), 6–24.

Radloff, J., & Guzey, S. (2016). Investigating preservice STEM teacher conceptions of STEM education. *Journal of Science Education and Technology, 25*(5), 759–774.

Rocard, M., Csermely, P., Jorde, D., Lenzen, D., Henriksson, H. W., & Hemmo, V. (2007). Science Education Now: A New Pedagogy for the Future of Europe. European Commission Directorate General for Research Information and Communication Unit. Retrieved February 10, 2022, from https://www.eesc.europa.eu/en/documents/rocard-report-science-education-now-new-pedagogy-future-europe

Sherman, B. J., Bateman, K. M., Jeong, S., & Hudock, L. A. (2021). Dialogic meta-ethnography: troubling methodology in ethnographically informed qualitative inquiry. *Cultural Studies of Science Education, 16*(1), 279–302.

Sondergeld, T. A., Peters-Burton, E. E., & Johnson, C. C. (2016). Integrating the three dimensions of next generation science standards: Issues and solutions for authentic assessment of student learning. *School Science and Mathematics, 116*(2), 67–70.

Tseng, F. C., & Kuo, F. Y. (2014). A study of social participation and knowledge sharing in the teachers' online professional community of practice. *Computers & Education, 72*, 37–47.

Turkish Higher Educational Council. (2018). *New Curricula for the Teacher Education Bachelor Programs (Yeni Öğretmen Yetiştirme Lisans Programları).* https://urldefense.com/v3/. https://www.yok.gov.tr/kurumsal/idari-birimler/egitim-ogretim-dairesi/yeni-ogretmen-yetistirme-lisans-programlari__;!!KGKeukY!lq8DdP2zp5XSXdMtII Uip_rxp6cSHMch_n5mtsk5bbPDyb9pBqCgeAzarGlAugYtkpI$

Wenger, E. (1998). *Communities of practice: Learning, meaning, and identity.* Cambridge University Press.

Yamak, H., Bulut, N., & Dündar, S. (2014). The impact of STEM activities on 5th grade students' scientific process skills and their attitudes towards science (5. Sınıf öğrencilerinin bilimsel süreç becerileri ile fene karşı tutumlarına FeTeMM etkinliklerinin etkisi) []. *Gazi University Journal of Gazi Educational Faculty, 34*(2), 249–265.

Yilmaz, A., Gülgün, C., Çetinkaya, M., & Doganay, K. (2018). Initiatives and new trends towards STEM education in Turkey. *Journal of Education and Training Studies, 6*(11), 1–10.

Zollman, A. (2012). Learning for STEM literacy: STEM literacy for learning. *School Science and Mathematics, 112*(1), 12–19.

CHAPTER 14

Greater than the Sum of its Parts: Centering Science Within Elementary STEM Education

Deepika Menon, Amy S. Bauer, Katie L. Johnson, Elizabeth F. Hasseler, Amanda Thomas, Ricardo Martinez, and Guy Trainin

Introduction: Why STEM Learning?

Reform efforts in K-12 STEM (i.e., Science, Technology, Engineering, and Mathematics) education have been prevalent in the past decade to respond to the future needs related to the global STEM workforce

D. Menon (✉) • A. S. Bauer • K. L. Johnson • E. F. Hasseler • A. Thomas • G. Trainin
University of Nebraska-Lincoln, Lincoln, NE, USA
e-mail: dmenon2@unl.edu; asokollbauer2@huskers.unl.edu; kjohnson160@huskers.unl.edu; ehasseler@huskers.unl.edu; amanda.thomas@unl.edu; gtrainin2@unl.edu

R. Martinez
Pennsylvania State University, State College, PA, USA
e-mail: Rfm5798@psu.edu

S. M. Al-Balushi et al. (eds.), *Reforming Science Teacher Education Programs in the STEM Era*, Palgrave Studies on Leadership and Learning in Teacher Education,
https://doi.org/10.1007/978-3-031-27334-6_14

(National Academy of Engineering and National Research Council, 2014). Locally and throughout the U.S., science receives relatively little emphasis in elementary grades. A large-scale national survey found that an average of only 20 minutes per day are spent teaching science in elementary, compared to 87 minutes for reading/language arts and 58 minutes for mathematics (Plumley, 2019). The survey also found that elementary teachers felt less prepared to teach science, engineering, and coding, while findings from a different survey indicated that U.S. pre-service elementary teachers agreed that STEM education was important at the elementary level (Madden et al., 2016). It is prudent to re-envision teacher preparation programs, so the next generation of teachers is competent and confident to teach STEM in a K-12 setting in ways that excite future generations of students for STEM-related careers (Atkinson & Mayo, 2010; Chen et al., 2021).

Early exposure to STEM learning increases student's foundational knowledge in STEM (Chen, 2011), develop students' critical thinking skills and literacy (Paugh & Wendell, 2021), and increases students' motivation and interest in STEM career fields (Nesmith & Cooper, 2020; Wang, 2013). Integrating across STEM subjects has shown promise as a strategy for improving students' knowledge in STEM disciplines, connecting, and transferring knowledge among STEM disciplines, developing creativity and technological skills, and cultivating positive attitudes and interest in STEM subjects (e.g., Century et al., 2020; Martín-Páez et al., 2019; Miller, 2019). When STEM learning experiences are incorporated into the teacher preparation programs, pre-service teachers have a deeper understanding of integrated STEM instruction (Pimthong & Williams, 2021) and are more likely to incorporate them in their future lesson plans (Maiorca & Mohr-Schroeder, 2020). Reform efforts include rethinking ways in which pre-service elementary teachers (PSTs) are currently prepared within teacher preparation programs (Darling-Hammond & Bransford, 2007). In response to this challenge, our team engaged in the process of conceptualizing STEM Integration and redesigning Integrated STEM curriculum for our STEM Semester.

Conceptualizing STEM Integration

For our reform efforts, the fundamental question to consider was, "What is STEM learning, or what should count as STEM learning?" The different models and definitions for Integrated STEM education range from

STEM disciplines traditionally taught as separate and distinct content areas to integration among the four STEM disciplines (NAE and NRC, 2014; Stohlmann et al., 2012). Teacher educators are often challenged to design STEM learning experiences within teacher preparation courses that prepare for the reality of classrooms while presenting pedagogical alternatives (Corp et al., 2020). Many researchers, for instance, Roehrig et al. (2012) distinguish between content and context integration of STEM. Content integration requires the blending of knowledge from different content fields into a single curricular activity or unit to build a collective knowledge of STEM from multiple content areas (Roehrig et al., 2012; Wang et al., 2011) while context integration, "primarily focuses on the content of one discipline and uses contexts from others" to make the content more relevant (Roehrig et al., 2012, p. 9). Most researchers conclude that STEM integration should involve the merging of some or all the STEM disciplines to solve real-world problems (Moore et al., 2020; Rinke et al., 2016).

Our conceptualization of STEM integration stems from (1) Dewey's work (1938) that highlights learning as an *active* process that involves students engaged in experiences situated in and connected to the *real world* and, (2) ideas based on social constructivism developed by Vygotsky (1978) that emphasize learning via social interactions among individuals within a social setting. Constructionist theory (Ackermann, 2001; Harel & Papert, 1991; Papert, 1980) also framed learning experiences in the integrated STEM semester. Teaching Integrated STEM calls for pedagogies that promote active learning that engages students in social interactions while working collaboratively in teams (Moore et al., 2014), and knowledge that is constructed via social discourse (Stohlmann et al., 2012). Other pedagogies that are fundamental to conceptualizing STEM learning are inquiry-based and hands-on strategies promoted in the *Next Generation Science Standards* (Bybee, 2009; NGSS Lead States, 2013), problem-based learning that involves a problem to solve (Shaughnessy, 2013), and connections to real-life experiences (Kelley & Knowles, 2016).

In leading our curriculum reform effort, we draw upon the viewpoint that STEM curriculum must involve both content and context integration. Figure 14.1 illustrates our conceptual framework for re-structuring our elementary STEM Semester. Our framework positions science at the center placing emphasis on scientific inquiry (Kelley & Knowles, 2016). Integrated STEM education has strong ties to inquiry processes allowing students to formulate questions, participate in investigations that facilitate

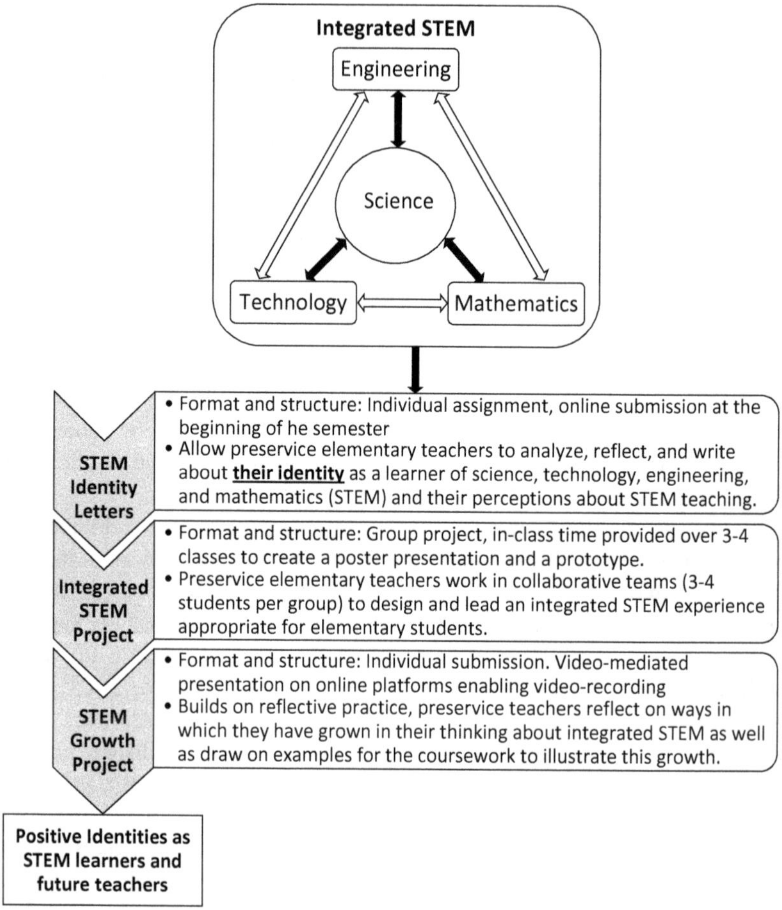

Fig. 14.1 Framework and shared assignments for integrated STEM for curriculum reform

engineering design, and integrate technology and mathematics to design solutions to complex real-world problems (Kennedy & Odell, 2014; Moore & Smith, 2014). Figure 14.1 depicts the interconnected relationship between disciplines where engineering, technology, and mathematical knowledge provide a context for meaningful science learning and vice versa. The framework served as a guide to inform our Integrated STEM curriculum design and STEM pathways (shared assignments) across multiple courses within the STEM Semester as explained in the subsequent sections.

STEM Curriculum Reform: A Constant Flux

The need to emphasize STEM subjects in elementary teacher preparation prompted curriculum reform to create the STEM Semester within an elementary education program at a large mid-western university. The program typically admits 70–80 PSTs per semester. This effort was led by a multi-disciplinary team of STEM educators and researchers including faculty and graduate students in science and engineering education, mathematics education, and technology education. Prior to this reform effort, the elementary teacher education program was organized in four semesters, taken sequentially after admission to the professional phase of the program: Math Block, Literature Block, "Methods" Block, and Student Teaching. The Math Block included integrated mathematics content and mathematics methods courses, a 1.5-day per week practicum in a local elementary school, as well as an innovative learning technologies course, and a course and associated practicum focused on English Language Learners (ELL). At that time, the science methods course was part of the "methods block," and was not associated with a field experience. Math Block, initially developed with support from National Science Foundation (NSF) (DUE #9981106), offered a successful model of collaboration among instructors and departments. Math content and methods courses were scheduled back-to-back, in the same classrooms, with instructors frequently sitting in on one another's courses, and students cohorted by sections. A unified syllabus and key assignments were shared between the math content, math methods, and practicum courses (Heaton & Lewis, 2011).

Extending the existing Math Block logic, we used a design process to reimagine the STEM Semester to integrate across the three methods courses: Math methods, Science methods, and Innovative Learning Technologies (ILT). The process included:

- Challenging pre-existing beliefs and status quo situated within each discipline,
- Reaching common ground with a shared understanding of STEM integration as a dynamic process,

- Strategizing the flow of STEM learning across various courses within the program,
- Implementing the curriculum,
- Continuing reflection and revision.

Faculty and graduate student instructors met during the summer prior to the first STEM Semester iteration to compare existing course content, find areas of potential overlap among classes, and create a flexible framework that would allow a mutually agreeable balance of disciplinary content and integrated STEM content. This approach included shared assignments focused on developing positive identities as STEM learners and future teachers, and embedded thematic topics that would be integrated across the three methods courses (see Fig. 14.1 above for more details related to structure and format of shared assignments).

The team of course instructors collaboratively designed, implemented, and assessed three shared assignments that complemented the discipline-based lesson plans and assignments students did within individual courses. The shared assignments (see Fig. 14.1) included STEM identity letters, an integrated STEM project, and a STEM growth presentation. STEM identity letters asked PSTs to present their initial definition of STEM and reflect on their identities as learners and future teachers of STEM subjects. The integrated STEM project was an opportunity for PSTs to work in teams, design an integrated STEM learning experience for elementary students, and reflect on what they learned from that experience. The culminating semester project was a STEM growth presentation for which PSTs selected and showcased artifacts of their work to support reflections about their development as learners and teachers of integrated STEM and its constituent disciplines. During the inaugural STEM semester, a coding and robotics theme was integrated across courses and a second theme of sustainability was added the following semester. These thematic pathways are detailed later in this chapter.

The design of the STEM Semester was intentionally flexible to encourage disciplinary autonomy within courses, anticipate changes in instructors over time, allow for research-based best practices, and amplify the assets and priorities each instructor brings to their course. STEM Semester instructors continued to meet regularly to collaborate around shared assignments, STEM-themed class activities, and PST needs and concerns. While the initial structure of the STEM Semester remains, the shared assignments undergo revision each semester and the STEM themes are implemented differently by new instructors within and across courses. The COVID-19 pandemic tested the flexibility of the STEM Semester in a unique way, but instructors collaboratively rose to the challenge and continued to implement the STEM Semester framework, often with alternative activities or revised assignments.

The STEM-Themed Pathways

The integrated STEM semester drew upon existing models of STEM integration (e.g., Kelley & Knowles, 2016; Moore et al., 2014) by connecting STEM content areas within communities of practice, defining STEM as an effort to integrate some or all STEM content areas, and making purposeful connections to enhance learning. Playing, creating, and minimalist teaching approaches maximized PSTs' opportunities to learn through exploration, in turn, preparing them to do so with elementary students.

Cross-Course STEM Themes

Two themes were integrated across the STEM Semester courses: robotics/coding and sustainability. The robotics theme was emphasized primarily in the ILT course and reinforced in mathematics and science methods courses. PSTs also reflected individually on how each tool could be aligned with STEM standards and instruction in elementary classrooms. The sustainability module provided a model of collaborative STEM integration within and across courses, culminating in an engineering design challenge. Unlike shared assignments which involved out-of-class work, STEM themes occurred primarily during scheduled class time.

Robotics and Coding. The robotics theme was introduced with a block-based coding activity in Scratch that aligned with elementary mathematics standards. PSTs learned introductory coding principles and developed a foundation for engaging with educational robotics throughout the semester. Rather than emphasizing one or two robots/coding tools, PSTs explored several robots and coding tools throughout the semester. In mathematics methods courses, PSTs learned to use BeeBots (see Fig. 14.2 left side) for engaging young learners in coding and algorithmic thinking while learning about connecting multiple mathematical representations. In science methods courses, PSTs learned to program and use micro:bits as tools for collecting moisture, temperature, and light data in an environmental science inquiry activity and designed their own NGSS-aligned

Fig. 14.2 Using BeeBots to Connect Mathematical Representations (Left side) and Testing Flood Mitigation Designs on an Enviroscape Floodplain Model (Right side)

science lessons using micro:bits. During the ILT course, PSTs engaged in structured play with Cubelets, Ozobots, Edison bots, and Osmo and discussed connections with mathematics and science standards.

PSTs also learned to code and use Dash bots in an integrated STEM activity during the mathematics methods course (Fig. 14.2). PSTs designed a 120 cm path (Goo, 2019) within a science context of their choice (e.g., zoo, solar system, water cycle), programmed Dash to give a tour with at least five stops (each identifying science content, distance traveled, and fraction of the whole length), and demonstrated Dash's tour with classmates. Similarly, PSTs learned to use Sphero robots during an ILT class by designing a maze, coding Sphero to drive through the maze, and aligning to the area and perimeter standards (Fig. 14.2). PSTs could use any of the educational robotics in their Integrated STEM Projects and although most students did not elect to do so, some teams incorporated BeeBots, Ozobots, and Dash bots.

Sustainability. The second STEM Semester theme resulted from instructors' participation in a university-wide Sustainability Curriculum initiative. STEM Semester instructors used a multi-disciplinary approach, incorporating related science content in science methods, math content during mathematics methods, and technology and engineering during multiple ILT class sessions. The components of the project were purposefully sequenced within and across courses and drew upon published materials from the Interdisciplinary Teaching about Earth for a Sustainable Future (InTeGrate) project (DeBari et al., 2020) and Water Warriors design challenges (Jason Learning, 2019).

In science methods, PSTs learned about the hydrologic cycle, aquifers, floodplain management, and common misconceptions while drafting 5E lesson plans (Bybee, 2009) and engaging with a university hydrologist. In a subsequent mathematics methods class, PSTs used authentic data, interpreted graphs of precipitation and river discharge, calculated recurrence intervals, used probability to define 100- and 500-year floods, and interpreted floodplain maps and graphs. In the ILT class, PSTs visited a maker space to scale and 3D-print house models and designed mitigation strategies to protect their houses from flooding on an Enviroscape floodplain model (see Fig. 14.1 right side). PSTs then placed their 3D printed houses at assigned locations on the Enviroscape. To test and discuss the effectiveness of PSTs' flood mitigation design strategies, a civil engineer who specialized in surface water hydrology and watershed management joined the ILT classes. Two types of flooding were approximated on the Enviroscape. First, water was sprinkled over the model to mimic rain over a continuous period. Then, water was poured rapidly, mimicking the deluge of a dam break (a phenomenon that had recently occurred in the region). The engineer helped students interpret the effectiveness of their strategies and compare their designs with strategies used in the real world. Locations of houses on the model also impacted the effectiveness of PSTs' designs, intentionally inviting discussions of resources, power, privilege, and justice in the context of the project.

Evidence of Success with the STEM Semester

This section represents themes that resulted from preliminary qualitative analysis of PSTs' ($N = 76$) perceptions of STEM at the beginning and end of the STEM Semester. We discuss: (1) initial themes from the STEM identity letters that PSTs wrote at the beginning of the semester documenting their personal and professional experiences with science/STEM and their perceptions about STEM teaching and learning and (2) final themes from focus-group video sessions on PSTs' experiences with the integrated STEM project and individual video-mediated STEM growth project presentations (see Table 14.1).

Table 14.1 Sample coding scheme for themes at the beginning and end of the semester

Themes	*Code*	*Sample Excerpts*
Beginning of the semester		
Naïve conceptions about STEM integration	Intimidating, don't know much about STEM	I think people can be intimated by the acronym STEM. I know STEM stands for science, technology, engineering, and mathematics; however, there is much more than just that that I do not know
Lack of confidence in STEM content or STEM teaching	Not sure to incorporate different components into one lesson	I am not so sure about how I would incorporate so many different components [science, technology, engineering, and mathematics] into one lesson
STEM stereotypes	Only for guys, rare to see a woman in STEM	When I think of STEM, I think of a lot of stereotypes and stigmas. I think about how STEM is "only for guys," or how rare it is to see a woman in STEM
End of the semester		
Increased value and importance for integrated STEM in K-5 classrooms	Come together, integrated, skills and interest in STEM	Four different pillars need to come together and be integrated so that students can develop skills and an interest in STEM that can help them understand how our world works and how to adapt to it
Shifting away from biases: STEM for *ALL* learners	Encourage every student, creative, can do it	It is important for teachers to encourage each and every one of their students to think critically in these subjects. I also think STEM can be creative and therefore, any student can do it
Increased confidence in planning and designing integrated STEM lessons	Confident, integrate into one lesson	I feel confident in my ability to integrate all of these subjects into one lesson effectively, more so than before

Initial Perceptions of STEM

At the beginning of the semester, we found that PSTs had naïve conceptions of STEM likely due to a lack of exposure to STEM learning in K-12 classrooms. Unsurprisingly, when responding to "what STEM means to them," a majority of PSTs stated that they did not know what STEM means and indicated little or no exposure to STEM prior to college. As one PST mentioned, "Growing up we didn't learn much of STEM specifically, it was mostly just math with a very few basic science lessons." Further, negative dispositions toward STEM disciplines resulted in low personal affinity or interest toward creating STEM lessons and STEM teaching overall. For instance, a PST wrote, "STEM is a hard thing to wrap our heads around. It has to do with science, technology, engineering, and mathematics. These are some hard subjects that do not come easy to many people." We also found that PSTs demonstrated assumptions about societal stigmas and gender bias: "I think of 'left brain' people succeeding in STEM. More than anything, I think teachers need to encourage girls to participate in STEM."

Change in Perceptions

We found that the STEM Semester experiences helped PSTs recognize the value and importance of Integrated STEM in elementary classrooms and develop positive attitudes toward Integrated STEM instruction. As one PST mentioned, "At the beginning of the semester I thought that Integrated STEM was science and math while playing games on the computer. Now, after going through various courses, I would say STEM is any educational tool, lesson, curriculum, or activity that has a basis in one or more of the fields of math, science, technology, and engineering." Furthermore, after engaging with the STEM Semester curriculum, we noted a shift in PSTs' perceptions. Students began to view STEM as critical for *all* students, not just left-brain individuals and males. One PST noted, "[STEM is] especially important for all young students, but especially young girls and racially diverse students who may feel excluded." Most PSTs explicitly talked about the importance of real-world STEM connections, noting that STEM lessons can provide young children "a variety of learning opportunities put together to teach new perspectives." PSTs realized that STEM helps student build new skill sets as STEM allows "students and educators to get creative with their work. They get to think, build, be a leader, try new things, and learn." We also found that PSTs' confidence in integrated STEM planning and lesson design increased as they completed the STEM Semester. For instance, one PST acknowledged the interconnectivity between STEM disciplines to create a lesson:

> *Before this semester, STEM classes were individual and lived on their own, separately. Math was math, science was science, and they just stayed that way. This semester really taught me that these classes can join forces to create a really successful lesson.*

Challenges Faced and Lessons Learned

No effort to renovate a teacher preparation program comes without challenges. Unsurprisingly, PSTs reported concerns considering their first exposure to integrated STEM instruction. We describe these challenges and lessons learned with an aim to provide meaningful insights that maximize student learning in STEM methods courses.

- *Increased time commitment in designing Integrated STEM lessons.* We recognize that there is an increased time commitment and accountability for PSTs to brainstorm ideas, create Integrated STEM lessons that integrate two or more disciplines, and coherently apply knowledge learned from different STEM methods courses. Having patience and lending seamless support to students is the key to students' success in achieving this challenging task. This can be well achieved by providing time within classrooms for students to work on projects rather than out-of-class work where immediate feedback is not available.
- *Collaborating with peers who have varied perceptions and affinity toward STEM subjects.* Pre-service teachers arrive in methods courses with varied beliefs and perceptions about STEM subjects owing to their prior experiences in science (Knaggs & Sondergeld, 2015) or other disciplines in STEM (Huziak-Clark et al., 2015). Working on collaborative projects where STEM interest, motivation, and comfort level differs from individual to individual can be intimidating. This is quite understandable, because we found PSTs were concerned about their lack of STEM background knowledge. Continuous support and mentoring are needed throughout the program so that PSTs can overcome fear as they continue to engage in collaborative

group tasks such as Integrated STEM lesson designs (Menon & Sadler, 2016, 2018).

- *Negotiating between how STEM was taught to them (personal prior learning experiences) while learning new pedagogiesthey are expected to teach in the future.* It is important to realize that most students learned STEM disciplines in a traditional way where each of the disciplines was taught in a discrete way. New pedagogies to deliver integrated STEM instruction can put PSTs under pressure while they are negotiating with their own personal teaching philosophies. Creating a classroom environment and culture where their ideas are valued, providing the time they need to process the "conceptual change" encompassing STEM teaching, and offering opportunities to ask questions freely will help PSTs value STEM instruction (Delahunty & Kimbell, 2021; Ryu et al., 2019).

Take-Aways for STEM Educators

Thomas Kuhn, in his writings about scientific revolutions (1962), posited that "paradigm shift" comes with its own challenges and the process of change may not be straightforward but achievable. Based on the experiences described throughout this chapter, we provide a set of recommendations for future teacher educators, who as a group of champions coming together, are willing to restructure their elementary education programs for STEM integration.

Recommendation 1. *Social discourse to develop a shared understanding of Integrated STEM among STEM educators.* In our experience, social discourse among the team has strengthened our collective understanding of Integrated STEM. Although everyone has a busy schedule, meeting biweekly as a STEM Semester team allowed open communication about the steps needed to ensure seamless implementation of shared assignments, reflect critically on our implementation of the curriculum, revise our shared activities and assessments, and brainstorm ideas to address any concerns students have while engaged in this experience.

Recommendation 2. *Negotiating roles and responsibilities amongst the team of STEM educators to ensure the seamless integration of STEM disciplines.* We believe that treating STEM as a culture for pre-service teacher preparation program is one way to ensure that there is ongoing motivation and dedication within the team of STEM educators. This requires social dialogue and constant communication about roles and responsibilities that each member of the team agrees to and is held accountable. A dedicated and highly motivated team is needed despite negotiating personal teaching philosophies, discipline-specific identities and developing personal STEM teacher educator identity.

Recommendation 3. *A consistent mentoring structure for training graduate student STEM instructors.* A significant number of our instructors are graduate students pursuing PhD degrees in science, technology, and mathematics education. Although highly motivated to teach, graduate students often lack the time to devote to coursework and research and may sometimes become challenged by the demands of teaching in a newer Integrated STEM environment. Having a structured mentoring program in place will help graduate students to transition into this teaching role much more smoothly.

Recommendation 4. *Departmental and administrative support including resources and time-release to facilitate the curricular reform.* Any effort toward STEM curricular reform is not a one-event activity (Sunal et al., 2001) but requires a significant time investment from faculty and graduate students who may already be overburdened with responsibilities. Departmental and administrative support that includes resources (such as materials, technology support) and time for facilitating curricular reform is crucial for a sustainable change.

Recommendation 5. *Maintain a critical stance toward students' positioning in STEM.* It is essential that the emphasis on Integrated STEM does not ignore the reality that the practice of STEM is not culturally neutral. As teacher educators, we must attend carefully to the biases that may emerge. Any team attempting STEM integration should maintain a critical perspective that includes identifying and supporting PSTs who may not be equitably positioned in STEM learning and celebrating PSTs' diverse voices and perspectives about STEM. We suggest that STEM teacher educators employ a critical lens as they reflect on their teaching practices and tailor to diverse student needs each semester.

References

Ackermann, E. (2001). Piaget's constructivism, Papert's constructionism: What's the difference. *Future of learning group publication, 5*(3), 438.

Atkinson, R., & Mayo, M. (2010). Refueling the US innovation economy: Fresh approaches to science, technology, engineering and mathematics (STEM) education. *Information Technology and Innovation Foundation.* https://itif.org/files/2010-refueling-innovation-economy.pdf

Bybee, R. (2009) *The BSCS 5e: Instructional model and 21st century skills.* Presentation. The National Academies.

Century, J., Ferris, K. A., & Zuo, H. (2020). Finding time for computer science in the elementary school day: A quasi-experimental study of a transdisciplinary problem-based learning approach. *International Journal of STEM Education, 7*(20). https://doi.org/10.1186/s40594-020-00218-3

Chen, G. (2011). The rising popularity of STEM: A crossroads in public education or a passing trend? http://www.publicschoolreview.com/articles/408

Chen, Y. L., Huang, L. F., & Wu, P. C. (2021). Pre-service preschool teachers' self-efficacy in and need for STEM education professional development: STEM pedagogical belief as a mediator. *Early Childhood Education Journal, 49*(2), 137–147. https://doi.org/10.1007/s10643-020-01055-3

Corp, A., Fields, M., & Naizer, G. (2020). Elementary STEM teacher education: Recent practices to prepare general elementary teachers for STEM. In C. C. Johnson, M. J. Mohr-Schroeder, T. J. Moore, & L. D. English (Eds.), *Handbook of research on STEM education* (pp. 101–114). Routledge.

Darling-Hammond, L., & Bransford, J. (Eds.). (2007). *Preparing teachers for a changing world: What teachers should learn and be able to do.* John Wiley & Sons.

DeBari, S., Gray, K., & Monet, J. (2020). Interactions between water, earth's surface, and human activity. In A. Egger (Ed.), *InTeGrate.* https://serc.carleton.edu/integrate/teaching_materials/energy_and_processes/index.html

Delahunty, T., & Kimbell, R. (2021). (re) framing a philosophical and epistemological framework for teaching and learning in STEM: Emerging pedagogies for complexity. *British Educational Research Journal, 47*(3), 742–769. https://doi.org/10.1002/berj.3706

Dewey, J. (1938). *Experience and education.* Simon and Schuster.

Goo, J. (2019). *Fraction street STEM project.* https://teachers.makewonder.com/curriculum/fraction-street-stem-project.

Harel, I. E., & Papert, S. E. (1991). *Constructionism.* Ablex Publishing.

Heaton, R. M., & Lewis, W. J. (2011). A mathematician-mathematics educator partnership to teach teachers. *Notices of the AMS, 58*(3), 394–400.

Huziak-Clark, T., Sondergeld, T., van Staaden, M., Knaggs, C., & Bullerjahn, A. (2015). Assessing the impact of a research-based STEM program on STEM majors' attitudes and beliefs. *School Science and Mathematics, 115*(5), 226–236. https://doi.org/10.1111/ssm.12118

Jason Learning, Inc. (2019). *Water warriors.* https://jason.org/portfolio_item/waterwarriors/

Kelley, T. R., & Knowles, J. G. (2016). A conceptual framework for integrated STEM education. *International Journal of STEM education, 3*(1), 1–11. https://doi-org.libproxy.unl.edu/10.1186/s40594-016-0046-z

Kennedy, T., & Odell, M. (2014). Engaging students in STEM education. *Science Education International, 25*(3), 246–258.

Knaggs, C. M., & Sondergeld, T. A. (2015). Science as a learner and as a teacher: Measuring science self-efficacy of elementary pre-service teachers. *School Science and Mathematics, 115*(3), 117–128. https://doi.org/10.1111/ssm.12110

Kuhn, T. (1962). The nature and necessity of scientific revolutions. na.

Madden, L., Beyers, J., & O'Brien, S. (2016). The importance of STEM education in the elementary grades: Learning from pre-service and novice teachers' perspectives. *The Electronic Journal for Research in Science & Mathematics Education, 20*(5).

Maiorca, C., & Mohr-Schroeder, M. J. (2020). Elementary pre-service teachers' integration of engineering into STEM lesson plans. *School Science and Mathematics, 120*(7), 402–412. https://doi.org/10.1111/ssm.12433

Martín-Páez, T., Aguilera, D., Perales-Palacios, F. J., & Vílchez-González, J. M. (2019). What are we talking about when we talk about STEM education? *A review of literature. Science Education, 103*(4), 799–822. https://doi.org/10.1002/sce.21522

Menon, D., & Sadler, T. D. (2016). Pre-service elementary teachers' science self-efficacy beliefs and science content knowledge. *Journal of Science Teacher Education, 27*(6), 649–673. https://doi.org/10.1007/s10972-016-9479-y

Menon, D., & Sadler, T. D. (2018). Sources of science teaching self-efficacy for pre-service elementary teachers in science content courses. *International Journal of Science and Mathematics Education, 16*(5), 835–855. https://doi.org/10.1007/s10763-017-9813-7

Miller, J. (2019). STEM education in the primary years to support mathematical thinking: using coding to identify mathematical structures and patterns. *ZDM, 51*, 915–927. https://doi-org.libproxy.unl.edu/10.1007/s11858-019-01096-y

Moore, T. J., Johnston, A. C., & Glancy, A. W. (2020). STEM integration: A synthesis of conceptual frameworks and definitions. In C. C. Johnson, M. J. Mohr-Schroeder, T. J. Moore, & L. D. English (Eds.), *Handbook of research on STEM education* (pp. 101–114). Routledge.

Moore, T. J., & Smith, K. A. (2014). Advancing the state of the art of STEM integration. *Journal of STEM Education, 15*(1), 5.

Moore, T. J., Stohlmann, M., Wang, H. H., Tank, K. M., Glancy, A. W., & Roehrig, G. H. (2014). Implementation and integration of engineering in K-12 STEM education. In S. Purzer, J. Strobel, & M. E. Cardella (Eds.), *Engineering in pre-college settings: Synthesizing research, policy, and practices* (pp. 35–60). Purdue University Press.

National Academy of Engineering and National Research Council. (2014). *STEM integration in K-12 education: Status, prospects, and an agenda for research.* The National Academy Press. https://doi.org/10.17226/18612.

Nesmith, S. M., & Cooper, S. (2020). Elementary STEM learning. In C. C. Johnson, M. J. Mohr-Schroeder, T. J. Moore, & L. D. English (Eds.), *Handbook of research on STEM education* (pp. 101–114). Routledge.

NGSS Lead States. (2013). *Next generation science standards: For states, by states.* National Academy Press. https://doi.org/10.17226/18290.

Papert, S. (1980). *Mindstorms. Children, computers and powerful ideas.* Basic Books.

Paugh, P., & Wendell, K. (2021). Disciplinary literacy in STEM: A functional approach. *Journal of Literacy Research, 53*(1), 122–144. https://doi.org/10.1177/1086296X20986905

Pimthong, P., & Williams, P. J. (2021). Methods course for primary level STEM pre-service teachers: Constructing integrated STEM teaching. *EURASIA Journal of Mathematics, Science and Technology Education, 17*(8), 10.29333/ejmste/11113.

Plumley, C. L. (2019). *2018 NMSSE+: Status of elementary school science.* Horizon Research, Inc.

Rinke, C. R., Gladstone-Brown, W., Kinlaw, C. R., & Cappiello, J. (2016). Characterizing STEM teacher education: Affordances and constraints of explicit STEM preparation for elementary teachers. *School Science and Mathematics, 116*(6), 300–309. https://doi.org/10.1111/ssm.12185

Roehrig, G. H., Moore, T. J., Wang, H. H., & Park, M. S. (2012). Is adding the E enough? Investigating the impact of K-12 engineering standards on the implementation of STEM integration. *School Science and Mathematics, 112*(1), 31–44. https://doi.org/10.1111/j.1949-8594.2011.00112.x

Ryu, M., Mentzer, N., & Knobloch, N. (2019). Pre-service teachers' experiences of STEM integration: Challenges and implications for integrated STEM teacher preparation. *International Journal of Technology and Design Education, 29*(3), 493–512. https://doi-org.libproxy.unl.edu/10.1007/s10798-018-9440-9

Shaughnessy, M. (2013). By way of introduction: Mathematics in a STEM context. *Mathematics Teaching in the Middle school, 18*(6), 324. https://doi.org/10.5951/mathteacmiddscho.18.6.0324

Stohlmann, M., Moore, T. J., & Roehrig, G. H. (2012). Considerations for teaching integrated STEM education. *Journal of Pre-College Engineering Education Research, 2*(1), 4. https://doi.org/10.5703/1288284314653

Sunal, D. W., Hodges, J., Sunal, C. S., Whitaker, K. W., Freeman, L. M., Edwards, L., Johnston, R. A., & Odell, M. (2001). Teaching science in higher education: Faculty professional development and barriers to change. *School Science and Mathematics, 101*, 246–257. https://doi.org/10.1111/j.1949-8594.2001.tb18027.x

Vygotsky, L. S. (1978). *Mind in society: The development of higher psychological processes.* Harvard University Press.

Wang, H. H., Moore, T. J., Roehrig, G. H., & Park, M. S. (2011). STEM integration: Teacher perceptions and practice. *Journal of Pre-College Engineering Education Research, 1*(2), 2. https://doi.org/10.5703/1288284314636

Wang, X. (2013). Why students choose STEM majors: Motivation, high school learning, and postsecondary context of support. *American Educational Research Journal, 50*(5), 1081–1121.

CHAPTER 15

U.S. Next Generation Science Standards: Possibilities, Not Prescriptions for STEM Teacher Education

Valarie L. Akerson and Gayle A. Buck

Introduction

There are many calls for STEM education in the United States of America (U.S.) due, in part, to the Next Generation Science Standards' (NGSS). The NGSS is a document containing science education standards, or educational goals, that provide a statement of the science competencies that all U.S. students should be able to demonstrate at the various stages of a K-12 education. The NGSS was developed by a consortium of 26 states in the U.S. and other stakeholders in science, science education, higher education, business, and industry. The document serves as a common guide for the various states to use in developing their own standards. In turn,

V. L. Akerson (✉) • G. A. Buck
Indiana University, Bloomington, IN, USA
e mail: vakerson@indiana.edu; gabuck@iu.edu

S. M. Al-Balushi et al. (eds.), *Reforming Science Teacher Education Programs in the STEM Era*, Palgrave Studies on Leadership and Learning in Teacher Education,
https://doi.org/10.1007/978-3-031-27334-6_15

these state standards set the stage for how teacher education programs prepare future teachers.

To be able to develop STEM conceptions, science teachers need to be educated in STEM methodology. The NGSS can be a guidepost to STEM teacher education if it is clear where the possibilities can be found within the document. In this chapter, we explore how these discussions about STEM impact teacher education. STEM has been defined in several ways, and it is important to conceptualize these various ways that can differ depending on the person delivering the instruction. For instance, Bybee (2013) described nine different perspectives of STEM education that influence teacher education. These nine perspectives vary in the amount of emphasis placed on the individual disciplines that comprise "STEM" (science, technology, engineering and mathematics), and the detail of emphasis on connections among the disciplines. These perspectives range from teaching each discipline independently to emphasizing one discipline (e.g. science) and connecting the other STEM disciplines to the main focus. The fully integrated STEM is where all disciplines have equal emphasis in terms of content instruction, and connections are made among all disciplines to highlight the integrated nature of the disciplines. Additionally, each of the STEM disciplines has its own perspective of the type of knowledge it seeks to create. For example, there are various natures of the knowledge of each discipline—a nature of science, nature of technology, nature of engineering, and nature of mathematics. Knowledge of the nature of these disciplines is necessary for "teaching STEM" as connections do need to be made across the disciplines and conceptualizing the natures of these disciplines is important in making these connections. For a more complete discussion about definitions and perspectives of STEM, and the natures of the individual disciplines, please see Chapter 1. In the sections below we look deeply into the NGSS to determine where and how STEM is being represented, and illustrate possibilities that the NGSS provides for STEM teacher education. We also provide some examples for programs within our university that are responding to these possibilities.

NGSS: Not a Prescription for STEM Teacher Education

Given the contemporary discussions and the fact that NGSS serves as a guidepost to most teacher education programs, a document analysis was completed on the NGSS to determine how STEM is represented within it. Document analysis is a process whereby written documents are interpreted by the researchers to give voice and meaning (Bowen, 2009). The process involves coding content into themes similar to how interview transcripts are analyzed (O'Leary, 2014). Of course, the main text in this process was the NGSS. However, secondary texts were included to aid in the evolving interpretations. These included the Common Core State Standards for Mathematics (National Governors Association Center for Best Practices & Council of Chief State School Officers, 2010), and the ISTE National Educational Technology Standards (2000), and Engineering in K-12 Education: Understanding the Status and Improving the Prospects (2009). The process included establishing both etic (brought in from the field) and emic (emerge from the experience) codes. The etic codes included STEM, science, technology, engineering, and technology. Examples of emic codes that emerged in the process included 'initial learning,' 'reinforcement knowledge,' 'subject bias.'

The literal definition of STEM in the NGSS is an acronym made of four distinct disciplines: science, technology, engineering, and mathematics. The actual acronym, STEM, is used very sparingly, although the separate disciplines are used extensively within the document. The few instances show that STEM is used to refer to various careers, or pipelines into those careers, that involve these disciplines. Example statements include, "The NGSS provide an opportunity to include medicine, engineering, forensics, and other applicable sciences in course that deliver the standards in ways that interest students and may give them a desire to pursue STEM careers." (page xviii) and "The National Science Foundation also reports that there are currently between two and three million unfilled positions in the STEM areas of science, technology, engineering and mathematics" (NGSS, Appendix C, page 11). There is a science focus in the context of these references, namely science lays groundwork for advanced work in careers that involve the multiple STEM disciplinary fields. There is one instance of referring to STEM-engaged citizens. The NGSS overall conveys an understanding that K-12 academic standards are to come from the separate disciplines of science, technology, engineering, and mathematics—there are not STEM standards. STEM is used to refer to the set of disciplines or opportunities when the different disciplines' standards may be brought together.

The various disciplines that make up STEM are very evident throughout the document. First and foremost, the NGSS document is about developing **science** standards. It was developed by the National Science Teachers Association (NSTA) and the American Association for the

Advancement of Science (AAAS), Archive Inc., and the National Research Council (NRC). It was developed in collaboration between states and other stakeholders in science, science education, higher education, business, and industry. Science is described as a critical field with many statements such as, "Never before has our world been so complex and science knowledge so critical to making sense of it all" (p. xiii). The document itself provides a complete set of educational goals for a K-12 education in science from "all animals needing food to live and grow" (grade K) to "multicellular organisms individual cells grow and then divide via a process called mitosis" (high school). The document provides a complete set of educational goals for science and addresses the nature of science, albeit indirectly. This document can stand as the lone set of science outcomes for a school district.

Though the NGSS is first and foremost about science, one could argue that it is also about **engineering**. The NRC, one of the collaborators in the development of NGSS, is the operating arm of the National Academy of Sciences and the National Academy of Engineering. There are differences that emerge, however, in the relationship of this discipline to science. In parts, engineering is treated like one of the sub disciplines of science. The core ideas include essential engineering, technology, and applications of science alongside three other major domains (physical, life, Earth, and space). The engineering area is discussed throughout in a similar manner to 'life science' and 'physical science'—as one of the sub disciplines within science. In other parts of the NGSS, however, engineering is treated like an equal, but separate, partner to science. Throughout the document, the term engineering often follows science (e.g. "science and engineering"). Engineering specific standards are found in both the disciplinary core ideas and practices. Key engineering ideas that were deemed necessary for students to be able to evaluate and select reliable sources of scientific information and allow them to continue their development well beyond their K-12 school years as learners, users of scientific knowledge, and perhaps producers of science knowledge were identified and included. One of the engineering standards is "Science and engineering complement each other in the cycle known as research and development (R&D). Many R&D projects may involve scientists, engineers and others " (HS-ESS1, 2 & 4). In the practice dimensions, engineering design is raised to the same level as scientific inquiry by emphasizing the core ideas of engineering design and technology applications. Every standard area has science and engineering practices. However, it is the same few standards throughout. The NGSS document provides a complete set of educational goals, albeit a limited scope, for engineering.

At many points, the NGSS portrays **Mathematics** as a separate subject that is outside of science but critical to the understanding of science and vice versa. Like engineering, mathematics is listed alongside science. Yet, a closer look also shows that mathematics is seen as a part of science. NGSS notes that "Science is a quantitative discipline, which means it is important for educators to ensure that students' learning in science coheres well with their learning in mathematics" (p. xxi). In this way, the very nature of science is perceived to be mathematical. The idea that Mathematics is a totally separate discipline is evident in practice. It is assumed that states using the standards are also using the Common Core State Standards for Mathematics (CCSSM) (National Governors Association Center for Best Practices & Council of Chief State School Officers, 2010) in its K-12 system. The developers noted that they were careful to not "outpace or otherwise misalign to the grade-by-grade standards in the CCCSM" (p. xxi). Specific standards are brought into the NGSS document from the CCCSM document to demonstrate how the standards can overlap and reinforce each other. Thus, the actual math standards listed were created outside of the NGSS and brought in to enhance the science learning on a prerequisite basis or included to provide reinforcement of the mathematics already learned in math class. Although these standards can be found throughout the NGSS, the actual standards are limited to a few mathematical standards from the larger set that are used repeatedly. These include such standards as (1) Reason abstractly and quantitatively, (2) Model with mathematics, and (3) Use ratios and rate reasoning to solve real-world and mathematical problems. These standards are taken verbatim from CCCSM and not included until after they are taught in math. Given this view of mathematics, the nature of mathematics itself, as noted above, is not evident in the NGSS. The document does not establish educational goals for mathematics, instead it uses the educational goals developed by others and places them in carefully considered order within the science standards.

The review of NGSS found that **technology** is explicitly referred to as a separate discipline; but it is implicitly portrayed as a component of science and/or engineering. Explicit statements such as " interdependence of science, engineering, and technology; and influence of engineering, technology and science on society and the natural world" (p. 3) are found throughout the document indicating it is equal and separate. Furthermore, the name is found in the category 'Connections to Engineering,

Technology and Applications of Science' and an emphasis on 'Science, Technology, Society and the Environment are prominent in the document. However, a closer look shows the listed technology standards are those of the other two disciplines. Technology is also included within the mathematics common core standards that are brought into the document. In the analysis, it was hard to code any references to technology that were not also coded as engineering, science, or mathematics. Thus, technology is referenced as a separate entity, but only acknowledged as a component of the other STEM disciplines. This is an approach that is recommended by the International Society for Technology in Education (ISTE) (2000) in their emphasis on defining technology within specific content standards. In the NGSS, technology is valued and intertwined with the math, engineering, and science standards in this document.

In conclusion, the NGSS is not a document that lists STEM standards, but rather a conglomerate of different standards from the various disciplines noted in that acronym. In this document, subject bias emerged as a code due to the fact that although the term STEM and the various disciplines within were reviewed, the authors of the NGSS were clearly focused on science and the other disciplines are noted in terms of their relationship to science. In other words, it is **S**tEm where science is emphasized with a bold capital S, engineering is emphasized, but to a lesser extent, with a capital E, and t and m are used to support or provide avenues to reinforce science and engineering ideas. It is with this lens, that the document provides example topics that are considered STEM. These examples revolve around science topics. Waves is one such example. NGSS brings in math by using mathematical representations to describe models where students develop a model to describe that waves are reflected, absorbed, or transmitted through various materials. In addition, they integrate qualitative scientific and technical information to support the claim that digitized signals are a more reliable way to encode and transmit information than using analog signals. Engineering is brought in when students apply their understanding of energy to design, test, and refine a device that converts energy from one form to another. Other example topics can be found in the Earth and space sciences. Again, these areas hold many traditional science standards. In addition, however, mathematical standards are emphasized such as patterns, scale, proportions, as well as engineering and technological standards such as obtaining and analyzing data that support theories of the formation of the solar system and universe.

NGSS: Possibilities for Teacher Education

There are no STEM standards in NGSS. Yet, teachers are being expected to meet the calls for STEM education. Given this, it is up to teacher education programs to help their students to understand and deliver the STEM possibilities within the document. STEM is an acronym used in the science standards to cover a group of individual disciplines with varying types of relationships between them. Within those variations, however, science or engineering are always dominant. Teacher preparation programs can use NGSS to show highlight that while these are science and engineering standards, they can be used to target other STEM disciplines. NGSS was developed in an educational system where science and math standards have historically been taught separately and national standards for each are provided as guides for states. How STEM is actually realized in the classroom is up to the states and districts, and ultimately the teachers. Thus, one will not find a prescription for educators in the document, but there are possibilities. These possibilities are new to the standards. So how can NGSS aid teachers and teacher educators with STEM teaching and learning? We explore some of these possibilities in this section.

Given the many different definitions noted earlier, we begin by establishing the definition(s) of STEM we use in this exploration of the possibilities. We use the definition from Akerson and Buck (2020) which is similar to the ninth perspective described by Bybee (2013) and is as follows: "STEM is a meaningful interdependence among all disciplines that comprise STEM. In other words, all individual disciplines of STEM are included in ways that are meaningful and showcase the interdependence of the fields. (p ix)" In this way future teachers are shown that their students can learn all four disciplines as connected in interdependent and meaningful ways.

Following a similar definition of STEM, Johnson et al. (2016) advocate for meaningful integration of the STEM disciplines and have created curriculum road maps that can be used to help teachers design such instruction. Each STEM Road Map includes six elements to ensure deep learning of STEM disciplines. These elements include (1) a motivating and engaging context for STEM learning, (2) include engineering design challenges of relevant technologies, (3) allow students to learn from failure and redesign based on what is learned, (4) include standards-based mathematics and/or science objectives in the learning activities, and go beyond STEM disciplines, (5) content should be taught in a student-centered manner to enable them to grapple with ideas and deepen their content knowledge, and (6) STEM learning environments should emphasize teamwork and communication abilities appropriate for life in a twenty-first century workforce.

Johnson et al. (2019) have further developed guides for pre-service and in-service teachers to be able to implement instruction using the STEM Road Map, such as the Natural Hazards guide for second grade, and the Influence of Waves for first grade (2020). They describe the STEM Road Map Curriculum as being organized around five real-world STEM themes that cause issues and dilemmas for current and future generations. These themes include (1) cause and effect, (2) innovation and progress, (3) the represented world, (4) sustainable systems, and (5) optimizing the human experience. These themes are used as springboards to connect real-world problems that will enable students to then connect the STEM disciplines meaningfully in their learning. This curriculum was created to aid teachers in efforts to teach STEM meaningfully.

Indeed, such a curriculum can be helpful, as most teachers have not been prepared to meaningfully teach each of the individual disciplines that comprise STEM in their teacher preparation programs. Most elementary preparation programs, for example, do not include a single course on engineering, but rather engineering is embedded in science methods courses, likely taught by an instructor who also has no background in engineering (Akerson et al., 2018). It would follow then, that they would be unlikely to be able to teach about the nature of the individual disciplines, or how the disciplines likely meaningfully connect. It is a problem that compounds without intervention through teacher preparation programs.

Johnson (2011) also established pathways to STEM education reform for secondary science education, including the importance of connecting all STEM disciplines meaningfully. There are further chapters that describe model programs for including STEM within various content areas, such as mathematics, science, and even literacy. Samples of programs are provided in both rural and urban districts. Additionally, there is a chapter that focuses on policy development, to provide suggestions for districts who desire to have STEM programs on their development of such programs. Johnson refers to the importance of *turbulence* in influencing districts and teachers to focus on STEM. This *turbulence* can influence development of STEM programs, but can also refer to influences against STEM programs, such as personnel, scheduling, standardized testing, and other issues.

Thus, developing a STEM program is difficult, and can be even more difficult to connect to various standards, such as NGSS.

Other such curricula and associated professional development programs could combine ideas about NGSS as well as STEM, ensuring that teachers have resources to not only "teach STEM" but also to help their students meet the science standards that are the focus of the NGSS. Wojnowski and Pea (2014) provided a guide for those who wish to provide STEM Professional development, and also includes connections to NGSS. This guide provides an overview of models of STEM professional development, along with a section that includes chapters describing state and district models for STEM professional development. These chapters include models for STEM professional development as well as science professional development models in grades kindergarten through twelve, and for rural and urban districts. One important component advocated in this book is development of professional learning communities that enable educators to focus on STEM professional development. In the professional learning communities science, mathematics, engineering, and technology instructors can work together to develop meaningful learning experiences for students across disciplines. Teachers can develop shared values and goals for STEM learning, create their own definitions of STEM, and connect them to NGSS, as well as other standards should they see fit. In this way they can choose one (or more) of the Bybee (2013) definitions of STEM and develop best practices associated with how their district chooses to define it, and to target learning for their students. These professional learning communities can evolve over time and teachers can adapt instructional practices to fit new programs, content, and grade levels, perhaps even revising their definitions of STEM teaching and learning over time depending on district priorities and learning goals.

NGSS does include a few small examples of combining disciplines, but no sample lessons. Thus, there are possibilities provided for STEM education (or at least interdisciplinary instruction). It is not a stand-alone document to support teachers in teaching STEM. As previously mentioned, it is most supported with science and engineering instruction as a guidepost for where teachers can target student learning goals. There are tangential connections to mathematics made, and small attention paid to technology.

STEM Possibilities Being Realized in Science Teacher Education

There are many concrete examples of teacher education programs that are preparing teachers to address the STEM possibilities within the NGSS. For example, at Indiana University we have attempted to implement STEM education in science teacher education at the elementary level with a content course entitled "STEM for Educators." This course is a physical science course taken by all elementary pre-service teachers and counts as one of their science content courses. Because this course is taught in the science education program, it generally ascribes to the third perspective of Bybee (2013), that science is the focus but connections are made to the other three disciplines of STEM. The major goals from the course are as follows:

By the end of this course, you should be able to:

- demonstrate a thorough and integrated representation of your understanding of how Matter and Energy exist, are transformed, and are conserved in our natural world. Additionally, how Matter and Energy can be used for explaining everyday phenomena and be used to engineer a solution to relevant problems;
- develop models of the scientific phenomenon using various representational forms that integrate science concepts, practices, and crosscutting concepts shared by various disciplines of STEM;
- explain basic principles of computing, including data, compression, encryption, processing and others;
- apply principles of Engineering Design and Computational Thinking, as they relate to designing an integrated STEM learning experiences for use in grades K-8

This course meets twice a week for an hour and a half each meeting, and is a combination of learning science content and learning connections to other STEM disciplines to aid students in conceptualizing connections between the STEM disciplines. Like the NGSS, science is at the core of the objective of this course, but the conceptualized connections among the STEM disciplines are evident. Assignments include hands-on projects where students can raise questions and manipulate materials to answer those questions, build models (e.g. models of the atom), all while working in teams and making connections to engineering, technology, and mathematics. Because they are future teachers, they have a chance to practice mini lessons with their peers so they can initially see the kinds of questions, conversations, and engagements they will have with their students.

Another new initiative at Indiana University is the advent of an online Masters in Education in Teaching, Learning, and Curriculum. Within this program are core courses for in-service teachers, including the core of curriculum courses, equity courses, assessment, an inquiry course, and capstone course. Within this major, there are four tracks, one of which is the STEM and Arts Innovations, which includes a graduate course entitled Introduction to STEM Teaching, and another course entitled Demonstration and Field Strategies in Science, and an Art Methods for Non-Art Specialists. The idea behind having this initiative is to aid those who are already teaching science to engage in new strategies for incorporating STEM disciplines within their teaching, and helping teachers to find ways to support students in making connections among the disciplines. Again, because the course is offered through the science education program, the course takes the third perspective of Bybee (2013) where science is at the center, and the other disciplines are included and connections are made to them.

Additionally, Indiana University offers one day workshops to teachers who are interested in the intersection of global literacy and STEAM education. The Global STEAM workshops use exemplar classroom-ready hands-on lessons that teach global competencies through literacy and science and engineering practices. Teachers from all disciplines are invited to participate, with the goal of implementing engaging project, problem, and inquiry-based activities in their classrooms. The global competencies that are targeted include investigating the world, recognizing perspectives of other cultures, communicating with diverse audiences, and taking action. The program builds on the Novel Engineering program developed by the Center for Engineering Education Outreach at Tufts University as an integrated approach to learning STEAM through literacy. In this program, students collaborate to design and build solutions for problems presented in youth fiction and non-fiction. At Indiana University, the adaptation of the Novel Engineering program focuses on global issues by using stories from around the world. This program seeks to be at levels eight and nine of Bybee (2013).

A new initiative that Indiana University is pursuing is the development of a STEM education minor for PhD and EdD students. This minor is in development with faculty from four departments representing science education, technology education, engineering education, and mathematics education. It will be open to all PhD students, and will consist of courses from each discipline, as well as an integrated STEM course that will be developed and taught by faculty across the STEM disciplines. The motive for developing such a minor is for graduates of Indiana to be able to better provide STEM instruction in teacher education programs in which they will teach in the future. This program will offer courses at perspectives one and two of Bybee (2013), and also at levels eight and nine, to highlight the various perspectives of STEM education.

These are a few ways that we are trying to incorporate STEM into programs at Indiana University, to respond to the calls for STEM teaching and learning. Of course, much more could be done to ensure STEM is properly incorporated and all disciplines are taught well, including the natures of those disciplines.

Conclusion

Certainly, teacher education programs strive to prepare teachers to take advantage of the STEM possibilities with the NGSS. Knowing where these ideas about STEM exist can be helpful in aiding teachers into making connections across the discipline. The NGSS is flexible enough to enable STEM connections to be made, and to include STEM from many perspectives. We have included samples of STEM curricula and models of STEM professional development programs that can connect to NGSS. While these recommendations for STEM curricula and professional development exist, there are certainly other models that can be developed, and it can be explored what is "best" for different grade level bands and content areas. There are many possibilities for connecting NGSS to STEM education, and resources exist to enable teachers and professional developers to at least have a starting point for doing so.

References

Akerson, V. L., & Buck, G. A. (2020). *Critical questions in STEM education*. Springer.

Akerson, V. L., Burgess, A., Gerber, A., Guo, M., Khan, T., & Newman, S. (2018). Disentangling the meaning of STEM: Implications for science education and science teacher education. *Journal of Science Teacher Education, 29*(1), 1–8.

Bowen, G. A. (2009). Document analysis as a qualitative research method. *Qualitative Research Journal, 9*(2), 27–40. https://doi.org/10.3316/QRJ0902027

Bybee, R. W. (2013). *The case for STEM education: Challenges and opportunities.* NSTA Press.

International Society for Technology in Education. (2000). *ISTE national educational technology standards (NETS).* Authors.

Johnson, C. C., Peters-Burton, E. E., & Moore, T. J. (2016). *STEM road map: A framework for integrated STEM education.* Routledge.

Johnson, C. C., Walton, J. B., & Peters-Burton. (2019). *Natural hazards: STEM road map for elementary school.* NSTA Press.

National Governors Association Center, & for Best Practices & Council of Chief State School Officers. (2010). *Common Core state standards for mathematics.* Authors.

O'Leary, Matt. (2014). Developing a National Framework for the Effective Use of Lesson Observation in Further Education. Project Report. University and College Union.

Wojnowski, B. S., & Pea, C. H. (2014). *Models and approaches to STEM professional development.* NSTA Press.

CHAPTER 16

Current Trends in Science Curriculum Reforms in Response to STEM Education: International Trends, Policies and Challenges

Hassan H. Tairab and Shashidhar Belbase

Introduction

Over the last decade, the development and implementation of science and mathematics curricula in most countries around the world have undergone educational reforms in response to the science, technology, engineering, and mathematics (STEM) education movement, with the aim of providing relevant and solid knowledge and skills needed to prepare leaders of the future knowledge-based and competitive economy (OECD, 1996). Proponents of these reforms stress that while acknowledging the contribution of science curricula to building content knowledge and basic

H. H. Tairab (✉) • S. Belbase
College of Education, United Arab Emirates University,
Abu Dhabi, UAE
e-mail: tairab@uaeu.ac.ae; sbelbase@uaeu.ac.ae

S. M. Al-Balushi et al. (eds.), *Reforming Science Teacher Education Programs in the STEM Era*, Palgrave Studies on Leadership and Learning in Teacher Education,
https://doi.org/10.1007/978-3-031-27334-6_16

scientific skills, they rarely emphasize cross-disciplinary and innovative skills needed to solve today's problems (Corlu et al., 2014).

Despite the concerted efforts to develop and implement science and mathematics curricula in line with the interdisciplinary perspective of STEM education, problems related to the development and implementation of STEM education represent mounting challenges for educators and other stakeholders that might interfere with successful development and implementation of STEM-based curricula going beyond traditional factual knowledge-base to more creative and innovative skills (Corlu et al., 2014). One of the promising thoughts in STEM education can be the application of integrated curriculum practice that may provide opportunities for learning mathematics and science with relevant knowledge and skills within engaging and stimulating interdisciplinary contexts (Furner & Kumar, 2007). Czerniak et al. (1999) found that STEM-oriented learning approaches positively and significantly impacted student performance than those who did not learn via the STEM approach. Furthermore, the use of STEM-oriented curricula has been linked to improving students' attitudes, motivation, and interests (Erlandson & McVittie, 2001).

This chapter intends to analyze current trends of science and mathematics curricular reforms within the framework of STEM education to identify and highlight critical issues related to conceptualization, implementation, policies, challenges, and evaluation of outcomes. The available findings of previous studies suggested that an interdisciplinary approach to curriculum implementation remains a thorny and contentious issue (Venville et al., 2012) due to various factors that are likely to affect implementation.

Disciplinary or Interdisciplinary

Recent curricular reforms added more confusion with respect to STEM, whether as "integration" or as "education." In this context, STEM can be thought of as an *educational* priority to promote meaningful teaching and learning of science, technology, engineering, and mathematics in school or higher education, or as *integration* is much needed to clearly address curriculum policies implementation and challenges. Although there are no common and agreed definitions of STEM, there are various attempts to shed light on the perspectives that researchers use to define STEM and other related practices attributed to STEM. For example, The National Research Council (2014) defined STEM integration as "working in the context of complex phenomena or situations on tasks that require students to use multiple knowledge and skills from multiple disciplines" (NRC, 2014, p. 52, Cited by Wang et al., 2020). In this sense, STEM is regarded as the integration of knowledge and skills of disciplines to engage in activities purposefully to solve problems using existing knowledge and skills from all disciplines. Sanders (2009) conceptualized STEM as a pedagogical approach based on the foundations of two or more disciplines of science, technology, engineering, and math. Likewise, Moore et al. (2014) defined integrated STEM as a process of facilitating the integration of the four disciplines of science, technology, engineering, and mathematics as a unitary learning experience for students.

On the other hand, others tried to define STEM as an "amalgamation of content and concepts from multiple STEM disciplines" (Nadelson & Seifert, 2017, p. 221). Such amalgamation may be likely to present STEM in terms of integrative approaches to models that mirror solving real-world problems using complex designs, knowledge, and skills that are drawn from STEM subjects in contexts of everyday learning (Bryan et al., 2016). Vasquez et al. (2013) provided a comprehensive approach to STEM where they emphasized different perspectives that ranged from disciplinary, interdisciplinary, and multidisciplinary perspectives.

English (2016) defines integrated STEM as the integration of content and concepts from multiple STEM disciplines. The integration takes place in ways such that knowledge and process of specific STEM disciplines are considered simultaneously without regard to the discipline but rather in the context of a problem, project, or task. In schools, integrated STEM is typically associated with a project or problem-based learning approach where the outcomes can vary widely, and the knowledge needed is distributed across STEM disciplines. It follows that STEM involves the application of STEM-related knowledge and practice across STEM disciplines not exclusive to a single discipline.

Current Trends of Science Curricular Reforms Within the Framework of STEM Education

During the last few years, trends in STEM education have shaped educational reforms nationally and internationally. Several concerned educational institutions and policy developers have expressed the need to improve knowledge and skills of STEM discipline to match the needed knowledge and skills of current and future STEM-oriented graduates

(Caprile et al., 2015). Furthermore, numerous reports and policies have all stressed the importance of STEM education in shaping the future STEM curriculum innovation and, consequently, the development of STEM-related skills. As noted by English (2016), STEM competencies are currently needed within and outside of specific STEM occupations. "Progress on STEM is critical to building a just and inclusive society" (National Science and Technology Council, 2013, p. vii).

On the other hand, in recent years, the call for new approaches to the development and implementation of STEM integration has been recommended by professional organizations such as the National Academy of Engineering (NAE) and the National Research Council (NRC). Approaches that are in line with current and future scientifically and technologically oriented contexts that focus on hands-on, interdisciplinary, and socially relevant aspects of STEM education to achieve the goals of STEM-related curricula (NRC, 2011). We have seen calls by developers of recent curricular initiatives such as the Next Generation Science Standards (NGSS) (NRC, 2012, 2013) for new perspectives to integrate STEM curriculum.

Conceptualization, Implementation, Policies, and Challenges

Given the lack of consensus on the educational views on the conceptions and the importance of STEM education as measured by specific national and international indicators, many nations are now re-examining their curricula and the future educational initiatives to enhance the development of STEM as a discipline in terms of conceptualization, development, and implementation. English (2016) suggested advancing STEM as a stand-alone discipline requires a need to focus on STEM as both content knowledge and as an interdisciplinary-oriented process to nurture skills in terms of procedural knowledge in addition to conceptual knowledge. This focus on skills and conceptual and procedural knowledge is likely to lead to the development of what we now know as twenty-first-century skills: problem-solving, creativity, and critical thinking. (English & Gainsburg, 2016). According to Mansour and Deghaidy (2021), this focus will shift the teaching environment from traditional lecture-based approaches to those that are based on inquiry, project-based, and problem-solving learning strategies.

Nevertheless, effective STEM implementation requires skilled STEM leadership that can spearhead curriculum development and implementation, as well as teacher preparation that supports such development and implementation of curricula that include cross-curricular real-world challenges for students to challenge. Indeed, well-prepared teachers for teaching STEM are one of the critical requirements of successful STEM implementation.

Despite the success of the implementation of STEM-related curricula, various research studies reported challenges facing educators in implementing integrated STEM education programs. For example, Kubat (2018) reported several challenges faced by teachers when trying to implement STEM integration in science classrooms. Challenges such as crowded classrooms that are difficult to manage; a traditional curriculum that is too broad to adopt the STEM integration; and teachers lack the necessary professional background both at content and pedagogical knowledge levels to teach using the STEM approach. Thibaut et al. (2018) suggested that STEM integration requires restructuring the interdisciplinary curriculum in line with the STEM approach and providing the needed support for both teachers and students.

Nadelson and Seifert (2017) identified two challenges related to teaching and implementing a STEM curriculum. The first challenge is the efforts needed to implement an approach that has not been done previously using the four STEM disciplines in a context that is used to segregation of disciplines. The second challenge is the teachers' readiness and their professional background. Other challenges identified by previous research studies are the lack of solid conceptual understanding of the nature of science and technology and the interactions between them among science teachers (Tairab, 2001; El-Deghaidy & Mansoor, 2015). In the absence of science teachers' sound understanding of the nature of science and technology, the intended STEM integration process would not be possible to achieve.

How Do Science Curricula Globally Respond to the STEM Education Movement? Samples of Global Curricular Reform Initiatives

There are governmental and professional organizational efforts in curriculum reform movement in science and mathematics that were considered seriously in the post-Sputnik era. The United States government formed different committees to study the status of science and mathematics education and recommended actions for improvement. United States President Eisenhower signed a law known as National Defense Education

Action (NDEA) in 1958 to promote mathematics and science education in US schools through reform programs and initiatives (Hunt, 2021). These initiatives were followed by the standards movement in science and mathematics education.

Global Initiatives

STEM Initiatives in North America

In the United States, there are four kinds of schools in terms of how they implement STEM education. The four schools are named "Elite STEM focused schools," "Inclusive STEM focused schools," "STEM focused career and technical education (CTE)," and "STEM programs in comprehensive schools" (NRC, 2011). The first kind of school (Elite STEM schools) focusses on high ability students to prepare them for STEM careers. The second kind of school (Inclusive STEM schools) focusses on minority groups in STEM fields. The third kind of school (CTE Schools) focuses on a broader range of STEM programs for students to continue their education without dropping out. The fourth kind of school is not STEM focused, but support students prepare for STEM education and related career. The reform in the science curriculum in the US with the introduction of recent Next Generation Science Standards has expanded the integrated STEM vision with an interdisciplinary connection of teaching and learning science with mathematics and engineering by using appropriate technological tools (Oliver & Hodges, 2014).

Likewise, the STEM initiative in Mexico has been promoted with educational programs, such as Movimiento STEM, Teritorios STEM Model, and United States-Mexico Foundation for Science (FUMEC). These initiatives have enriched STEM activities in the schools. For example, Movimiento STEM emphasizes an engineering-based program in Queretaro to motivate students toward technical and other vocational education (Roja & Segura, 2020). In this context, the gender gap in the STEM discipline has been a major concern in Mexico, and school-based programs have been launched to bring more female students into STEM disciplines through elite STEM and non-elite STEM initiatives in schools (Ngo & Dustan, 2019). There are several ongoing STEM initiatives in Canada, such as the Science, Technology, and Innovation Council emphasizes the need to strengthen science, technology, and engineering education to meet the global competitiveness gap (Science, Technology and

Innovation Council, 2015). The government of Canada formed a comprehensive policy in 2007 to promote STEM discipline and related workforce in the country (DeCoito, 2016; Krug, 2012).

STEM Initiatives in Europe

A vast majority of European countries have emphasized STEM education with a high priority at the national level (Kearney, 2016). Nistor et al. (2018) recommended more support for innovative STEM education emphasizing inquiry-based teaching and learning; the governments should offer more opportunities for STEM-related professional development, introduce an innovative approach to curriculum development and assessment practices, and promote transdisciplinary collaboration among teacher preparation institutions. European countries have initiated STEM programs in schools to attract young people to the field. For example, Iceland, Poland, France, Faroe Islands, and Norway had a joint project Edu-Arctic as an innovative program to bring young people into the field of science, technology, math, and engineering (EDU-ARCTIC, 2016). Likewise, another program named Key Competencies for Life-long Learning was initiated by fourteen European countries to initiate reform projects with integrated STEM education to develop competent teachers in the field (European Schoolnet, 2018).

STEM Initiatives in Africa

Barrett et al. (2019) emphasized implementing high-quality STEM education in Sub-Saharan Africa through Education for All (EFA) and a vision of a knowledge economy in the region. The EFA policy guides and promotes life skills, skills for sustainability, and twenty-first-century skills. The vision of a knowledge economy encompasses the powerful implications of ICTs and other technological tools across STEM disciplines. In this context, the new vision of Pan African Sustainable Development has been introduced by the African Union as a policy agenda for a knowledge-based economy through the enhancement of STEM in schools (Barrett et al., 2019). With this call to enhance the STEM field in the region, Tanzania introduced compulsory science education at the lower secondary level. Botswana introduced a Strategic Plan 2015–2020 for Education and Training Sector to promote STEM education for economic growth. Likewise, Kenya unveiled Vision 2030 to improve STEM education

(Barrett, 2017). Blom et al. (2016) analyzed STEM research and found that several countries in Africa joined collective efforts to improve their STEM education through a Join Call for Action in Kigali, Rwanda, to develop a knowledge-based society meeting the generational gap. For this action to be materialized, they joined the STEM initiative with the support of the World Bank under the program called Partnership for Applied Science, Engineering and Technology (PASET). In Egypt, the science curriculum was developed traditionally as activities in the first three grades, significantly different from the mathematics curriculum, where it was formally developed within the traditional approach commonly found in Egyptian curricula where the emphasis is on the teacher-centered approach (Mansour & El-Deghaidy, 2021).

STEM Initiatives in Asia

STEM initiatives in Asia are expanding. Many Asian countries and autonomous regions, for example, Hong Kong, Malaysia, Philippines, Thailand, Singapore, and South Korea, have introduced STEM-related policies in teacher education, school curriculum and research activities in higher education (Teo et al., 2022). Lee et al. (2018) emphasized designing STEM as an integrative unit in schools, equitable representation of each discipline in STEM, technologically enhanced collaborative STEM, modular-based STEM challenges, contextualization of STEM, and design-based STEM in Asia Pacific nations. China recently introduced a vision of the "Chinese Dream" to be a world-class innovation hub with the promotion of a STEM environment for transforming into an innovation-driven economy by 2050 (Han & Appelbaum, 2018). Ma (2021) has proposed that China should consider STEM education as a praxis within three dimensions: lived, historical, and ethical, in order to promote situated interdisciplinary lenses in the theory and practice of integrated STEM. India is also focusing on improving education by introducing STEM education policies. For example, Innovation in Science Pursuit for Inspired Research, Science and Engineering Research Board, Institutes for Nanoscience and Technology, Translational Research Institute, Biotech Mission 1998, and Nano Mission 2002, Science Express, to name a few (Vivekananda International Foundation, 2019). With these strategic governmental and institutional policies, the school mathematics and science teaching-learning and curriculum practices have been reformed with a motive to promote STEM education in India.

STEM Initiatives in Australia and Oceana

Australia has emphasized STEM as an enterprise at all levels of education, from schools to universities including pre-service teacher preparation institution, to strategically promote social, cultural, and economic prosperity (Office of the Chief Scientist, 2013). The Office of the Chief Scientist (2013) suggested key actions to develop STEM programs and policies to implement the strategy by building a clear purpose and course of actions, policy coordination, and establishing a high-level committee to execute the policies. They further state, "Not being left behind as a nation and designing our future with STEM as a critical element ought to be the goals of governments as they make their choices" (p. 9). This way, the Office of the Chief Scientist (2013) embarked upon the importance of STEM education policies and their implementations to strengthen the country's economic and social welfare through effective and strong foundations of school curriculum and pedagogy. Although there are several STEM initiatives in place in Australia, there are limited efforts to promote the STEM field in the other Oceania countries, such as Micronesia, Polynesia, and Melanesia (Baker et al., 2022).

STEM Initiatives in Caribbean, Central, and South America

There are several STEM initiatives ongoing in the Caribbean and Central and South American nations. For example, the Inter-American Teacher Education Network (ITEN) provides fellowships to mathematics, science, engineering, and technology teachers to promote STEM-related activities by enhancing teacher development and recruitment through a career pathway program (Hite et al., 2020). There are other programs, such as Girls4Tech, Technovation Girls, Girl Power Codesfest, STEM es para chicas, and Hulheres na Ciencia, to name a few, that promote STEM teacher education and engagement of more female students in STEM-related educational activities and skills development (Villavicencio et al., 2022). Likewise, there are STEM initiatives to promote the field in several South American countries. For example, STEM Brazil helps in teacher development in the field of science and mathematics and supports disadvantaged students in joining STEM disciplines in Brazil (Educando, n.d.). This program started in 2009 and provides 60 hours of professional development training to mathematics and science teachers in more than 1000 schools in

Brazil (Educando, n.d.). Likewise, Experimento Chile started in 2012 to promote STEM activities in several schools in Chile with the support of universities, the government, and local schools (Seimens Stiftung, 2022).

STEM Initiatives in Arab Region and the Middle East

The UAE Government has emphasized STEM initiatives in schools and higher education through different programs and policies (Al Murshidi, 2019). For example, the Emirate of Abu Dhabi introduced curriculum reform at the school level by focusing on STEM education (Moonesar et al., 2015), and the Government of the UAE introduced Science, Technology, and Innovation Policy in 2015 (Elsayary, 2021). This policy is aligned with the national goal to drive away from the economic dependency on limited oil resources by fostering sustainable innovation for economic diversity and promoting an innovation-friendly ecosystem and culture of innovation (United Arab Emirates Government, 2015). Likewise, other Arab nations have concerted efforts to build a strong STEM foundation in schools by introducing initiatives to improve mathematics and science curriculum and pedagogy and enhancement of technology integration across the disciplines. For example, Saudi Arabia has taken a bold move toward building a more competitive and knowledge-based economy through the promotion of STEM initiatives in schools and higher education institutions with Vision 2030 (Government of Kingdom of Saudi Arabia, 2021). However, there are limited opportunities for teachers to develop their knowledge, skills, attitudes, and values toward STEM discipline for themselves, and that might impact their roles in the classroom practices to promote STEM as an integrated interdisciplinary approach to teaching and learning mathematics and science (Madani, 2020). Other Gulf Cooperation Council (GCC) countries have emphasized STEM education in their respective schools with long-term policies, although there is more to be done to improve students' achievement in STEM fields in international tests, such as TIMSS and PISA (Kayan-Fadlelmula et al., 2022).

Discussion

STEM education has received acceptance around the world. Policy documents, new perspectives, pre-service mathematics and teacher preparation, and professional development programs for teachers have all been developed and implemented to improve knowledge and skills of STEM disciplines among both teachers and students. On the other hand, the popularity of STEM has also led us to believe in curricular reforms as a dynamic process to update the teaching, learning, and assessment practices that meet the demands of changing contexts. In this regard, the trends of science curriculum reform in response to STEM education show a feeble ray of hope of having any significant impact. The science curriculum reform in the United States shows a systematic and periodic historical effort with reports of the Committee of Ten in 1893, several curriculum projects funded by the National Science Foundation in the 1950s–1970s, and the report 'A Nation at Risk' by the Commission of Excellence in Education (Abell & Lederman, 2007). Sustained and continued review of STEM policies, implementation, and teacher preparation programs need to be reconsidered in light of the various perspectives of STEM.

Previous research findings on the development and implementation of curricular reforms suggested more considerations of not only the curriculum but also teacher-training programs, particularly at the pre-service level. Mansour and EL-Deghaidy (2021) suggested that teacher-training programs should focus on helping teachers develop new conceptual structures and perspectives to implement STEM integration in schools. Mansour and EL-Deghaidy (2021) also suggested that adequate considerations should be in place to provide accounts for both content and professional knowledge.

In a STEM integrated curriculum, students are expected to engage with their peers to realize personal responsibility to engage in group activities such as cooperative learning activities through creativity and innovation based on the concept of life-long learning (Belbase et al., 2021). Students in formal classrooms are likely to enhance the perspectives of a "learning community" that works within a collaborative approach throughout the year to guarantee effective implementation and hence, acquire the intended STEM-oriented learning outcomes.

Previous findings of studies on STEM education suggested a critical need for restructuring STEM disciplines in ways that facilitate integration to reflect better teaching and learning. However, integrated STEM, as recommended by previous studies on the development and implementation of STEM-based curriculum, requires different approaches and a significant move toward meaningful outcomes of teaching and learning activities. Development and implementation of the STEM approach to teaching and learning are likely to shape our understanding of how teacher preparation and in-service programs are developed and implemented

Conclusion and Recommendations for Teacher Preparation Programs

Science, technology, engineering, and mathematics (STEM) education or integration may have drawn considerable attention to not only the process of reforming school science and mathematics curricula, but also to reforming teacher preparation programs. There are theories and practices of STEM, either as an integrated approach or as an educational practice, to promote meaningful teaching and learning of science and mathematics. However, there seem to be no conclusive findings or model practices that convince the actors of the STEM field to feel the wave and evidence-base to effectively design and implement it either in schools or in teacher preparation programs. Much of the energy and environmental factors in STEM appear to be peripheral echoes rather than transformations at curricular and pedagogical epicenters. That said, we feel that STEM education or integration has merit only when teachers are well trained in STEM theory and practice, both in curricular and pedagogical actions. Leaders and stakeholders should consider it as a possibility, but not as an ultimate goal to transform educational practices. The stakes are high in either direction, not focusing on it and going with the disciplinary curriculum practices despite the demand for integrated knowledge, skills, and attitudes; or focusing on it despite the mounting challenges due to lack of readiness of the teachers, poorly integrated or forcefully interlinked pedagogical actions, which are rather more distractions. Therefore, we recommend reconsidering STEM education or integration beyond the interdisciplinary or transdisciplinary bandwagon. It should be seriously planned with a long-term vision, teachers well trained, and the curriculum well reformed as a unitary-whole approach.

References

Abell, S. K., & Lederman, N. C. (2007). *Handbook of research on science education.* Routledge.

Al Murshidi, G. (2019). STEM education in the United Arab Emirates: Challenges and possibilities. *International Journal of Learning, Teaching and Educational Research, 18*(12), 316–332. https://doi.org/10.26803/ijlter.18.12.18

Baker, J., Keahi, K., Cogbill, J. T., Naeole, C., Grabowsky, G., Keahiolalo, R., Stokes, A. J., & Turner, H. (2022). Dimensions of culturally-intensive STEM education: Looking to the source. In P. Pangelinan & T. McVey (Eds.), *Learning and reconciliation through indigenous education in Oceania* (pp. 150–169). IGI Global. https://doi.org/10.4018/978-1-7998-7736-3.ch009

Barrett, A. M. (2017). Making secondary education relevant for all: Reflections on science education in an expanding sub-sector. *Compare: A Journal of Comparative and International Education, 47*(6), 962–978. https://doi.org/10.1080/03057925.2017.1343127

Barrett, A. M., Gardner, V., Joubert, M., & Tikley, L. (2019). *Approaches to strengthening secondary STEM & ICT education in Sub-Saharan Africa.* Mastercard Foundation. https://mastercardfdn.org/wp-content/uploads/2019/07/Strengthening-STEM-ICT-in-Sub-Saharan-Africa-v.F.pdf

Belbase, S., Mainali, B., Kasemsukpipat, W., Tairab, H., Gochoo, M., & Jarrah, A. (2021). At the dawn of science, technology, engineering, arts, and mathematics (STEAM) education: prospects, priorities, processes, and problems. *International Journal of Mathematical Education in Science and Technology.* https://doi.org/10.1080/0020739X.2021.1922943

Blom, A., Lan, G., & Adil, M. (2016). *Sub-Saharan Africa science, technology, engingering, and mathematics research: A decade of development.* World Bank Group.

Bryan, L. A., Moore, T. J., Johnson, C. C., & Roehrig, G. H. (2016). Integrated STEM education. In C. C. Johnson, E. E. Peters-Burton, & T. J. Moore (Eds.), *STEM road map: A framework for integrated STEM education* (pp. 23–37). Routledge.

Caprile, M., Palmen, R., & Sanz, & Dente, G. (2015). *Encouraging STEM studies for the labor market.* European Parliament. https://tinyurl.com/342tzytm

Corlu, S., Capraro, R., & Capraro, M. (2014). Introducing STEM education: Implications for educating our teachers in the age of innovation. *Education and Science, 39(171)*, 74–85.

Czerniak, C. M., Weber, W., Jr., Sandman, A., & Ahern, J. (1999). A literature review of science and mathematics integration. *School Science and Mathematics, 99*(8), 421–430. https://doi.org/10.1111/j.1949-8594.1999.tb17504.x

DeCoito, I. (2016). STEM education in Canada: A knowledge synthesis. *Canadian Journal of Science, Mathematics and Technology, 16*(2), 114–128. https://doi.org/10.1080/14926156.2016.1166297

EDU-ARCTIC. (2016). *Engaging students in STEM education through Arctic research.* Retrieved May 28, 2022, from https://edu-arctic.eu/about/objectives

Educando. (n.d.). *STEM Brasil: Bringing innovation to public schools.* Accessed May 24, 2022, from https://educando.org/stembrasil/

EL-Deghaidy, H., & Mansour, N. (2015). Science teachers' perceptions towards STEM education in Saudi Arabia: Possibilities and challenges. *International Journal of Learning and Teaching, 1*(1), 51–54. https://doi.org/10.18178/ijlt.1.1.51-54

ElSayary, A. (2021). Using a reflective practice model to teach STEM education in a blended learning environment. *EURASIA Journal of Mathematics, Science, and Technology. Education, 17*(2), em1942. https://doi.org/10.29333/ejmste/9699

English, L. D. (2016). STEM education K-12: Perspectives on integration. *International Journal of STEM Education, 3*, Article 3. https://doi.org/10.1186/s40594-016-0036-1

English, L. D., & Gainsburg, J. (2016). Problem solving in a 21st century mathematics curriculum. In L. D. English & D. Kirshner (Eds.), *Handbook of international research in mathematics education* (3rd ed., pp. 313–335). Taylor & Francis.

Erlandson, C., & McVittie, J. (2001). Student voices on integrative curriculum. *Middle School Journal, 33*(2), 28–36. https://doi.org/10.1080/00940771.2001.11494660

European Schoolnet. (2018). *Science, technology, engineering and mathematics education policies in Europe*. European Schoolnet.

Furner, J. M., & Kumar, D. D. (2007). The mathematics and science integration argument: A stand for teacher education. *Eurasia Journal of Mathematics, Science & Technology Education, 3*(3), 185–189. https://doi.org/10.12973/ejmste/75397

Government of Kingdom of Saudi Arabia. (2021). *Vision 2030*. The Author. https://www.my.gov.sa/wps/portal/snp/content/saudivision

Han, X., & Appelbaum, R. P. (2018). China's science, technology, engineering, and mathematics (STEM) research environment: A snapshot. *PLOS One, 13*(4), e0195347. https://doi.org/10.1371/journal.pone.0195347

Hite, R., Vieyra, R. E., Milbourne, J., Dou, R., Spuck, T., & Smith, J. F. (2020). STEM teacher leadership in policy. In C. C. Johnson, M. J. Mohr-Schroeder, T. J. Moore, & L. D. English (Eds.), *Handbook of research on STEM education* (pp. 470–480). Routledge.

Hunt, T. C. (2021, August 26). *National Defense Education Act. Encyclopedia Britannica.* https://www.britannica.com/topic/National-Defense-Education-Act

Kayan-Fadlelmula, F., Sellami, A., Abdelkader, N., & Umer, S. (2022). A systematic review of STEM education research in the GCC countries: Trends, gaps and barriers. *International Journal of STEM Education, 9*(2), 1–24. https://doi.org/10.1186/s40594-021-00319-7

Kearney, C. (2016). *Efforts to increase students' interest in pursuing science, technology, engineering and mathematics studies and careers: National measures taken by 30 countries Report*. European Schoolnet. http://www.eun.org/resources/detail?publicationID=783

Krug, D. H. (2012, November 24–27). *STEM education and sustainability in Canada and the United States.* Paper presented at the 2nd International STEM in Education Conference, Beijing, China.

Kubat, U. (2018). The integration of STEM into science classes. *World Journal on Educational Technology: Current Issues, 10*(3), 165–173. https://doi.org/10.18844/wjet.v10i3.3557

Lee, M. H., Chai, C. S., & Hong, H. Y. (2018). STEM education in Asia Pacific: Challenges and development. *Asia-Pacific Educational Research, 28*(1), 1–4. 101007/s40299-018-0424-z.

Ma, Y. (2021). Reconceptualizing STEM education in China as a praxis: A curriculum turn. *Sustainability, 13*, 4961. https://doi.org/10.3390/su13094961

Madani, R. A. (2020). Teaching challenges and perceptions on STEM implementation for schools in Saudi Arabia. *European Journal of STEM Education, 5*(1), 03. 10.20897/ejsteme/8468.

Mansour, N., & El-Deghaidy, H. (2021). Promotion of STEM Education in Schools through Partnerships. In N. Mansour & H. El-Deghaidy (Eds.), *STEM in Science Education and S in STEM. From Pedagogy to learning*. https://doi.org/10.1163/9789004446076

Moonesar, I., Mourtada, R., Shaer, S., Al-Eisawi, D., & Elomari, L. (2015). Persistence in the Abu Dhabi STEM Pipeline. *Preparing Emirati Youth for Science and Technology Careers in The Innovation Economy*. Mohamed Bin Rashid School of Government. Dubai, United Arab Emirates.

Moore, T., Stohlmann, M., Wang, H., Tank, K., Glancy, A., & Roehrig, G. (2014). Implementation and integration of engineering in K-12 STEM education. In S. Purzer, J. Strobel, & M. Cardella (Eds.), *Engineering in precollege setting: Synthesizing research, policy and practices* (pp. 35–60). Purdue University Press.

Nadelson, L. S., & Seifert, A. L. (2017). Integrated STEM defined contexts, challenges, and the future. *The Journal of Educational Research, 110*(3), 221–223. https://doi.org/10.1080/00220671.2017.1289775

National Research Council. (2011). *Successful STEM education: A workshop summary*. The National Academies Press.

National Research Council. (2012). *A framework for K-12 science education: Practices, crosscutting concepts, and core ideas*. The National Academies Press. https://doi.org/10.17226/13165

National Research Council. (2013). *Next generation science standards: For states, by states*. The Academies Press. https://doi.org/10.17226/18290

National Research Council (NRC). (2014). *STEM integration in K012 education: Status, prospects, and an agenda for research*. The National Academies Press. https://doi.org/10.17226/18612

National Science and Technology Council. (2013). *Federal science, technology, engineering, and mathematics (STEM) education 5-year strategic plan*. Committee of STEM Education, National Science and Technology Council.

Ngo, D., & Dustan, A. (2019). *Closing the STEM gender gap: Choice, access, and policies in Mexico City high schools*. Accessed May 24, 2022, from https://andrewdustan.com/pdf/stem_mexico_ngo_dustan.pdf

Nistor, A., Gras-Velazquez, A., Billon, N., & Mihal, G. (2018). *Science, technology, engineering and mathematics education practices in Europe*. Scientix Observatory Report. European Schoolnet.

Office of the Chief Scientist. (2013). *Science, technology, engineering, and mathematics in the national interest: A strategic approach*. Australian Government. https://www.chiefscientist.gov.au/sites/default/files/STEMstrategy290713FINALweb.pdf

Oliver, J. S., & Hodges, G. W. (2014). Rural science education: New ideas, redirections, and broadened definitions. In N. G. Lederman & S. K. Abell (Eds.), *Handbook of research on science education (vol. 2)* (pp. 266–283). Routledge.

Organization for Economic Cooperation and Development (OECD). (1996). *The knowledge-based economy*. OECD. https://tinyurl.com/5cmk98nu

Roja, G., & Segura, L. (2020). Mexico's movimiento STEM and related developments in the State Queretaro. In C. Zintgraff, S. C. Suh, B. Kellison, & P. E. Resta (Eds.), *STEM in the Technopolis: The power of STEM education the regional technology policy* (pp. 203–224). Springer.

Sanders, M. (2009). STEM, STEM education, STEMmania. *Technology Teacher, 68*(4), 20–26. *The Journal of Educational Research, 110*(3), 221–223. https://doi.org/10.1080/00220671.2017.1289775

Science, Technology and Innovation Council. (2015). *State of the nation 2014. Canada's innovation challenges and opportunities*. Author.

SIEMENS Stiftung. (2022). *STEM education in Chile: Respecting traditions while embracing future knowledge*. Accessed May 24, 2022, from https://www.siemens-stiftung.org/en/foundation/education/stem-education-in-chile/

Tairab, H. (2001). How do pre-service and in-service science teachers view the nature of science and technology? *Research in Science and Technological Education, 19*(1), 235–250. https://doi.org/10.1080/02635140120087759

Teo, T. W., Tan, A. L., & Teng, P. (Eds.). (2022). *STEM education from Asia: Trends and perspectives*. Taylor & Francis.

Thibaut, L., Ceuppens, S., De Loof, H., De Meester, J., Goovaerts, L., Struyf, A., Boeve-de Pauw, J., Dehaene, W., Deprez, J., De Cock, M., Hellinckx, L., Knipprath, H., Langie, G., Struyven, K., Van de Velde, D., Van Petegem, P., & Depaepe, F. (2018). Integrated STEM Education: A systematic review of instructional practices in secondary education. *European Journal of STEM Education, 3*(1), 02. https://doi.org/10.20897/ejsteme/85525

United Arab Emirates Government. (2015). *Science, technology & innovation policy in the United Arab Emirates*. The Author. https://u.ae/-/media/Science-Technology-and-Innovation-Policy.ashx

Vasquez, J., Sneider, C., & Comer, M. (2013). *STEM lesson essentials, grades 3–8: Integrating science, technology, engineering, and mathematics*. Heinemann.

Venville, G., Rennie, L., & Wallace, J. (2012). Curriculum integration: Challenging the assumption of school science as powerful knowledge. In B. J. Fraser,

K. G. Tobin, & C. J. McRobbie (Eds.), *Second international handbook of science education* (pp. 737–749). Springer.

Villavicencio, X., Myers, C., & Coflan, C. (2022). *STEM skills initiatives for adolescent girls in the Latin America and the Caribbean Region*. UKaid and The World Bank. https://doi.org/10.53832/edtechhub.0085

Wang, H., Charoenmuang, M., Knobloch, N., & Tormoehlen, R. (2020). Defining interdisciplinary collaboration based on high school teachers' beliefs and practices of STEM integration using a complex designed system. *International Journal of STEM Education (2020), 7*, 3. https://doi.org/10.1186/s40594-019-0201-4

Index[1]

[1] Note: Page numbers followed by 'n' refer to notes.

S. M. Al-Balushi et al. (eds.), *Reforming Science Teacher Education Programs in the STEM Era*, Palgrave Studies on Leadership and Learning in Teacher Education,
https://doi.org/10.1007/978-3-031-27334-6

T

CPSIA information can be obtained
at www.ICGtesting.com
Printed in the USA
LVHW051047110623
749453LV00007B/489

9 783031 273339